Chicken Soup, Cheap Whiskey
and Bad Women

To Angie —

August, 2000

Chicken Soup, Cheap Whiskey and Bad Women

A True Life Murder Trilogy

BY JOHN FULKER

ORANGE FRAZER *PRESS*
Wilmington, Ohio USA
2000

ISBN 1-882203-65-8
Copyright 2000 by John Fulker

Additional copies of *Chicken Soup, Cheap Whiskey and Bad Women* or other Orange Frazer Press publications may be ordered directly from:

Orange Frazer Press, Inc.
Box 214
37 ½ West Main Street
Wilmington, Ohio 45177

Telephone 1.800.852.9332 for price and shipping information
Web Site: www.orangefrazer.com

Illustrations by Meryl Sklut-Lettire
Jacket design by Tim Fauley

Library of Congress Cataloging-in-Publication Data

Fulker, John, 1929-
    Chicken soup, cheap whiskey and bad woman : a true life murder trilogy / by John Fulker
        p. cm.
    Contents: Mrs. Ragan's chicken soup -- Cheap whiskey and bad women -- More bad women.
    ISBN 1-882203-65-8 (pbk. : alk. paper)
    1. Murder--Ohio--Miami County--History--19th century--Case studies. 2.
    Trials--Ohio--Miami County--History--19th century--Case studies. I. Title.

    HV6533.05 F85 2000
    364.15'23'0977148--dc21

                                                            00-035976

They are, all of them, for NJ

TABLE OF CONTENTS

You may charge me with murder —

or want of sense —

(We are all of us weak at times)

Lewis Carroll

The Hunting of the Snark

Book One

***

Mrs. Ragan's Chicken Soup

Chapter One

THE MAN WAS PERCHED, scarcely seated, on the leading edge of a spartan, cane-bottomed armchair, like an intensely agitated ferret. Although he had been wringing his hands ceaselessly since his arrival he seemed utterly unaware of the exercise.

"I'll allow as how she might have done it, Mr. McKinney," he conceded. "But I don't want to think it."

They were in the second floor offices of S. S. and J. F. McKinney, Lawyers, located on Main Street, "above F. Geyer", in Piqua, Ohio. The ferret-like man was smallish in stature, lean and sinewy. He appeared to be in his middle forties. He was clean-shaven and deeply tanned. His full dark hair was shot through with streaks of iron-grey. He had the look of a working man decked out in his Sunday best for the occasion. This was Martin Cunningham, a cooper by trade, and the father of Jane Elizabeth Ragan.

On the opposite side of the ancient, lightly cluttered oak desk, across from Mr. Cunningham, a matching oak swivel chair overflowed with the person of Samuel Scott McKinney, the elder of the two McKinney brothers. Sam McKinney was a man of substance in every sense of the word. Not yet thirty-seven years old, he had already served as the town mayor. He had distinguished himself as a lawyer and had prospered financially. He also weighed nearly 300 pounds.

McKinney brandished a single sheet of lined white paper. "Well, Mr. Cunningham, the question of your daughter's guilt or innocence will ultimately be determined by the courts, but as matters now stand, she has most certainly been charged. What I have here is a copy of the Coroner's Inquest. I secured it this morning from the coroner after I learned that you wished to consult about the matter." Then, because the document was hand-written and because Mr. Cunningham was not particularly literate, McKinney led him through it.

"I expect you'll know Dan Ellis...Daniel F. Ellis...he's the county coroner. You need to know that whenever anyone dies suddenly or under suspicious circumstances, or if the reason the person dies is not obvious, the coroner is required by law to inquire into the matter and to determine the cause of death. That inquiry," he explained, "is what's known as a coroner's inquest. And, if the coroner figures he might need help — or maybe just validation — he can impanel a jury to look at the available evidence and render a coroner's verdict.

"Well," McKinney continued, "that's what Mr. Ellis has done in this situation. He impaneled a jury of six men, and I suspect that he did so for the precise purpose of validating his own findings. He submitted his evidence, whatever that might have been, and took their verdict. You'll see that all six of them signed it here at the bottom." The lawyer slid the paper across the desk, turned it around and stabbed its lower right quadrant with the index finger of his bear-like forepaw.

"And what they've said is that after having heard the evidence and having examined the body they decided that this fellow Ragan 'came to his death by poison.'" McKinney retrieved the paper, hesitated somewhat theatrically and cleared his throat for emphasis. "The next sentence of the verdict is of especial significance." He smoothed the paper on the desktop and read, "'And we the jury do further find that the said poison was administered by Elizabeth Ragan, wife of said Arthur Ragan.'"

Almost imperceptibly Cunningham had stopped wringing his hands. Now he rolled them upwards and stared into his palms, as though he were seeking answers to questions not yet formulated. "It seems that everything has happened so quick. Surely the matter has not yet been decided? You do not mean to tell me that it's all over and done with? Not this soon?" When his own calloused hands failed to provide the information he sought, he looked up at McKinney. "Should there not have been a proper trial — time to — to do something? Shouldn't there have been a lawyer?" he stammered. "Somebody? Something? Ragan only died Tuesday evening, day before yesterday, and my girl's been in jail since late last night. It don't seem right that — "

Now it was McKinney's turn to gesticulate with his hands. He extended them across the desk, palms down, as if to quiet troubled waters. "No, no, Mr. Cunningham," he said. "Nothing is over. Nothing has been decided. The coroner's verdict doesn't convict anyone of anything. There will be time, there will be a defense, there will — "

"I don't understand. You tell me there's been a verdict that says — "

And McKinney, himself a difficult man to interrupt, interrupted back. "Please, Mr. Cunningham. Listen to what I have to say. You must understand that the coroner's verdict forms the basis the basis only, for the filing of a formal charge that your daughter in some manner poisoned her husband. Then, upon the filing of that charge, there must next be a preliminary hearing before a magistrate — a judge or a justice of the peace — and then that officer will make a determination as to whether there is probable cause to believe both that a crime has been committed and that your daughter is the person who committed it. And, if he so determines, then the magistrate will bind her over to the Grand Jury, which, in turn will hear the State's evidence and decide whether or not to return an indictment.

"Now, then, when and if all those things should happen and your daughter should ultimately be indicted by the grand jury, then she will be tried to another jury, what we call a petit jury. That jury will consist of twelve persons, all of whom must reside here in the county. And in the event of such a trial, she will have every opportunity to defend herself and she will most certainly be entitled to the advice and assistance of counsel.

"So, you see, nothing is over. We are presently in a very early stage of the process. Do you understand?"

Martin Cunningham was a simple man, virtually without formal education, but he was not unintelligent. He permitted himself a moment to digest the lawyer's remarks, then nodded. "Yes sir, I believe I do. I think you've just told me that my daughter is in jail only because she has been charged, but not convicted, by this so-called coroner's verdict. And that before this business is finally over there'll probably have to be a trial — but she'll be able to have a lawyer and she'll be allowed to tell her side of the matter?"

"Precisely," confirmed McKinney, tilting his chair some degrees backward and assuming a posture better suited to his girth.

"Something I don't yet understand though," offered Cunningham, "is how come they've arrested Jimmy Mowrey. Does that coroner's paper say anything about him?"

McKinney snapped to an upright position in his swivel chair. The question had quite literally caught him off balance. "Mowrey?" he queried. "Who in God's name is Jimmy Mowrey? Was someone named Mowrey arrested also?" And when Cunningham nodded affirmatively, the lawyer demanded, "What? In connection with Mr. Ragan's death?"

Martin Cunningham nodded again and Sam McKinney tried to factor this new and unanticipated information into the context of what he already knew. "Your question is a most excellent one, Mr. Cunningham. Rather obviously, I have had no knowledge concerning this Mowrey person. As you know, I have only this morning procured this copy of the coroner's verdict and I have seen no other papers touching upon Mr. Ragan's death or persons alleged to have been involved. I can assure you, however, that there is no mention of any Mowrey in the coroner's verdict." And, after a thoughtful pause, he continued, "It sometimes happens — and such may be the case here — that some officer of the law, usually the Sheriff, may himself deem it appropriate to arrest and charge a person whom he believes to have been involved in the commission of a crime. In the present circumstance, a homicide, it would be most extraordinary, an anomaly indeed, for the Sheriff to take such a course; however ..." McKinney allowed the sentence to hang fire. Absently, he stroked his neatly-trimmed beard and abandoned himself to his thoughts.

"Perhaps," he said upon the return of his attention to Mr. Cunningham, "you would be good enough to acquaint me with the facts of this affair as you apprehend them to be. Tell me, if you will, something about your daughter, Jane Elizabeth, I believe, and about the deceased, Mr. Ragan, and this other man, too, this Mowrey person."

The wringing and kneading of Martin Cunningham's hands resumed as he began his recitation. Less articulate than the lawyer, his discourse did not come easy. "Well, sir," he said, "I don't suppose you'd have met my daughter, but I expect if you had, you'd've remembered her well enough. She's a tiny thing, barely five feet tall, and probably don't weigh much over a hundred pounds. She's well-made, though, and kinda perky too. No doubt she's the best-looking of all my girls, but I'd guess that's beside the point.

"As you know, her name's Jane Elizabeth — we call her Libby — or just Lib, for short. She and Ragan would have been married five years in July, the day before Independence Day. That makes it easy to remember. She was only seventeen at the time. I had to sign so she could get a license. Ragan was a few years older. Not much, but some. I knew him before she did. We're both coopers and the two of us've worked together from time to time.

"They had a baby, a little girl, about three years ago. And Libby was a good mother to her. She nursed her, took real good care of her — you know, she dressed her up, kept her clean, everything you'd expect a mother to do. She was a bright little thing and we were all real attached to her. She got the cholera, though, and died, before she was sixteen months old. I think the baby's death bothered them both a lot at the time, but they got through it alright. They tried to get her familywise again, but it didn't seem to happen. That wasn't too surprising though. It had taken them more'n a year to get it done the first time.

"Anyway, everything seemed to be moving along right for them. Ragan had enough work to keep him busy and Libby was occupied with her church work — she teaches Sunday School pretty regular, goes to the church quarterlies, services and such. Then, just last Friday, Ragan took sick to his stomach. Fact is, he never even got out of bed that morning. Said his belly hurt something terrible, like it never had before. He got all pale and sweaty, threw up everything he tried to eat. Libby got real concerned and sent for Doc Brownell. He got there pretty quick and soon's he did, Lib took him off into the front room and told him she thought Ragan had taken arsenic. She said he'd gone out the night before and when he came home he was drinking some kind of powder from a glass. When she'd asked him what it was, he told her it was cream tartar. I don't know whether Doc asked Ragan about it, but he did examine him and gave him some medicine. He stopped by again on Saturday and still again on Sunday to see how he was doing and to give him more medicine.

"Well, then, along about Sunday afternoon Ragan started to feel a little better, and Monday he seemed real good. In fact, Doc Brownell saw him that morning and said the only thing he needed was a cathartic. I think that's all he gave him. In the afternoon, though, Ragan got sick again and Libby had to send word to the doctor to come back. He got there just before dinner and found Ragan to be every bit as sick as he had been on Friday, if not worse. He told Libby he thought Ragan had got more poison. I don't know how that could be because there were people in and around the house just about all day every day from Friday on.

"Anyway, Ragan didn't get any better this time. He just got sicker and weaker, 'till he died. That was early Tuesday evening. Then the next day, yesterday, Jim Tamplin told me Doc Brownell had done a post-mortem that showed Ragan had died of poison and that there were suspicions that Libby was the person who had given it to him. Joe Kelly came by and told me the same thing.

"Well, as soon as I'd heard that I went straight to my daughter and asked her direct if she was the one. She was mightily distressed by the question, but she answered it firm. She looked me right in the face and said, 'By God, I am not.' That's pretty strong language for Lib. Then, last night, they came and arrested her. They said the charge was murder. They took her to Troy and she's been in the jail ever since."

Martin Cunningham permitted his hyperactive hands a well-earned respite from their nervous massaging of one another. He wrested them apart, inspected them closely and deliberately applied them, viselike, to the solid arms of the chair on which he perched. Raising his eyes above the level of the brass gaboon at the foot of McKinney's desk he looked askance at the lawyer. Was there anything else?

"Mowrey? Jimmy Mowrey. Who is he and where does he fit?" prompted McKinney with an uncharacteristic gentleness.

"Oh. Yes. I'm sorry. I almost forgot." Cunningham was embarrassed by the lapse. "I don't know how I could have done so, but I clearly did. Jimmy's a young fellow from down around Cowlesville. I've known him for six or seven years. He's a cooper too, so I've worked with him from time to time. There's work for coopers at Cowlesville. In fact Ragan had been down there working most of the winter.

"You see, I've lived most of my life in Cowlesville. There was a time when we were neighbors with Jimmy Mowrey. Jimmy used to be kinda sweet on Libby — that was before either of them was married, five, six years ago. He's got a nice wife and a couple of little ones now. Course, I'll still see him in the trade. And Libby, and maybe Harriet or Josephine, those are my other daughters, will run into him sometimes when they're in Tippecanoe or Cowlesville for the quarterlies. Sometimes Jimmy comes to Piqua to pick up an order or make a delivery. He might stop around her house if he's got the time.

"What I think is, that some people have got the idea that maybe Jimmy and Libby had somehow got involved with each other and decided to get rid of Ragan. I think that's why he got arrested."

Sam McKinney scarcely stirred in his chair. He was too keen an observer of the human condition, and too good a lawyer, to have missed the implications of what he'd just heard. Neither was he likely to have misapprehended the probability curve as applied to the facts which had been described to him. However, in order that he might not be perceived to have prejudged the issue, he attempted to mask his reaction to this most recent intelligence by not reacting at all. Without changing expression, McKinney returned Cunningham's glance. "Do you consider," he asked in a low tone, "such a hypothesis to be possible?" And when the answer was slow in coming, he chided, "We can best position ourselves to help your daughter, sir, by getting to the truth of the matter. We cannot afford the comfortable, but costly luxury of ignorance."

"It's possible," Cunningham conceded, "but the thought is painful for me to bear. I don't want to think on it. There have been some rumors."

The lawyer nodded his acknowledgment. "If you believe it to be possible, then we must explore it." He let it sink home. "Mr. Cunningham, it is necessary that you realize that in the ordinary course of events, your daughter will doubtless be charged with murder in the first degree. Implicit in that charge are the elements of malice and premeditation. If convicted, she will be publicly hanged. That is the penalty prescribed by law and will be imposed — unless, and only unless, the jury should recommend mercy. And in that event, her mandatory sentence will be life imprisonment.

"If your daughter is truly innocent of her husband's death, we must, of course, insist on a full and unconditional exoneration." He paused. "If, on the other hand, we are so extensively compromised by the facts that we cannot reasonably expect to accomplish such a total exoneration, then it is imperative that we examine other options."

Martin Cunningham had not quite winced at the lawyer's suggestion that his daughter might have to face the gallows and the hangman's noose, but he had certainly paled noticeably and his manner became still more diffident. It was his turn to nod acknowledgment. And acceptance.

"What should I do?" he asked tentatively.

McKinney was ready for the question. "First of all, sir, you should retain counsel. May I fairly presume that you have arranged this consultation for that purpose?" And, when Cunningham appeared to be befuddled by the attorney's stilted language, McKinney simplified it. "Do you wish to formally engage me as counsel?"

"Yessir, for my daughter, that's why I'm here."

"Has she authorized you to do so? To retain counsel on her behalf?"

"Well, no," Cunningham answered. "Not in so many words. She didn't tell me to go find her a lawyer. We haven't really had a chance to talk about it. This just came up yesterday. We didn't even know she was accused 'till last night when the sheriff came and arrested her. And, of course, she's been in jail since then.

"But I'm sure I can speak for her. I'm her father after all. And she'll be wanting some help with this. Apart from her three sisters, her mother and I are all she's got. Her husband's dead." Realizing how his last sentence must have sounded, he stammered, "I mean..."

Sam McKinney waved him off. "I understand, Mr. Cunningham. I understand. Let's do this. Let's consider that I will be available to represent your daughter if she elects to retain me. I will want you to discuss that with her at your first opportunity. Alright?"

"Yessir. I'll do that first thing. I'm sure that's what she'll want."

"Good," responded McKinney. "Now then, if I am retained in the matter, I will want to involve my brother, J. F. McKinney. He is younger and less experienced than I, but he's a member of this firm and a good lawyer. He will be helpful to us. Is that acceptable?" At a nod from Cunningham, McKinney continued, "Also, because this is a capital case the stakes are very high and will doubtless entail an arduous and lengthy trial, I deem it necessary that your daughter retain yet another lawyer with experience to assist in her defense. I would suggest Mr. James H. Hart. Do you know Mr. Hart?"

Cunningham was not immediately responsive. He had a question of his own. "That'll make a total of three lawyers," he noted. "Mr. McKinney, I want to help my daughter all I can, but I'm not a wealthy man. I work for coopers' wages." He shook his head sadly. "It'll be about all I can do to afford one lawyer."

Sam McKinney waved him off, "I don't want you to worry about that Mr. Cunningham. I will arrange for a division of my own fees among the other lawyers. It is much too early in the process to know what will be required, but you may be assured that I shall be mindful of the fact that you are a person of limited resources. I am, first and foremost, a practicing attorney, and I do expect to be paid for my time and effort. I am also," he added, "a public servant and an officer of the court. I shall see to it that your daughter receives the representation she deserves at a price you can afford."

And when Cunningham signified his acceptance, McKinney continued, "Now then, about Mr. Hart, do you know him?"

"Know of him. I think he used to be in Troy, then moved to Piqua sometime back. Yeah, he'll be fine, if you think we need him," came the prompt response. "Whatever you say."

"Very well, then," McKinney continued. "I should like for you to visit your daughter at the jailhouse and secure her approval concerning these arrangements. Please be certain that she understands and approves that I am to be retained as her counsel, and that I am also authorized to involve my brother, J. F. McKinney, and James H. Hart, to assist. These matters need to be addressed at once."

Martin Cunningham shifted his feet, preparing to rise. He thought the interview to be over. "I can do that," he said.

"And," McKinney ignored the movement. "While you are speaking with her, please press her as to any knowledge she may have concerning the role in this affair, if such there be, played by Jimmy Mowrey."

Cunningham wanted to know, "Will that help Libby?"

"Let me share my thoughts with you," began McKinney as though settling in for a protracted dissertation. "We have already acknowledged the likelihood that Jimmy Mowrey has been arrested because of a suspicion that he was in some manner involved, with your daughter, in the poisoning death of her husband. We have also acknowledged at least the possibility that that suspicion may be justified. Let's accept those separate acknowledgments, then, as a predicate for what I am about to say.

"If it should develop that each of them, this Mowrey and your daughter Libby, bears a measure of responsibility for Mr. Ragan's death," McKinney waggled a cautionary finger. "And if the State possesses or develops sufficient evidence to prove its case," the lawyer spread his palms, thick fingers extended, as though the syllogistic conclusion were obvious. "Then your daughter is doomed."

Martin Cunningham appeared to be stunned by the lawyer's revelation. He had certainly been aware that his daughter's predicament was serious, but the full import of her situation had not yet been appreciated. He looked at the lawyer, hoping for encouragement.

A silence developed as the two men stared across the desk. After Cunningham averted his glance, McKinney sought to attenuate his remarks, "Mind you, now. I said 'if'."

"Yessir. I heard that," said Cunningham. "And I think I understand you. What should we do?"

"Business," answered McKinney. "If we can. If the facts are as we have supposed, and if the State has the wherewithal to prove it, then we should try to do business with them as soon as possible."

"What kind of business?" queried Cunningham, seemingly overwhelmed at the direction in which the conversation had turned.

"Well," mused the lawyer, barely audible in the sobered ambience of the room. "In the event it should happen that all these other 'ifs' should be true ..." He didn't complete the sentence.

"Yes?" prompted Cunningham.

"Then she might want to think about giving evidence against Mowrey," McKinney finished. "It may well be her best chance."

"And, if all this be true, and if she was to give evidence," Cunningham stammered, "what might she expect in return?"

"I can't answer that, Mr. Cunningham. I don't know." Sam McKinney heaved his bulk upward and into a standing position. The interview was nearly ended. "We don't have enough information. First of all, we don't yet know what really happened. Second, and most importantly, we don't know what the State will be able to prove."

Cunningham had also risen from his chair. He accepted the lawyer's proffered hand, which engulfed his own, and allowed himself to be guided towards the office door. "I'll talk to Libby right away," he assured.

"And press her," admonished McKinney. "Press her hard. Her very life may depend on it."

"I will, sir. I truly will."

McKinney had one final instruction. "Please report back to me as soon as you have spoken with your daughter. In the meanwhile, I will make some inquiries of my own."

Chapter Two

THE YEAR WAS 1855. England's Queen Victoria was in the 18th year of her 64-year reign. Napoleon III was emperor of France and Frederick William Hohenzollern IV was King of Prussia. Further east, in what seemed another world, Alexander II had just succeeded his father, Nicholas I, as Czar of all the Russias; the Crimean War was a significant part of his inheritance.

This same year, Italian audiences thrilled to fresh performances of Giuseppe Verdi's newest and most popular operas, *Rigoletto*, *Il Trovatore* and *La Traviata*. The German composer, Richard Wagner, had barely commenced the score for his epic tetralogy, *Der Ring des Nibelungen*, and France's Charles Gounod had not yet completed his hauntingly lyrical opera, *Faust*. Two London teenagers, William S. Gilbert and Arthur S. Sullivan, would remain strangers to one another for yet another decade. And a second pair of schoolboys, Russia's Peter Ilyitch Tshaikowsky and Nicolai Rimsky-Korsakov, had not yet distinguished themselves or become aware of each other's existence.

In literature, Charles Dickens and Charlotte Bronte depicted widely disparate strata of London society while Victor Hugo wrote eloquently of humanity, tragedy and morality in the hidden recesses of Paris. And in art, French impressionists Manet, Monet, Renoir and Degas developed an innovative and conceptual approach to their work and thereby introduced a new age.

On this side of the Atlantic, Franklin Pierce was President of the 31 United, but sorely troubled, States. The trouble, of course, was the slavery issue. Illinois' Senator Stephen A. Douglas had sponsored the newly enacted Kansas-Nebraska Act, which sounded the death knell for the Whig Party, spawned the "Know-Nothing" Party, witnessed the birth of the Republican Party, and directly precipitated the bitterly fought War for Bleeding Kansas. Mrs. Stowe's enormously provocative tale of life among the lowly polarized public opinion and contributed mightily to the dark storm clouds on the nation's horizon.

The recent discovery of Gold at Sutter's Mill produced an unprecedented rush for riches; Commodore Perry had just concluded his treaty for trade with

Japan and the opening of the Soo Canal was expected to provide cheap transportation of iron ore and to promote the development of the steel industry.

From his home in Tarrytown, New York, Washington Irving entertained the nation with tales of Rip Van Winkle and Ichabod Crane and a place called Sleepy Hollow. Herman Melville wrote about the whaling industry and about an obsessive Captain Ahab. Nathaniel Hawthorne and Oliver Wendell Holmes wrote moralistic essays and novels, and poets William Cullen Bryant, Henry Wadsworth Longfellow and James Greenleaf Whittier separately contributed to an American anthology of metered classics.

American civilization, along with its attendant commerce, industry and prosperity, had pushed its way westward. In the process, it had also pushed the North American Indian tribes in the same direction. So well had that enforced migration been accomplished that by 1855 there was no longer an Indian menace anywhere east of the Mississippi. A series of Congressional land grants had enabled the construction of railroads connecting some of the principal population centers east of that dividing river with the Atlantic Seaboard.

And, so as not to lose perspective altogether, in New Rumley, Ohio, George Armstrong Custer had just last December celebrated his 15th birthday.

THE TOWN OF PIQUA had been laid out and systematically constructed along the meanders of the Great Miami River in the gently rolling terrain of Southwestern Ohio. Not surprisingly, it had been neither the first nor the only establishment to have been located at that particular bend in the river. It had, in fact, been erected both over and amongst the ruins of myriad earlier settlements dating back to the prehistoric mound-builders. In more recent times, it had been the situs of a principal village of the Miami Indian tribe which had occupied the territory for generations untold. It was the Miamis from whom the town derives its name. According to one of their ancient traditions, a group of warriors had been gathered around the smoldering embers of a ritual fire in which a captured enemy had been burned alive when they were greatly startled to see a large puff of white smoke issue from the glowing coals and resolve itself into a fullbodied and intensely angry enemy chieftain. In fear and bewilderment, more than one of the Indians gasped aloud, "Otah-he-wagh-Pe-Qua!" That phrase, translated from a phonetic language which has no alphabet, means "He has risen from the ashes!"

Then, with the coming of the white man, the village became a major center for commerce between the Indians and the frontiersmen. Both the trading post and the fort built there by the British were destroyed in the first battle of the French and Indian War; eleven years later, in 1763, the last battle of that war was waged a single mile to the north.

After that war had ended, the fierce Shawnee tribe seized possession of the territory and occupied it for the next twenty-odd years. The legendary Tecumseh and his brother, The Prophet, were born at Piqua during the Shawnee occupation. The Shawnees remained in control until General George Rogers Clark defeated them and destroyed their villages in the course of his 1782 Expedition. Shortly after that event General "Mad" Anthony Wayne rebuilt Fort Piqua on the site of its predecessor and General William Henry Harrison commanded it as a supply base during the War of 1812.

Over the course of its history the Miamis' Pe-Qua evolved into and became the American town of Piqua. And because it had historically played a significant role in the recurrent confrontations with the bordering French forces, the settlement was appropriately, and successively, dubbed the "border village", the "border town" and, finally, the "Border City".

Piqua was also located near the northern border of Miami County. Some eight miles downriver and nearer the geographic center of the county was Troy. Despite the fact that it was slightly smaller than Piqua, Troy had become the seat of county government, primarily because of its more centralized location. When General Clark led his expedition from Kentucky in 1782 he had ordered a part of his army to cross the Great Miami at a broad ford just east of Troy. A few miles further on, the General brought the rest of his army across and the combined force followed the west bank on the march northward to attack the Shawnees. A bridge long since built across the ford has ever been known as the Broadford Bridge and Main Street, in both towns, follows General Clark's trail.

Just before the turn of the century General Wayne had soundly defeated the resident Indian tribes in the Battle of Fallen Timbers. That victory, and the resulting Treaty of Greenville, had effectively removed the "Indian menace" and opened the entire Miami Valley for settlement. Now, in 1855, Piqua was a well-established, peaceful, and burgeoning community. Its population consisted of some 4000 souls and it boasted not one, but two newspapers, and a telegraph office. It also had a first-rate fire department, graded schools, and a growing number of churches. The needs of the locals, coupled with the availability of suitable watercourses, had spawned a varied proliferation of mills along the river and its tributaries. There were saw mills, grain mills and even a linseed oil mill. There were also leather tanneries and distilleries in abundance. Ready access to more distant markets was accomplished with the extension of the Miami-Erie Canal, which ran directly through the center of town, and the two nearly completed railroads that would soon intersect one another near the center of town.

THE SECOND FLOOR OFFICES of Attorneys S. S. and J. F. McKinney overlooked Main Street in Piqua. It was a fine day, unseasonably warm, this first Saturday in April, 1855. The brothers McKinney were stationed near the front windows, Sam seated at a work table and Frank standing, where they too might overlook the activity in the street below. Saturday was market day and the muddy thoroughfare was nearly choked with the wagons and traps of farmers and tradespeople, the buggies of shoppers and visitors, and the occasional cluster of livestock that wandered aimlessly about the street. The leather-booted pedestrian traffic confined itself, as best it could, to the relatively drier, more negotiable boardwalks alongside the array of offices, saloons and storefronts.

True to his word, Sam McKinney had already involved his younger brother in the Ragan affair. Within an hour of his Thursday interview with Martin Cunningham, he had conferred with Frank and acquainted him with all that he had learned from Cunningham. When he inquired if Frank knew anything of this Jane Ragan, he was surprised at the answer.

"Good God, man! I had thought that every red-blooded man in the county knew something of the woman. Have you never seen her about? Or have the ravages of age, good food and strong drink so dulled your perceptions that you can remain thus far oblivious to her extraordinary physical charms?"

"Spare me the rhetoric, please," Sam had growled. "Just tell me what you know about her."

At 28, Frank McKinney was nine years younger, and more than 100 pounds lighter, than his brother. And while he felt genuine affection for him and had enormous respect for his talents, he was scarcely in awe of him.

"I don't actually know Mrs. Ragan," he had acknowledged. "But I could hardly be unaware of her. She is the most stunningly provocative woman I've ever laid eyes on. She is smallish in stature, almost petite, but full bosomed and nicely formed. Her hair and complexion are dark and her eyes — mm — her eyes — they're deep, dark blue and sultry." He had paused to consider the description. "That's it," he said. "She's small, dark and sultry. Had you told me that some man or other had killed out of desire for her, I should not have been surprised.

"If murder has been done," he had continued, "I'll warrant it was out of an illicit attraction for this woman. For that reason, if for none other, we may want to know more about this James Mowrey."

Because Sam had already scheduled a series of unrelated commitments for Friday, the two men had concluded that Frank would make inquiries, both in Troy and in Piqua, in order to learn what the prosecution might be expected to prove and to better understand their own client's situation. He had been engaged in those activities all day Friday and they had not seen one another until this morning.

As they watched the street scene below, they were at leisure and their conversation easy and desultory. They had not yet referred to the subject at hand. Finally Sam McKinney tilted himself back into his chair, lit his first cigar of the day, and raised an eyebrow at Frank. "So tell me, little brother, what you learned as a result of yesterday's peregrinations about the countryside. Anything useful?"

Frank maintained his stance at the window, left shoulder resting on the post, and shifted his attention to his brother's question. "As a matter of fact I learned a great deal, both officially and unofficially. Whether any of it turns out to be useful remains to be seen. I guess you'll have to be the judge of that.

"As you know," he continued, "Mrs. Ragan was arrested directly after her husband's death. The coroner's jury went against her and the prosecutor charged her immediately. She has neither sought nor been admitted to bail and is at this moment confined in the county jailhouse as the guest of Sheriff Hustler. And, of course, I have not spoken with her.

"I think you also know about this James Mowrey person. Even though the coroner's verdict made no mention of him, he was also charged and arrested directly after Ragan's death. The prosecutor filed the charge himself, on information and belief, with the result that Mr. Mowrey may also be found in residence at the sheriff's establishment.

"Now, just yesterday afternoon, it seems that Harvey Sellers and Charles Morris have appeared as counsel for Mowrey and demanded an immediate hearing on the question of probable cause. That's set for the 9th, next Monday, before Justice Sage."

Sam McKinney extended his open hand to signal an interruption. "The charge against Mrs. Ragan is murder, that she poisoned her husband. What's the charge against Mowrey?"

"That he was an accessory, *particeps criminis*, to the murder," answered Frank. "The thrust is that he encouraged and induced her to kill her husband and that he actively helped her secure and administer the poison."

"Why?" asked Sam, as if he hadn't known the answer.

"So he could have the spicy wench to himself," chortled Frank with an exaggerated leer. "I tell you this woman is an exciting piece of goods. And while her rather obvious charms may not yet have launched a thousand ships, she's certainly got Mowrey's canoe going pretty good. Rumor has it they're former sweethearts who have rediscovered one another. They've apparently been sneaking around together for a couple of years. Now, it seems, if Arthur Ragan could be gotten rid of, Mowrey would simply leave his wife and children and the two lovebirds could build themselves a new nest in some other community."

"Is this the prosecutor's theory or is it just the common gossip?"

"Both," responded Frank to his brother's query.

"Which prosecutor are we talking about?"

"*The* prosecutor," answered Frank. "The estimable Mathias H. Jones. And I expect Ebenezer Parsons will assist at the probable cause hearing on Monday. I spoke with Ben about the matter yesterday. They'd like for Mrs. Ragan to testify."

Sam McKinney raised an eyebrow, "For the State? Against her boyfriend? Why do they think she would do that?"

"Well," Frank drawled, "Ben suggested it might be to her advantage to do so."

"In what way," Sam pressed, "did he suggest it would be to her advantage?"

"He didn't say," Frank admitted. "Only that it might be to her advantage. I think his remark was intended to be an overture."

"Ben Parsons knows she can only help the State by incriminating herself," Sam observed. "If she were to testify that Mowrey helped her to poison Ragan, she would thereby acknowledge her own flagrant culpability."

"That's true enough," Frank conceded. He waited for Sam to work it through.

"They must be very confident of their case against Mrs. Ragan," mused Sam McKinney, "to make such a suggestion."

And, when Frank nodded agreement, he continued, "What do they have? How strong is the evidence against her?"

"It's pretty strong, Sam. I recognize that we're just at the threshold, but at this juncture the evidence seems most compelling."

"Tell me, then. What have they got?"

"Well," Frank consulted his notes, "first of all, they can demonstrate that Ragan died of arsenic. Doc Brownell was his attending physician. He suspected poisoning and so he and Doc Neff did a post mortem. Examined Ragan's stomach and contents. They even sent samples to Columbus for analysis. There's a Dr. Wormsley who lectures in chemistry at some medical college. They, all of them, concluded that Ragan died of poisoning and that the specific poison was arsenic. Doc Brownell even recovered some of Ragan's vomit after he died. I mean," he stammered, "stuff he'd vomited up before he died — Doc recovered it afterwards. Anyway, they examined that too, and found it full of arsenic. Before he died, he'd been puking arsenic."

"Alright," Sam McKinney nodded. "So he died of arsenic. How do they tie that to Mrs. Ragan?"

"Actually, they don't," Frank reviewed his notes. "Not directly, that is. But there is rather an impressive lot of circumstantial evidence against her. For example, do you know that she is known to have gone to a great deal of trouble to purchase a very small amount of arsenic the day before her husband died?"

"No, of course I don't know that. I've had no opportunity to inquire."

"Well, she did," Frank rejoined. "And in the clumsiest way imaginable. It seems that on Monday morning — just last Monday — Mrs. Ragan sent a little neighbor girl, with a note, over to Ashton's Drug Store to buy just three cents worth of arsenic. The little girl's name is Cornelia Gabriel; she's barely nine years old. Anyway, the note was signed 'Mrs. Sanders' and asked Ashton's to give her three cents worth of arsenic. Cornelia had Mrs. Ragan's three cents, but Bill Ashton wouldn't take it and he wouldn't sell her the arsenic. He told her they didn't sell it in such small quantities. But he kept the note. Then, no more than ten or fifteen minutes after she'd left, the little girl came back for the note. She said Mrs. Ragan wanted it. Ashton wouldn't give it to her so she ran along home.

"The next thing, just a couple hours later, at ten or eleven o'clock, a young lad named George Kelly came into the store and bought a dime's worth of arsenic from Ashton's brother — that'd be Asa. Seems that young Master Kelly was at Mrs. Ragan's house that morning and she told him she was bothered with rats so much she could hardly sleep at nights. She wanted George to go to the drugstore and buy her three cents worth of rats-bane. He told her he thought maybe his mother might want some too. So Mrs. Ragan goes over to see Mrs. Kelly — they're neighbors — and asks if it's alright to send George to the drugstore for three cents worth of arsenic. Mrs. Kelly says she told her she didn't think they'd sell less than a dime's worth. But since she needed some too, they each put in five cents and sent George off to the store. Mrs. Ragan specifically told the boy to go to *Starrett's* Drugstore, but because it was closer, he went to Ashton's and bought it from Asa."

"Hold on a minute. When was this, again?" Sam McKinney interrupted.

"Monday morning. Remember Ragan had got sick the first time on Friday. By Monday, he was feeling a little better. It looked like he was going to get well. Then Monday afternoon, right after Mrs. Ragan got the arsenic, he got really sick. He died the following day."

McKinney was astonished. "Good, God, Frank! Can they prove all this?"

"Sure can," said Frank. "Ben Parsons let me look at the statements from the Ashton brothers, the little Gabriel girl, the Kelly boy and his mother, Mrs. Kelly. He even showed me the note the Gabriel girl brought to Ashton's. That's the note that was supposed to have been signed 'Mrs. Sanders'? Well, they've got a statement from the only 'Mrs. Sanders' in town and she says she never sent to Ashton's for arsenic and never sent the Gabriel girl anywhere for anything. Says she lives in the neighborhood with Mrs. Ragan, but has never spoken with her.

"Tell you what else they've got," Frank clucked. He sorted through the pages of his notebook till he had found the right item. "They've got another neighbor, a Mrs. Wise. She was with Mrs. Kelly, George's mother, that day. Last Monday. Mrs. Ragan came in and told them her husband was much better. The doctor had said he was out of danger. Then she'd asked Mrs. Kelly about sending George to the drugstore for arsenic. They gave the boy five cents apiece and sent him to Starrett's. When he came back with the poison, Mrs. Ragan divided it equally and took her portion home. Then, about an hour later, just at dinnertime, she came running back and said her husband was worse. He was as bad as he was on Saturday. She came back again a couple of hours later, two, three in the afternoon, and said he was a whole lot worse. She wanted them, Mrs. Kelly and Mrs. Wise to come. Well, of course, they did. Mrs. Wise says in her statement that she found Ragan in a spasm. He was complaining that his tongue was stiff. When she gave him a mouthful of whiskey, he said that made it a little better, but he was sure he was going to die.

"She and Mrs. Kelly went back to the Ragan home later that evening. Mrs. Kelly found Mrs. Ragan's portion of the arsenic they had divided that morning. They opened the packet and noted that it was about half gone. That seemed to confirm their suspicions and they dropped the rest of it into the stove. Apparently both women had heard Doc Brownell say, over the preceding weekend, that he thought Ragan might have been poisoned."

Frank McKinney adjusted his spectacles, paged further through his notes, and glanced toward his brother. "There's more, of course, on that subject, but that's the gist of it."

"Jesus," murmured Sam McKinney, softly. "Jesus Christ."

Chapter Three

MARTIN CUNNINGHAM DID NOT return to town until late afternoon. The shadows cast by the low buildings along the west side of Main Street had crept across the rutted thoroughfare and now approached the bottom members of the wooden walkways to the east. The unaccustomed midday warmth had yielded to a coolness that reminded of the winter just completed. The market day throngs, having finished their business, had largely disappeared so that there remained only a few loungers and fewer pedestrians along the walks and not more than a handful of stray dogs in the center of the street.

Cunningham secured his mare to the rail in front of Ashton's Drugstore and clomped his way across the muddy boards, past "F. Geyer" and up the stairway that led to the upstairs offices of the brothers McKinney. There was a barely perceptible sag in his shoulders and a heavy weariness in his gait. He had had a long day. Up before daylight, he had hitched his mare to the buckboard and travelled the river road to the southern part of the county. He had gone first to his home in Cowlesville to collect some barrel orders and to see about his family, then back to the jailhouse in Troy to visit with his daughter. He had just now completed the circuit and both he and his mare were spent.

The door at the head of the stairway stood full open. Sam McKinney had been expecting Cunningham, had heard his tread on the stairs, and had now risen to greet him.

"Come in, Mr. Cunningham," McKinney boomed. "Do come in and sit awhile. I should like to introduce you to my brother, J. F. McKinney. Frank, this is Martin Cunningham. I expect he'll have some news of his daughter, Mrs. Ragan."

Sam McKinney turned his attention back to his visitor. "Mr. Cunningham, you will remember that you authorized me to engage Frank to assist in this matter." And when Cunningham nodded, McKinney continued, "Well, sir, I have done so, and Frank has agreed to become involved. As a matter of fact, he spent nearly all of yesterday inquiring about the prosecution's case.

"Now then," he resumed after Cunningham had lowered himself into the same cane-bottom chair he had occupied on his previous visit. "Tell us of Mrs. Ragan. What have you learned from your interview with her?"

"Nothing good, I'm afraid." Cunningham seemed totally dejected. "It seems to be all that I'd feared. It's what everybody's been saying."

"What's that? That she poisoned her husband?" McKinney demanded in consternation.

"Well, no. She didn't actually tell me that, but ..."

"What did she tell you?" McKinney interrupted. "We can't help her unless we know the truth of it."

"Yessir. I know that." Tawny, sinewy hands on knees, arms outstretched, bearing the weight of his fatigue, Cunningham seemed thoroughly dejected. "I guess you'll recollect that Libby told me right off that she'd thought Ragan had taken arsenic himself. She told that to Doc Brownell first time he came by. Then, later, when I asked her direct if she'd given it to him she denied it straight out."

"I remember," said McKinney.

"Well, now the jailer tells me she's been mostly unconscious these past two days. Some sort of fit, I suppose. But she was herself today. I told her I suspicioned she was the one had given Ragan the poison. She hemmed and hawed about it for awhile and wouldn't answer. Then, after I caught her eye and looked deep, she finally told me that James Mowrey was at the bottom of it."

"What does that mean, 'at the bottom of it'?" McKinney queried.

"I asked her that," answered Cunningham. "I asked her to start at the beginning and tell me exactly what had transpired. Well, sir, she did. And it seems that the beginning was about five years ago, before she was married to Ragan. Libby wasn't yet seventeen when she and Mowrey got to be pretty close. This was down in Cowlesville and we were neighbors with the Mowreys. The two of them were together a lot — and I suppose they might have been intimate — though she didn't say so. Anyway, I'd thought that was over when she married Ragan. Especially after the baby came. But then, summer before last, it seems to have started up again. They'd come together somehow and then began to see each other again. At first it had been in Tippecanoe or in Cowlesville, at the quarterlies or in church. Then later he'd come to Piqua, even to the house when Ragan was away. Apparently it got pretty thick and Mowrey tried to get her to run off with him, to go west somewhere. He was prepared to leave his wife and children behind. Libby said she wouldn't do that because it wasn't right.

"Well, apparently that's when Mowrey began to urge her to poison Ragan. But she wouldn't do that either. He finally said he'd do it himself. What he said was he'd give him poison and that'd stretch him out cold. Told her Ragan would go out one day and not come back. They'd bring him back dead and nobody'd ever know the difference. Then the two of them could be together all the time."

"Did she say to you," Sam McKinney wanted to know, "that James Mowrey administered poison to her husband?"

"No sir, she didn't," answered Cunningham. "She wouldn't say who it was that actually gave him poison. All she'd say was that James Mowrey was at the bottom of it. And then she'd cry and look away. I couldn't get anything more out of her."

"It would be good to know the straight of it," mused Sam McKinney pensively. "But at least we know that Mowrey was involved. We also know that the prosecutor, Mr. Jones, and probably Mr. Parsons also, would like to hold James Mowrey accountable. They'd like an indictment against Mowrey and I think your daughter should help them along. It just might induce them to treat her more leniently if they can find a way to do so."

Frank McKinney had paid close attention to the colloquy between his brother and Martin Cunningham. Then, at Sam's invitation, he rehearsed for Cunningham's benefit all that he had learned of the prosecution's case against his daughter. "It appears to me," he concluded, "that they've got a very compelling case against her. It's all circumstantial, I know, but it's also very damning."

"I think," said Sam McKinney, stroking his beard, "that your daughter should be encouraged to co-operate with the prosecutors. She should make a clean breast of the matter — regardless of the question which of them actually administered the poison. I suspect that in their zeal to implicate Mr. Mowrey the prosecutors may be induced to consider your daughter to be a victim, albeit not an entirely innocent victim, of James Mowrey's evil designs, his unholy lust and his unattenuated malevolence. I think, sir, that your daughter may well be perceived as an unwitting tool in the hands of this ruthless man who would stick at nothing, not even murder, in his wanton quest to make your daughter his concubine."

"Sam, Sam," interjected Frank McKinney. "Save the rhetoric for the jury. Trial's a long way off."

Sam McKinney acknowledged his brother's mild reproof with a self-deprecating grimace. "You're right, Frank," he said. "Quite right. That was a bit much, wasn't it?" Then, back to Martin Cunningham, he continued, "I may, indeed, have overstated that which appears to me to be our best hypothesis. Nonetheless, sir, it would seem to offer an opportunity."

He allowed a moment's pause, time for the concept of Libby Ragan as a victim to register. Would it wash? Could he mold it into a realistic, viable defense to a murder charge? Sam McKinney wondered. He would have to see how it played out. For the moment, he needed to know, "Will your daughter give state's evidence? Will she testify against James Mowrey?"

"I don't know, sir," answered Cunningham. Everything about him, his posture, his face, his eyes, bespoke despair and dejection. "I'm having trouble understanding any of this. I'm not real sure I know my own daughter. That she could be a part of something like this, that she could let herself be tempted in such a way. I know she's pretty young, but she's been raised right. She's always been a decent girl — wasn't ever any trouble to us, her mother and I.

"She's been saved, you know. Couple of years ago, now. She took up with Jesus and became a member of the church. Since that time her religion's been important to her. What with the prayer meetings and the Sunday sessions and the quarterlies, she doesn't have much time to do other things. She teaches Sunday School, too, at different times and places."

His voice trailed off and he stared at his hands. He realized he hadn't answered the lawyer's question. "I'm just trying to say I don't truly understand how all this has come about. I have to believe that it's somehow Jimmy Mowrey's fault and I want Libby to tell about it. That's what I want her to do, but I truly don't know whether she will. She doesn't believe she's done anything wrong, so it's anyone's guess what she'll be willing to admit to."

Sam McKinney rose to signal that the interview was at an end. He patted Cunningham on the shoulder and sought to assure him. "We needn't guess, Mr. Cunningham. I intend to visit your daughter tomorrow. That will provide an opportunity to plan our strategy and to set matters aright. Then, as soon as that has been accomplished, I can meet with the prosecutors and negotiate an understanding of sorts."

Cunningham's countenance fell. "She won't see you, sir," he stammered. "Not yet, anyway. She's set in that. She told me specifically you were not to come. She said she appreciates your willingness to help, but she wants to wait till after Mowrey's hearing to decide what she wants to do."

"But, but," Sam McKinney spluttered, "That may be too late!"

"I told her that," said Cunningham, "but she's got her mind made up. She won't see you now. Says that's her right." His hands kneaded one another mercilessly.

"Please understand," continued Cunningham. "She wants you as her lawyer. She says that's a comfort to her. But, at least for the time being, she doesn't want to talk with anyone, not even her lawyer."

This time it was Frank McKinney who reacted. "That's unacceptable," he snapped. "We cannot — "

And Cunningham interrupted, "Sir, I know it's unusual and I know it's hard to believe. I guess I forgot to mention that my girl is headstrong." His eyes beseeched them. "But I'm hoping you'll stay with us anyway. We'll be needing your help soon enough."

The brothers McKinney exchanged a look of mutual dismay. Sam McKinney redirected his attention to Martin Cunningham and shook his head sadly. He didn't like the situation at all. It was as though he'd have to spot the prosecutors his queen, both rooks and the move. "Very well," he conceded with ill-disguised chagrin. "She shall have it her way. We will simply stay out of the way, for the nonce, and remain at the ready. She will wish to consult soon enough."

Chapter Four

THE FOLLOWING MONDAY, APRIL 9TH, the charges against James Mowrey came on for hearing before the resident justice of the peace for Washington Township. That person was Joseph Sage, Esquire, a tall spare man whose dark beard and deep-set eyes were entirely complemented by the unrepentent flat black color of the only suit of clothes he had ever been known to wear.

The specific charge was that James Mowrey was guilty of the murder of Arthur Ragan by virtue of his having been *particeps criminis*, an accomplice whose participation in the crime was such that he was himself, in the eyes of the law, as guilty as the principal. The purpose of the hearing before Justice Sage was to determine whether there was sufficient cause to bind Mowrey over and to refer the matter to the next grand jury. And, because these proceedings were not technically directed against Jane Ragan, the McKinney brothers, as her counsel, would take no active part in this particular phase of the criminal process. Nonetheless, Frank McKinney had been elected by his older brother to attend, and to monitor, the entire event. He had been instructed to take copious notes of the testimony, to assess the credibility of the witnesses, and to report his conclusions.

The assignment was entirely welcome to Frank McKinney. He was already greatly intrigued by the persona and the charms of their client and he had become so far engrossed in his investigations that he was eager to learn all that he could about the circumstances. He had arrived before daybreak, waited on the doorstep, and had been the first to enter when Squire Sage unlocked his front door at 7:30. He explained his role in the affair to the justice and claimed a seat on the front bench of the small room that served as a courtroom. The appointments and furnishings were rude, but entirely serviceable. There was a broad oak desk for the justice, two small tables for the lawyers, and a plain, straight-backed chair for the witnesses. Members of the press and interested spectators were accommodated in the three rows of rough benches located only slightly behind the counsel tables.

Frank McKinney was not surprised to find the central arena of the courtroom to be nearly as crowded as the spectator section when court was opened promptly at 8:00 o'clock. He was aware that the State of Ohio would appear in the persons of Mathias Jones and Ebenezer Parsons and he had expected the defendant to be represented by local attorneys Charles Morris and Harvey Sellers. He correctly guessed that the slight, even-featured man seated between the two defense lawyers was James Mowrey. Squire Sage presided from behind his flat-topped desk opposite the counsel tables, and the bailiff, a bright-faced older gentleman specifically employed for the occasion, sat on a stool in the corner of the room, near the door through which he would escort the witnesses as they were called.

Because Squire Sage's J. P. Court was an inferior court, not one of record, there was no court reporter. The testimony of the witnesses would be memorialized only in the notes of the participants and the reports of the several newspapers, The Troy Times, The Piqua Register and The Dayton Gazette. And, of course, pursuant to his brother's explicit admonitions, Frank McKinney maintained his own hand-written synopsis of the proceedings:

Sam: Here are my:

Notes of Mowrey Preliminary Hearing
(beginning April 9, '55)
JFM

STATE'S EVIDENCE

Dr. Brownell

Is a practicing physician in Piqua. Was called to see Arthur Ragan and attended him during his whole sickness; first saw him on the 30th of March. Symptoms were nausea, vomiting and abdominal tenderness; dryness of the mouth and throat; eyes much injected; pulse at 60 (all indicating inflammation of the stomach). Upon arrival Mrs. Ragan took him to another room and said she thought Ragan had taken arsenic; said he went out the night before and when he came back he was drinking some kind of a powder from a glass; she asked him what it was and he said it was cream tartar. Dr. B said he had suspected poison and treated accordingly.

— Ragan remained critical until late Sunday, and by Monday he seemed to be getting better. Dr. B thought no more medicine necessary except a cathartic. That afternoon, about four o'clock, Dr. B found Ragan's name on the slate at his office; he called and found patient laboring under the same symptoms as before. Took Mrs. Ragan to another room and told her that the patient must have had some more poison; said he believed her former statement and told her it looked as though he had taken some more himself or some one else had given it to him; her reply was that she didn't know how that could be because she had given him everything he had taken; Dr. B said he must speak to him about it, but Mrs. Ragan begged him not to for if he recovered he would take her life for telling on him; she said he confessed to her that he took it. Dr. B told Ragan's sister of his suspicions and asked her to speak to him about it; also told a Mr. Tamplin to ask him about it. Dr. B was informed that attempts had been made by Mrs. Ragan to obtain poison. Dr. B found that nothing could be done for his patient; called the next morning (Tuesday) and found him sinking very fast; patient died Tuesday evening at six o'clock (April 3rd).

Dr. B proposed to do an autopsy to determine the cause of death, but Mrs. Ragan begged him not to do so. Her offer of a "reward" to prevent such an examination was ignored and Dr. B performed a post mortem before the coroner on Wednesday morning in conjunction with Drs. Dorsey, Neff, Smith and O'Ferrell. They examined the stomach and found it to be "injected"; the mucous membrane was so disorganized that it could be separated by rubbing it with the thumb nail. The stomach appeared to be greatly inflamed as if subjected to some active corrosive poison. They came to that conclusion; said it might have been arsenic, but two or three other poisons would produce the same appearance. Dr. B made a second examination of the stomach at Columbus in conjunction with Dr. Wormsley. They applied five tests upon it and upon the rectum (which had been saved); all tests indicated arsenic clearly and indisputably. Dr. W is a teacher of Chemistry at Columbus; he lectures on that subject at Starling Medical College.

From all these tests and other circumstances, Dr. B reached the conclusion that Ragan came to his death by poison and that the specific poison was arsenic.

In a subsequent conversation with Mrs. Ragan, she told Dr. B that he was right in his suspicions; that she was fixing his bed the evening before and found a vial in the pillow slip. Dr. B took the vial and found it to contain arsenic. He asked where she threw what he vomited from his stomach; she showed him and he scraped up some of the earth at that place on Friday morning; upon analysis, the earth showed traces of arsenic.

(Note to Sam — *Dr. Brownell is an excellent witness. — We will not wish to quarrel with his testimony.*)

Dr. Neff

Also a practicing physician in Piqua. He attended the postmortem examination and concurs generally with the testimony of Dr. B. The result of the examination was that Ragan died of poison, and there were some peculiarities which would raise the presumption that the poison was arsenic.

Wm. B. Ashton

Is in the drug business in Piqua. Monday, April 2nd, between 7 and 8 o'clock in the morning, Mrs. Gabriel's little girl came to the store with a note, signed "Mrs. Sanders," asking for three cents worth of arsenic. He took the note, told her they did not sell it in so small a quantity, and sent her off. He kept the note and gave it to Dr. Brownell. The little girl said Mrs. Ragan had sent her with the note; ten or fifteen minutes later the girl came back for the note, saying Mrs. Ragan sent for it, but Ashton refused to return it. George Kelly came in soon after and bought some arsenic from Ashton's brother.

(Sam — *At this point, Dr. Brownell was recalled to authenticate the note. It was offered as State's Ex. 1. I've copied it verbatim:*

Mr. Ashton, — Send me three cents' worth of arsenic; I wish to kill the rats.

It was signed Mrs. E. Sanders or Mrs. R. Sanders — can't tell which. It's slightly blurred.)

Miss Cornelia Gabriel

She's nine years old. Says she took a note to Ashton's store for arsenic. Mrs. Ragan sent her. She did not get it. Gave the note to Ashton. Mrs. Ragan later told her to go back and get the note as the arsenic was not for Mrs. Sanders but for herself. Wanted her to go somewhere else and get it. Cornelia went to get the note, but Ashton said he had let it go. Mrs. Ragan said it made no difference because she really didn't have many rats. She took back the three cents.

Prudence Gabriel
(Cornelia's mother)

Mrs. Ragan came in on Monday and said her husband was much better. She asked Cornelia to go for some medicine; said she had a note the doctor wrote. Cornelia left with the note; Mrs. Ragan went out with her and they talked a good little bit at the gate. Mrs. G. did not know of her daughter's going to Ashton's a second time.

Mrs. Sanders

Said she never sent a note to Ashton's for arsenic at any time. Does not live near Mrs. Ragan, never spoke to her, and never sent the little girl for anything.

George Kelly

He bought some arsenic last Monday off Asa Ashton. He was at Mrs. Ragan's that morning between 10 and 11 o'clock, and Mrs. Ragan said she was so bothered with the rats she could hardly sleep nights. She wanted him to get her some rats-bane — said she wanted to get three cents worth. George told her his mother wanted to get some too. Mrs. Ragan said his mother might give five cents and she would give five cents and put it together. They gave him the money and he went and got it; when he came back, Mrs. Ragan divided it and took hers home. She had told him particularly to go to Starretts, but he went to Ashtons because it was closer. When he told her he had gone to Ashtons she said it didn't matter.

Mrs. J. Kelly
(George Kelly's mother)

On Monday last week, Mrs. Ragan came in about 10 in the morning and asked if she had any arsenic. Said she had none and Mrs. Ragan asked if George could go and get three cents worth. Mrs. Kelly told her she didn't think they sold less than a dime's worth. Mrs. Ragan said the rats were very bad and she thought they were worse on her side now because she had had to move her flour from the platform. Mrs. Ragan asked if each could give five cents in order to kill the rats while the cold weather lasted. They did so. George went and got it. Later, he came in with Mrs. Ragan and asked Mrs. Kelly to divide it; she refused. He then asked Mrs. Wise and she said she would have nothing to do with it. Mrs. Ragan said "give it to me and I will divide it." She did so and took hers home. Mrs. Ragan returned at about one o'clock and said her husband was worse. Sometime after dark Mrs. Wise came in and said Dr. Brownell had told her his suspicions; Mrs. Kelly and Mrs. Wise went to the Ragan home to inquire about the arsenic. Mrs. Ragan gave it to them and said "there it is just as I got it. I did not use any of it." The two women put the arsenic into the stove. It seems the arsenic had been in the back kitchen up behind the studding; the room was not plastered.

Mrs. Wise

She went to spend the day with Mrs. Kelly on Monday last week. Mrs. Ragan came in and said her husband was a great deal better and that the Dr. considered him out of danger. She asked Mrs. Kelly if she had arsenic in the house; she had not. Mrs. Ragan wanted to know if George could go for some; she then asked if Mrs. Kelly would give five cents and she five and get some and divide it between them. Said the rats were so bad she could not stand it. George went and later returned with Mrs. Ragan; he asked his mother to divide it and she wouldn't do it. Mrs. Wise wouldn't either, so Mrs. Ragan divided it. At lunchtime Mrs. Ragan came running in and said her husband was just as he was when he was first taken and she was afraid he would get worse. Then at two or three o'clock she came in again and said he was much worse. She told Mrs. Kelly they ought to go in. Mrs. Kelly said the room was too small, but she would take care of the children while Mrs. Wise went. She found Ragan in a spasm and called for some hot water; he said his tongue was stiff. They gave him a mouthful of whiskey. He said it was better but he thought he must die, he felt so bad.

Later that evening Mrs. Kelly and Mrs. Wise went back and asked about the arsenic. Before they dropped it in the stove Mrs. Wise remarked that half of it was gone; her suspicions had been aroused before that by having heard what the Doctor said.

Sam—That's all for today — it's been a long one. Tedious at times.

As you'll see from these notes, none of the witnesses has implicated Mowrey, but their testimony is extremely damning to Mrs. Ragan.

LATER THAT EVENING, well after dark, the brothers McKinney reviewed Frank's notes and discussed the day's proceedings before Squire Sage. They were more or less comfortably seated at the large central table in their offices above J. Geyer. The cast-iron woodstove had been newly stoked against the chill of the evening and the cotton wicks of the twin lard-oil lamps were turned up high for greater visibility. They made their supper of hot biscuits, cold venison and cold beer, ordered up from the hostelry on the near corner of the public square.

Sawing manfully on an especially stubborn slab of venison, Sam McKinney demanded of Frank concerning the appearance, demeanor and credibility of each of the nine witnesses who had testified that day. Frank responded patiently and fully to each of his brother's inquiries and separately rehearsed the testimony given by the witnesses. Then, while they chewed on their dinners, they also chewed on the prosecution's evidence, catalogued it and tested it against their collective experience and their appreciation of the probabilities, i.e. what testimony was probable, and therefore credible, and what was not.

"Your conclusions, as expressed in your final note, are most certainly appropriate," Sam pronounced. "It seems clear that the State has not yet adduced a single shred of evidence in support of the charge against James Mowrey. And, as you have observed, the case against Mrs. Ragan becomes more and more compelling.

"As to the first point, I shall be much surprised if Messrs. Jones and Parsons are not presently poised to tie our Mr. Mowrey into the matter. And," he added ominously, "I greatly fear that they intend to make that connection with Mrs. Ragan's testimony — which must, perforce, inculpate herself as well as Mowrey."

Frank McKinney nodded agreement. "I see no help for it."

"Nor do I," conceded Sam. "There would be no point in her trying to deny the obvious. We have already advised her father to encourage her co-operation. I can only hope that her rendition of the truth does not destroy her completely."

He stoked his full beard thoughtfully. "When does she testify? Do you know?"

"First thing tomorrow," Frank replied. "I caught Ben Parsons after session and asked him. As you know, I've a pretty decent rapport with Ben and he's been willing to share information."

"I note," mused Sam McKinney, "that the State's evidence thus far has Mrs. Ragan attempting, both successfully and unsuccessfully, to procure a supply of arsenic on Monday, the day before her husband died. But he was first taken sick on the preceding Friday. Will it be the State's position that he became ill, or was poisoned, by some means independent of Mrs. Ragan and that she simply seized the opportunity to finish him off?"

"Not really, Sam. I wondered the same thing myself. In fact," Frank answered with no more than the hint of a twinkle. "I asked Ben Parsons about it. He said that was a nice convenient theory, but that we ought not get too comfortable with it. He's got a witness, fellow named John Wesler, who's a clerk in a drug store in Tippecanoe. Mr. Wesler has known Mrs. Ragan since she was a little girl. He'll testify that she came into his store the third week of March and bought half an ounce of arsenic."

Chapter Five

WHEN SQUIRE SAGE UNLOCKED HIS COURTROOM door at precisely 7:30 Tuesday morning he was greeted by a sizeable crowd of would-be spectators. Those stationed on his front porch and on its stout plank steps had arrived in the early morning darkness. Others, gathered in the small front yard and in the dirt street beyond, had come only slightly afterward. It was obvious that news of the proceedings against James Mowrey had spread through the township like an unchecked conflagration. The fact that Mrs. Ragan was expected to testify today had only intensified the general interest.

Frank and Sam McKinney had anticipated this morning's increased demand for spectator space within the small courtroom and had been among the earliest arrivals. They were also among the first in line when the Squire and his elderly bailiff opened the door and permitted no more than forty-odd people to take seating room along the wall behind them. Those persons not fortunate enough to be admitted accepted their exclusion equably and remained outside in hopes that they might ultimately gain entrance, or that they might at least catch a glimpse of the participants or receive a first-hand report of new developments.

Because Mrs. Ragan was scheduled to give her testimony this morning the brothers McKinney had determined that both of them should attend today's session. Neither had met or interviewed their prospective client and Sam had not so much as laid eyes on her. This latter circumstance, despite Frank's earlier monitory remarks, had not only caused Sam McKinney enormous frustration, but had also left him utterly unprepared for the general appearance, the understated elegance and the undeniable beauty of this woman, Jane Elizabeth Ragan. She was escorted into the courtroom not by the bailiff, but by her father, Martin Cunningham. Her hand rested lightly on his arm as they walked together, as if in a processional, to the witness chair. Cunningham seated her there, squeezed both her hands, spoke softly in her ear, and took a place against the wall where he could watch and listen.

No person in the courtroom could have failed to react to the presence of Jane Ragan. She was tastefully dressed in a trim and efficient dress of midnight blue, neatly cinched at the waist, with white linen cuffs and collar. She was of not more than average height, with graceful bearing and a firm, lithe figure. Long dark hair, center-parted, framed a smooth, intelligent face with even features, high cheekbones and eyes of muted sapphire.

Justice Sage administered the oath and Ebenezer Parsons, tall and studious, examined for the State. In response to his patient questioning, and in a firm clear voice, Mrs. Ragan told her story.

She had, she acknowledged, been acquainted with the defendant James Mowrey since they were teenagers. They had both lived in Cowlesville at the time and had enjoyed a mutual "affection". Although it was not articulated, there was a strong implication that they had been sexually intimate. Then, before she turned seventeen, her family had moved to Troy and the relationship ended. Shortly after the move she had met, and soon afterwards married, Arthur Ragan. That was in July of 1850. And, in March of '52, the baby came, a beautiful little girl with eyes the color of her own. Her emotional commitment to the child was so great, she said, that she became indifferent, and perhaps cold, to her husband.

"Then, in June of '53, while I was nursing my child at our home in Piqua, James Mowrey came to the door. Although I was greatly surprised to see him after the passage of nearly four years, I asked him to come in. He did so and immediately began to speak of former days and our former affection. He finally told me that he was still very much in love with me and that he was miserable and unhappy without me.

"I told him that it was useless for us to talk of such matters and I reminded him of his wife and children. I told him that he was a husband and father and I, a wife and mother. I said that it was wrong for us to think of our former passions.

"Then, when I refused to permit him to lure me into the sitting room, he said that he would leave, but he promised to return when he next came to town.

"I saw him a few weeks later when he came up with my sister, but nothing of importance happened on that occasion and I saw no more of him until September. By that time my child had died and I had been very ill. After I recovered I went to the church quarterly meeting at Cowlesville; actually the meeting itself was at Hyattsville. While I was there Mowrey came down as often as he could without exciting suspicion. His conversation was always the same. He repeatedly declared his affection and insisted that he could not live his life apart from me.

"Then, in the winter I went down to Cowlesville again to stay with my father and to attend the meetings at Hyattsville. One Sunday evening James Mowrey and I found ourselves together by the altar after everyone else had left. I begged him to go and get the others to come back so we would not be alone, but he would not do so.

"I came home the next day and he rode with me on the cars as far as Troy. He wanted me to write to him and said that if I didn't sign my name we would not be found out. He pleaded so earnestly that I finally agreed to write to him in care of the Troy postmaster."

Ebenezer Parsons rose from his chair at the counsel table to signal his intention to interrupt the witness' testimony. "And," he asked, "did you, in fact, write to the defendant as you promised to do?"

The answer came swiftly. "Yes. I wrote to him the next day and told him it was no use. I was a married woman."

"Did you ever write to him again?" Parsons demanded.

"Only the one time. In December of that next year — 1854. You have the letter."

"Alright," said Parsons. "We'll get to that. Let's go back to the winter of '53. When did you next see the defendant?"

"I didn't see him again until he came to Piqua to see me in the spring of

1854. Nothing of consequence happened on that occasion. I saw him again the last week of June just before I was to go to London. He came to Piqua because he had heard I was going away. He said he had a request to make of me. He wanted me to elope with him. He said he would sell all his property in order to provide for his family and we could go off to some distant place and make a new start in life. It made no difference that he wouldn't have a dollar in his pocket. He said that he would willingly sacrifice all that he had — his home, his wife and his children — if I would agree to go.

"I told him that I could not go with him. I said that I had a husband to think of. He continued to urge me to elope and finally said to me 'There's one thing I can do so you can be with me. I can give your old man a dose of arsenic that will stretch him out cold.'

"We saw one another again in the fall when he came to visit. He stayed until ten in the morning and then we went for a buggy ride. Before we went to ride he told me that I should administer poison to my husband. I could put it in his coffee, or his victuals, and he would simply go to town and be brought back dead. No one would suspect that I had done it. He said he would do it himself but that I would have a better chance.

"I told him I could not, with as tender heart as I had, bring myself to do it. I did tell him, though, that I cared as much for him as he did for me and that I would be glad if Ragan were not in our way."

Ebenezer Parsons was on his feet again. "That conversation took place before your buggy ride?"

"Yes."

"And what happened during the buggy ride?"

"We rode to the hill back of town, and over to the railroad, and then came back home."

"And" Ben Parsons persisted, "did you stop awhile? Out on the hill?"

"Yes. We did. For just a short time."

"Specifically," the prosecutor demanded, "did you have sexual intercourse with James Mowrey at that time — out on the hill — in the buggy?"

"I did not. We talked for a bit, mostly about our predicament. And he kissed me passionately several times. And he fondled me somewhat. I permitted that, but would go no further. He pressed me hard, but I refused and required that he take me home."

Ebenezer Parsons appeared to be satisfied with the answer and retreated from the witness. He resumed his seat at the counsel table and commanded, "Please continue."

"I next saw James Mowrey on December 6th — that's the date of the letter you have. My husband was away all day. Mowrey came soon after lunch and stayed until tea time. He said he came to tell me that if I could persuade Ragan to move to Cowlesville, or even to Tippecanoe, then he would himself have opportunity to administer the poison. When I told him that I had no such influence over my husband, he said that in that case I must administer it myself. He said that if I would do so then he would make arrangements to take me out West.

"As I said, he left about tea time, half past five, and my husband saw him as he was going back to Cowlesville. Later that evening my husband came home and would take no supper. When I asked him what was the matter, he seized me by the shoulders and shook me violently. He told me that I had been seen kissing James Mowrey on the river bridge that afternoon and that he knew we had spent the afternoon together. He said that if I would ever again admit James Mowrey to the house he would find the stoutest hickory switch this side of Cincinnati and wallop it across my back.

"As soon as he released me I went into the front room and threw myself onto the floor and cried. Then, after awhile, I got up and wrote the letter to Mowrey and sent it to the postmaster as he had told me to do."

Ebenezer Parsons pumped himself out of his chair, walked to the table behind which Squire Sage presided, and possessed himself of the unfolded letter which had lain in plain view throughout the course of Mrs. Ragan's testimony.

"Is this the letter to which you refer?" he asked, knowing full well that it was. "Dated December 6, 1854?"

"Yessir, it is," from the witness.

"Let me see here," began Parsons, scanning the letter from the station he had assumed just beside the witness. "This final paragraph is of interest. It seems to say," he began to read, "'Something must be done. We cannot continue in this way. It is too miserable for both of us. Unless you can find a way to eliminate this impediment, we must not see one another again.' Did I read that correctly?"

"Yes, you did. It's plain enough."

"And then," Parsons continued, "further down in the same paragraph, 'But if you could do that which I cannot, and remove that single obstacle, we could consummate our passion together, freely and utterly, and I could be yours to possess for the rest of our lives.'

"Did I read that correctly also?"

"Yes," came the shame-faced answer.

"And you wrote these words?"

"Yes."

"To the defendant, James Mowrey?"

"Yes."

"To what, or whom, did you refer as an 'impediment' and as an 'obstacle'?" demanded the prosecutor.

"To the fact that I was married," answered the witness.

"Oh come, now, Mrs. Ragan," pressed Parsons. "Didn't you really mean your husband, Arthur Ragan?"

"Yes. I suppose so."

"Not a mere concept, like a marriage, but a live, waking human being, such as your husband?"

Squire Sage struck the table resoundingly with his gavel. "Enough of that counsellor. You've made the point. This lady is not a defendant in these proceedings. And, I might add, she's your witness. I'll have no hectoring in this courtroom."

Ebenezer Parsons seemed unruffled by the rebuke. "I'm sorry, your honor. And Mrs. Ragan, please understand that I've meant no offense. I only wish to understand your meaning. Now, then, madam. Did you receive a response to your letter?"

Glad to move along, the witness answered, "No. I don't believe he ever received it. I think the postmaster delivered it to your people just last week — after Ragan died."

"Did you and the defendant Jimmy Mowrey have any discussion about it?"

"He told me that he didn't get my letter, even though he had inquired after it on several occasions. He also said that it didn't matter because he'd have no chance to poison my husband. He said that I must do it myself."

"And," coaxed the prosecutor, "did you agree to do so?"

"No, sir. I didn't actually agree to poison my husband. But I did, late last month, purchase a small amount of arsenic at the drugstore in Tippecanoe. From there I went into Morrison & Sicles store. Mowrey was there when I entered. I told him that I had purchased arsenic and he said that I should allow some time to pass before I gave it to Ragan. I went to church the following Sunday — also to Sabbath school and church again in the evening. Even though I have taught Sunday school classes for more than a year now, I am ashamed to say that I have been more of a professor than a possessor of my religion.

"I kept the poison those several days thinking whether I could do such a thing. Then, by Thursday, I was reminded how easy Jimmy had said it would be. I'd had no trouble with my husband that day, but I put a teaspoon full of arsenic in his coffee that evening. I put the poison in first, then the sugar and cream. I brought it in from the kitchen and he stirred it himself. He took a second cup of coffee and I gave him the rest of the arsenic in that one. He went out in the evening and came home very sick. I had been to prayer meeting, but returned home before my husband. When he arrived, he complained of stomach pain and went straight to bed. "I nursed him during his sickness and by Monday morning he seemed much better. Then, as you know, I set about procuring more arsenic from Ashton's Drug Store. Shortly before noon I asked my husband if he wanted anything and he said he'd like some chicken broth. I put arsenic in a pint-sized bowl and poured warmed chicken soup in after it, stirred it and gave it to him. I asked if it tasted good and he said that it did. He ate just a small portion at first and I set the bowl down on the hearth to keep it warm. Shortly afterwards he said he was ready for the rest. I gave him the bowl and he finished it off. He told me it was very good.

"Mrs. Davis had been in earlier and had tasted the chicken soup also — that is, without any arsenic in it. She had told me it was really very tasty.

"By two o'clock, of course, my husband was in excruciating pain. I think he knew that afternoon that he was going to die. I also believe that he knew he had been poisoned.

"By Tuesday morning it was obvious that my husband was dying and I sent for my father. I wanted him to be with me for comfort and solace. I was in and out of Ragan's room all that day, nursing him as best I could. It was then that my husband told me that he had instructed that his will be destroyed because he had heard some hard things. He wouldn't say what those things were. He told me that the will was made March 27th, just before he got sick, and that he had left me all his property.

"I was surprised to learn that he had made a will because he had not spoken of it before. I had thought about the matter earlier because I had once dreamed that he had died and I had wondered about what would happen to his property. But now he said that he had not only made a will, but had also ordered that it be destroyed. I could only guess what "hard things" he had heard to cause him to take such an action. He would not tell me anything more and only asked that I kiss him. Which, of course, I gladly did. Soon after that he died.

"I must add to this account — and this may seem very strange to you — but in spite of all that has happened, one thing is very certain and that is that I am grieved by my husband's death."

Ebenezer Parsons seemed satisfied with Mrs. Ragan's testimony on direct examination. He rose to his feet, nodded respectfully to Justice Sage, and proffered the witness. "You may examine," he said in the general direction of the defense counsel table.

Although that table was located almost directly in front of the witness chair and not more than ten feet away, Mrs. Ragan had thus far studiously averted her glance from the three men seated there. The defendant, James Mowrey, was flanked by his attorneys, Charles Morris and Harvey Sellers. The defense lawyers were almost a matched set. Each was in his early forties, each resided and practiced in Troy, and each had served a single term as mayor of that community. Sellers, the older and leaner of the two, conducted the cross-examination of Mrs. Ragan. In doing so, he revisited the principal points and events alluded to in her direct testimony. It was a long and searching process and was in many respects tedious and repetitive of her former descriptions. And yet, inevitably, new matter and a subtly different perspective developed as well.

At one point Harvey Sellers had asked Mrs. Ragan if she had loved her husband. She said that she supposed that she had "in the ordinary way." And when questioned about the quality of her marriage with Ragan, she answered that her husband was "cold toward me and I didn't think he had much affection for me. His attitude seemed to be that I was his concubine and was to perform as such when and if he commanded.

"But he was good to me when I did not displease him. He sometimes got things for me if in the right mood. Though he did tell me that coopers' wives need not wear silk dresses, so if I wanted one I must get it myself. And I did, too. I earned a little with my needle and was able to come by a few things in that manner."

Further along in his cross-examination Sellers asked the operative question, "Mrs. Ragan, you have freely acknowledged that you deliberately administered lethal dosages of poison to your husband. What is it that motivated your conduct?"

"I'm sorry. I thought I had made it clear that I acted as I did because of the urgings and the blandishments of Mr. Mowrey. It was all done because of him. He tempted me and he pressed me relentlessly until I did what he demanded."

"Isn't it true, Mrs. Ragan, that you poisoned your husband yourself because you were unable to persuade Mr. Mowrey to do it for you?" demanded Sellers.

"No. That's not true. It was Mowrey who wanted my husband poisoned. It was he who first suggested it and continued to insist on it. I only did it because he urged me to."

"Well, now, Mrs. Ragan," began Sellers archly. "We've all seen your letter of December 6th, haven't we?"

"Yes," from the witness.

"Is it not fair, Madam, to characterize that letter as an offer to exchange your sexual favors for your husband's murder?"

"Certainly not."

Sellers had snatched the letter from the center table. "Let's see here. Does it not say that if he would remove 'that single obstacle' — your husband — 'we could consummate our passion together, freely and utterly, and I could be yours to possess for the rest of our lives'? Does it not say that?"

For the first time that day Jane Ragan stammered. "No — Yes — Yes, it does say that, but ..."

"Is that not a promise of sex in exchange for murder?" demanded Sellers as Justice Sage gavelled for control.

"Enough of that Mr. Sellers," snapped the Justice. "You've made your point. Let's get on with it."

Sellers accepted the rebuke with total equanimity. "You need not answer that, Mrs. Ragan. Let me ask another. Do you contend that the poisoning of Arthur Ragan was accomplished by the acts of Defendant James Mowrey rather than by your own activities?"

Jane Ragan turned slightly in the witness chair and glared directly at James Mowrey as she answered in a firm controlled voice, "I do not. He is guilty and I am guilty. We conspired together to do the deed and we must each accept our punishment. I want James Mowrey to be punished, but not more severely than myself."

Harvey Sellers had a final question. "Mrs. Ragan, has anyone made you any promises in exchange for your testimony today?"

"No, sir. I say these things without any legal advice, or, for that matter, without any advice at all. I have not seen a lawyer, nor a minister, nor even my father. I say these things only because they are true."

BY THE TIME JANE RAGAN WAS FINALLY EXCUSED, she had been on the stand for more than nine hours and court was adjourned for the day.

Over the next two days another dozen witnesses were called by the prosecution. Their testimony was largely corroborative and cumulative. Another handful of witnesses was called by the defense to vouch for the character and reputation of James Mowrey. The Defendant himself invoked the Fifth Amendment and declined to take the stand.

At the conclusion of the proceedings, Justice Sage found probable cause and bound Mowrey to the Grand Jury. He refused to admit him to bail.

Chapter Six

AND THEN THEY had to do it all over again.

The ink had not yet dried on Squire Sage's order remanding James Mowrey to the county jail before both the order and the proceedings in the Justice's Court were challenged by Mowrey's attorneys. Claiming their client's entitlement to an immediate release from custody, the Messrs. Morris and Sellers petitioned Judge Joseph Pearson of the Miami County Probate Court for a writ of habeas corpus. The argument ran that the squire's order, finding probable cause and holding the defendant until such time as the grand jury might chance to convene, was tantamount to an order of indefinite commitment and that such an order clearly exceeded the authority of a justice of the peace. The fact that the justice had also refused to admit Mowrey to bail served to reinforce their contention that the defendant had been impermissibly deprived of his liberty without regard to constitutionally mandated due process protections.

Judge Pearson's response to the petition had been to set the matter for an immediate re-hearing on the question of probable cause. This "Second Examination of Mowrey" was held before Judge Pearson at the county probate courtroom in Troy. It began on Saturday, April 14th, just two days after completion of the first examination, and continued through the following Thursday. Not surprisingly, this second examination before Judge Pearson was a precise reprise of the first examination before Justice Sage. All of the same witnesses appeared and testified as before. All of the documents, including the note to Ashton's drugstore and Jane Ragan's letter of December 6th, were re-introduced. Most significantly, the lady herself testified again, precisely as she had before. And, once again, James Mowrey invoked his Fifth Amendment rights and refused to testify in his own defense.

Upon completion of the evidence and the arguments of counsel in this second examination of Mowrey, Judge Pearson announced his own findings to be consistent with those of Justice Sage. The writ of habeas corpus was denied, the defendant was bound over to the grand jury on the basis of probable cause, and bail was denied. The defendant was remanded to jail.

The county newspapers, the Troy Times and the Piqua Register, as well as the nearby Dayton and Cincinnati Gazettes, had fully and faithfully reported the proceedings in Justice Sage's courtroom. Virtually all of the testimony had been reproduced verbatim and featured prominently. That same quality coverage was then extended for the second examination before Judge Pearson. The net effect of the two examinations of Mowrey and the attendant news coverage was that by the end of April 1855, Jane Elizabeth Ragan had twice confessed, in two separate courtrooms, to having poisoned her husband, and those separate confessions had been reproduced and prominently featured in the public press throughout Miami County and all of southwestern Ohio. The perception was that while there might be room for controversy concerning James Mowrey's culpability, there was clearly no question concerning Mrs. Ragan's guilt. All of the published evidence was entirely consistent with her own confessions.

THAT WHICH HAD BECOME a warm and rainy springtime ultimately segued, in desultory fashion, into a hot, dry and dusty summer. In the early months the mosquitoes had been a constant menace and as the summer progressed the deerflies assumed their own vicious dominance over those persons whose activities required them to spend time out of doors. Matters were somewhat better, however, for those who resided indoors within the restricted confines of the Miami County jail. Located in Troy, and only recently completed, the jailhouse was an enormous, two-story building constructed entirely of Dayton limestone. Each of the separate stones was itself massive in size and had been interlocked with its neighbors by tongue and groove joints. The overall impression was that of a formidable, monolithic edifice, thick-walled and immensely secure. Because, then, of the thick stone walls, the interior of the cellblock remained cool all summer long and, because of the jailer's pride in his new facility, it had been maintained in near pristine condition. All in all, the county jailhouse had been a most comfortable accommodation for Jane Ragan that summer of 1855. The condition of the jail and Jane Ragan's own particular circumstance were noted and charmingly described by an unidentified young woman whose contemporary account of her own visit to the facility appeared in the July 26, 1855 edition of the Troy Times:

I went in to look in admiration at the convenient arrangements for the comfort of the prisoners; bath-rooms, ventilators in each cell; walls and floor clean as whitewash and soap and water could make them; all so cool and quiet, that I fully determined, should my lot ever be cast in Miami County to commit some petty larceny immediately, that I might secure myself such a comfortable retreat. The sun shone cheerfully down through the barred windows, upon the spotlessly white wall, and flickered on the bars of a cage hanging at the door of one of the cells, and the little canary within the cage burst out into a merry and ear-piercing song, as if he were hung in a drawing-room, or flying through the groves of his own tropical land.

"That is the cell of Mrs. Ragan, the woman who poisoned her husband," said the jailor; "Will you go in and be introduced to her?" I hesitated with a nervous unwillingness to intrude upon her, a shy feeling which came upon me, a fear of awkward doubt what to say, and fears of wounding her feelings. However, I plucked up courage and went in. There, in one of those clean quiet cells, furnished with a couple of tables, a few chairs, bedstead, some books, etc., sat a pretty young woman, surrounded by piles of embroidery and sewing materials. The formal introduction fell strangely on my ear — "Mrs. Ragan, Miss_____" sounded so incongruous in that place and under such circumstances, but the force of conventional habit was on me and I fell at once to talking of the embroidery, the weather, etc. — At last, I got presence of mind to look at her. You remember her story — she poisoned her husband with arsenic, giving him three separate doses, induced to the crime by love of another man, who is now confined in the same jail as his accomplice. The suspicions of the physicians were aroused, and at her husband's death she was arrested. She made a full confession of her guilt, never denying any circumstance, but giving a full account of everything, alleging no reason but love for this man Mowrey, whom she accused of being her accomplice, and whom she said, she now hates as much as she formerly loved him. The murder seems to have been committed with the most frightful coolness, letters having been found dated months back, which had passed between her lover and herself, discussing the manner of his taking off. The poison was administered at three times, so far apart that the victim had nearly recovered from the effects of the first dose before the second was given, and during all the time he was ill she had nursed him even though she was the same woman who was at that time committing a cold blooded murder. A frank, engaging young woman with a beautiful expression, not refined of course, but very womanly — blue eyes and an open clear forehead, and a mouth large, certainly, but opening with a pleasant smile and disclosing very beautiful teeth. A glance at her face was a whole volume of argument against Lavator.

— I talked with her some time, carefully avoiding any allusion to her situation; discussed the prison in its cheerful aspect; heard her tell how the moonlight fell upon the wall of her cell at night, asked her if she slept; "Yes," she said, her bed was very comfortable. At last I gathered courage and ventured to say something about her trial, which is fixed for September.

She was very hopeful. To be sure the suspense was bad, and sometimes she was down-hearted, but then friends would come in and encourage her; indeed, she was sure she would get clear some way or other. I bid her goodbye with a saddened, depressed feeling, from which I could not recover for the whole day.

THE HONORABLE RALPH S. HART was Judge of the Court of Common Pleas for Miami County. He had been, in fact, the first and only person to occupy that office since it was created by the Ohio Constitution of 1850. He had earned a reputation as a studious, hard-working lawyer and had achieved local prominence by having spoken out in favor of the temperance movement in Troy. On one occasion, some thirteen years earlier, he and fellow attorney Charles Morris had been pelted with rotten eggs while speaking against the Demon Rum at the nearby Dye Settlement. Two of the offenders had been arrested and subsequent demands for their release had led to an angry confrontation between a group of enraged farmers and the county sheriff. When the sheriff enlisted assistance from local infantry and cavalry units, the farmers disbanded and the whole affair, which came to be known as the Broad Ford War, was over.

Now, in late July of 1855, Judge Hart took an official interest in the predicament of this woman whom he fully expected to be indicted and ultimately tried in his courtroom. Despite his awareness that Mrs. Ragan was represented by the McKinney brothers, with assistance from his own brother, Troy attorney James H. Hart, Judge Hart made an order finding her to be in need of additional counsel and appointed former Judge John A. Corwin of nearby Urbana, Ohio, to assist in her defense. Because the order also found Mrs. Ragan to be indigent, Mr. Corwin would be paid by the county.

Upon the event of his appointment as additional counsel for Mrs. Ragan, John Corwin immediately scheduled and paid a courtesy visit on Sam McKinney. He wanted to insure that his entry into the case would be accomplished smoothly and without resentment. He had not sought the assignment, he said, and would not accept it without Sam's blessing. He also declared himself ready to assist and co-operate in the defense of Mrs. Ragan in whatever manner, and to whatever extent, Sam McKinney should deem appropriate.

For his own part, Sam acknowledged his need for assistance with such a difficult case and professed himself to be grateful for the opportunity to work with counsel of Mr. Corwin's caliber. He would make his files readily available for examination. The two men sealed their relationship as co-counsel with a handshake and proceeded to business. Sam McKinney described the case history from memory and offered his own notes, as well as those prepared by Frank, for Corwin's review.

"You should be aware," McKinney articulated, "That the lady has only recently consented to speak with us at all. For some strange reason, she has thus far kept her own counsel and has refused, until quite recently, to permit us to appear on her behalf, or for that matter, to be of any assistance whatever."

"Truly?" inquired Corwin. "That is certainly irregular."

"Indeed," replied Sam McKinney. "One might almost call it 'bizarre'. She did however consent to see me some ten days ago. However, even on that occasion she would say nothing other than what she has already said in her public testimony. She is quite confident that she will be fully exonerated when her own case comes on for trial."

John Corwin raised an eyebrow, "Upon what basis?"

"I truly cannot imagine," McKinney replied. "Her confidence seems most unwarranted. Unrealistic, under the circumstances. She did, however, finally agree to permit me to explore the prospect of securing some form of consideration in exchange for her testimony against Mowrey."

"A little late for that, isn't it?" asked Corwin.

"Somewhat," acknowledged Sam McKinney ruefully. "But at least, its a chance."

The lawyers agreed — if she would permit it — that Corwin might investigate the matter independently as he saw fit and that he would privately interview Mrs. Ragan at the jail. They agreed to meet again, with Frank and James Hart also, the following Friday, August 3rd.

"Do not be surprised, John," Sam McKinney admonished, "to find our client large with child. She's due to deliver in early September. God knows who the father is, but He hasn't spoken to the matter. I asked Mrs. Ragan, but she will only say that the child was conceived during wedlock and will therefore be quite legitimate."

John Corwin was taken aback. "She's to deliver while in jail?" He shook his head. "In early September? Isn't that when she's to go to trial?"

"Mmhm," McKinney acknowledged. "That's when it's scheduled."

Chapter Seven

WEDNESDAY, AUGUST 1ST, was the 21st anniversary of the West Indian Emancipation and was celebrated, at Piqua, by colored people from all over the southwestern part of the state. Many of the celebrants had themselves been the slaves of Congressman John Randolph of Virginia. Randolph had freed his slaves at his death and had provided funds with which lands located in Mercer County, Ohio, were purchased for them. Sadly, the canal boats which carried these former slaves north from Cincinnati were met by farmers armed with pitchforks and axes. The entire group was denied access to their promised lands and none were allowed to debark from the packets. Several hundred of them returned to Miami County and most of those had settled in the Piqua area. Because of the large concentration of the "Randolph People", it was natural that Piqua should have become a focal point for the celebration of Emancipation Day. And it was a gala, joyous event. There were delegations from Troy, Urbana, Dayton and other nearby communities. Each had come supplied with its own emblems, badges, banners and marching bands. Beginning early in the day and continuing until dusk, the festivities consisted of physical contests, foot races, wrestling matches, speechifying and band performances, all of which were sustained with vast amounts of Cronk's Beer and assorted piles of foodstuffs handsomely laid out on the several makeshift and borrowed tables. The separate table reserved for their white guests was equally well-provisioned.

Sam McKinney was traditionally included as one of the "white guests" and had accepted several warm invitations to attend this year's event. Because Sam's affinity with the "groaning board" was well-known, if not obvious from his sizeable girth, it was generally expected that he too would arrive early, stay late and consume a great deal. And, of course, he did not disappoint. True to his habit, he had come to the festival direct from his home and remained until mid-afternoon. He had permitted no court assignments and had scheduled no office appointments for the day. When he finally made the rounds, said his goodbyes and left the pleasant grove which was the situs of the festival, he headed, more of habit than of necessity, for his offices on Main Street.

He was surprised, upon arrival, to find Martin Cunningham seated on the stairway. Cunningham appeared to have been waiting quite a little while. He seemed agitated and he clutched a folded sheet of white paper.

"I haven't minded waiting for you, Mr. McKinney," he said while following the lawyer up the narrow stairway. "I didn't have an appointment, but I'd hoped that I might catch you anyway. Libby said I should bring this to you as soon as possible."

The two men had arrived at the second level, entered the law offices and seated themselves on opposite sides of the oak table. Cunningham offered the folded paper and McKinney took it from him.

"What is it?" he asked as he opened and scanned the paper. "Where did it come from?"

Martin Cunningham was quick to respond. "You'll see what it is, Mr. McKinney. Or, at least, what it seems to be. It's been in a drawer at my home these past two months."

"How's that?" demanded Sam McKinney.

"Well, sir," replied Cunningham. Right after the trial in Judge Pearson's court, I gave directions to my wife and daughters — that'd be Edith and Harriet — and Josephine, she's the youngest — to search Ragan's house for papers. I had thought we might have missed something earlier.

"And it happened that Edith remembered that she'd collected some papers right after Ragan died. She'd put them all inside a little ottoman and hadn't really looked at them since. Well, then, after I'd given orders to search for papers, she and Harriet went through the things that were in the ottoman. When they found this paper, Edith gave it to her mother and she passed it on to me. That would have been about the first of June. I placed it in my drawer and it's been there ever since. I spoke to Libby about it yesterday and she asked me to bring it to you."

Sam McKinney had only glanced at the paper while he listened to Cunningham's explanation. Now he flattened the loosely scrawled document on the table and read it aloud:

Piqua, March the 29th, 1855.

Dear Wife — When you see or find this on my person, it will tell you that I am my own murderer. Proudly do I boast of it, as I do not wish to live any longer in this world. I have no work to do, and I do not want to live any longer. Now, Elizabeth, you have been a faithful wife, ever ready and willing to do for me when it was in your power. You have been a kind, obedient, dutiful wife, and have borne with all my harshness without a murmur. I want you to be kind to everybody. I have willed all I have to you. You will find my will in the under drawer, in little Alice's hat. Forgive me — may God and my aged parents forgive me. You must not think hard of me. Bury me by the order to which I belong. No more. I take poison tonight, if not foiled.

AURTHR RAGAN

Sam McKinney looked askance at Martin Cunningham, then re-read the letter, to himself, twice more. For what seemed an eternity he spoke not a word, pondering that which he had just seen and heard. He rotated his bulk in his swivel chair and contemplated the blank north wall of the room. He swung back around to rest his elbows on the table, interlocked the fingers of his large, meaty hands, rested his chin heavily on the resulting temple, and closed his eyes. When he was satisfied that he could deal with this latest information, he looked up at Martin Cunningham.

"What do you take this document to be?" he inquired.

"Seems like it might be a kind of suicide letter," answered Cunningham.

"Do you believe it to be genuine?"

"I don't know, sir," Cunningham hedged. "I've told you how I came by it. I can't say if it's Ragan's handwriting or not. It might be."

"And then, again, it might not be," McKinney supplied.

"That's true," Cunningham conceded. "I've seen his handwriting, of course, but I'm no expert."

"Do you consider it likely that the man would have misspelled his own name when he printed it at the bottom of the letter?" asked McKinney pointedly.

And when McKinney directed his attention to the obvious error, Cunningham seemed mildly perplexed. "I don't know, sir," he answered. "None of us had really noticed it."

Sam McKinney studied the letter another few moments before changing tack. "What do you suggest I do with this document?" he asked.

"I don't know, sir. I think that'll have to be your decision. Libby thought you should see the letter right away. She said they'd have to release her as soon as they knew about it."

McKinney shook his head sadly. "No, Mr. Cunningham. That will not occur. I think I can assure you that the prosecution cannot be persuaded to release your daughter — by means of this document — or by virtue of any other evidence that may surface. She has already confessed her part in the matter." "Then what's to do?" inquired Martin Cunningham. He had reverted to his customary practice of wringing his hands. "There must be something."

"Not for the moment, I fear," intoned Sam McKinney. "As you may or may not be aware, I have finally been permitted some preliminary discussions with the prosecutors, but we can do nothing further until the grand jury brings back its indictments. That body is set to convene on Monday. If they return an indictment against James Mowrey, as I expect, the prosecution will want your daughter's testimony at his trial. I anticipate that they will be prepared to make some concessions in exchange for her co-operation.

"In the meanwhile, I should like to keep this document. I'll want to sleep on it, get used to it, and examine all its ramifications. I will also want to pass it by my co-counsel — I seem to have developed several of those fellows — my brother Frank, and James Hart, both of whom I have involved, and now, of course, the court has seen fit to appoint Mr. Corwin into the mix and I will want to consult with him as well.

"Then," he continued, "after full consideration by all concerned, we can decide what we should do, or not do, with this document."

On that somewhat equivocal note Sam McKinney heaved himself out of his chair and hauled himself to his feet. It was evident that the interview was over. Martin Cunningham took his leave and descended the office stairs at a disheartened pace. Any trace of his earlier excitement was gone.

ON HIS WAY HOME THAT EVENING Sam McKinney stopped by his brother's residence to acquaint him with this latest development in the Ragan case. He was greeted warmly by his sister-in-law. Louise Wood McKinney was an attractive, intelligent young woman of New England stock. She and Frank had married less than two years ago. Now she led Sam into Frank's small and cluttered study, kissed him lightly on the cheek, and withdrew.

Sam McKinney reported his earlier conversation with Martin Cunningham and spread the document on his brother's small writing table. Frank had listened quietly and scrutinized the document closely. His reaction was both incredulous and explosive.

"How remarkably childish!" he snorted. "It's clumsy! It's incredibly naive! Worse than that, it's an obvious and convenient fabrication."

"Do you think so?" asked Sam innocuously. "Why is that?"

Frank McKinney looked hard at his older brother trying to catch the hint of skepticism in his expression. "Do I really have to answer that? Are you putting me on?"

Sam smiled grimly. "No," he said, "you needn't answer. The question was purely rhetorical. I agree that the document is obviously — and egregiously — a fabrication.

"And," he added ominously, "I don't think I like what it portends."

Chapter Eight

"I TELL YOU AGAIN," insisted John Corwin, "that the lady says she is innocent."

"Do you really?" asked Sam McKinney, with poorly disguised acrimony.

"I do, indeed," replied Corwin. And when the brothers McKinney looked askance at one another and rolled their eyes in moues of mock disbelief, Corwin continued, "I tell you also, gentlemen, that upon that state of the case, we have no independent choice in the matter. We are duty-bound to plead her not guilty and to present her defense with all possible zeal."

Although John Corwin was younger by a year and lighter by a hundredweight than Sam McKinney, he had no cause to be intimidated by the older and larger man on either score. Corwin's initial training and his subsequent experience before the bar were vastly superior to that of either of the McKinney brothers.

He was the scion of Moses B. Corwin, Champaign County's most distinguished attorney, and he had begun his own legal career at the early age of twenty, fresh out of Decatur College and brimfull of the ideals and traditions of the law. After some ten years of practice in his father's offices in Urbana he had served a stint as judge of the county court. He was presently engaged in the private practice of law, having rejoined his father, along with his own younger brother Ichabod, to form the firm of Corwin, Corwin and Corwin. As a result of his short term on the county bench he would wear the respectful mantle "Judge Corwin" for the rest of his days.

And while he would have displaced considerably less water than would Sam McKinney, John Corwin was a strongly built six-footer with an imposing, formidable countenance. Despite his easy, courteous manner, he was clearly a force to be reckoned with on any level of activity.

The four defense lawyers, John Corwin, the brothers McKinney and James Hart, were gathered in McKinney's office. It was early evening of the Friday before the Grand Jury was slated to meet on August 9th. It was also just two days after Arthur Ragan's "suicide" letter had surfaced on Emancipation Day. The meeting had been scheduled to begin at four o'clock, but John Corwin had been excusably, if not predictably, delayed. He had risen early, saddled the big bay, stuffed his "Ragan File" into his saddlebag, and left home before daylight. The twenty-six mile ride to Troy was uneventful and he had arrived in good time for his early afternoon appointment with Mrs. Ragan at the county jail. That conference, however, had taken a great deal more time than anticipated. As a result, even though he had made the eight mile leg to Piqua at a near gallop, he was nonetheless more than an hour late for his meeting with the other defense lawyers.

Now, hungry from having missed his lunch and warm from his ride in the hot August sunshine, he paced restlessly across the rough flooring of the second story office room. Sam and Frank McKinney watched him warily from their stations at opposite ends of the big oak table. James Hart monitored the proceedings from his own perch on a cane-bottom in the corner. John Corwin had already described his earlier, and much protracted, interview with Mrs. Ragan and her newly-expressed determination to plead innocent. Sam and Frank McKinney, upon hearing that startling disclosure, had simultaneously exploded in consternation and disbelief. James Hart's eyes had merely widened as he tried to process this latest information.

It was Hart who finally articulated the common reaction. "But she can't," he blurted. "She can't do that." "Of course she can," answered John Corwin calmly. "All that is required is that she, or one of us on her behalf, stand up in court and utter the words 'Not guilty' when asked to plead. Nothing could be more simple."

"She just can't," insisted Hart.

"And why the hell not?" demanded John Corwin sternly. "Tell me why this woman may not stand on her constitutional rights and require the State to either prove her guilt, beyond a reasonable doubt, or set her free?"

"She may certainly do so," conceded Sam McKinney reasonably. "The issue is whether we can permit her to make such an ill-considered choice."

"Permit?" echoed John Corwin heatedly. "What's to permit? We have no authority either to 'permit' or not to 'permit' a decision taken by our client. We are her lawyers and, in that capacity, we are constrained to abide by her instructions."

"We are also her counselors," argued Sam McKinney, "and we have an affirmative duty to advise her concerning her best interests. We have a strong and compelling obligation to protect against her own foolishness."

John Corwin seemed to relent. "I quite agree. We owe our client our best advice. She is entitled to the full benefit of our informed and separate analyses of her situation and our best judgments concerning the potential consequences of her decisions. She is, in short, entitled to receive our recommendations." He looked to the others for acquiescence. Then, "However, the ultimate decision in the matter, whatever our recommendations might be, must be that of our client. It is her life and it must be her choice."

"It's her neck, you might have said," remarked Frank McKinney. "Because that's what they mean to hang her by."

"I'm sure that you realize," said Sam McKinney to John Corwin, "that Mrs. Ragan has already confessed her part in this affair, the poisoning death of her husband, in a public forum, and on the record."

"Twice," interjected Frank McKinney. "There were two separate preliminary hearings and she told the same story each time."

"And every newspaper in this part of the state printed her testimony verbatim," added Sam McKinney. "Each time."

"Can her testimony be used against her?" asked John Corwin. "Was there an agreement concerning her testimony against James Mowrey?"

"No, there wasn't," answered Sam McKinney resentfully. "There should have been, but there wasn't."

John Corwin's eyes narrowed. "Explain that. Why was there *not* an agreement?"

"I've already explained it," Sam McKinney groused. "You will remember, I expect, that we have not had occasion to speak with Mrs. Ragan until just last week. For reasons known only to herself, the lady adamantly refused to consult with us beforehand. The net result, then, is that she has blurted out the entire sordid story without benefit of any protection."

"Actually," Frank McKinney interjected, "there was an agreement of sorts." He placed his hand on his brother's shoulder to calm his obvious resentment. "I may well have overstepped my authority..." he chuckled, "I'm sure I did, since we had no authority. I haven't mentioned it to Sam, but I did, on my own responsibility, undertake to conclude an agreement with the prosecutors."

"You did what?" demanded Sam McKinney, his attitude somewhere between consternation and disbelief. "Without my knowledge? And without our client's approval?"

"Yessir, I did," Frank responded in a conciliatory tone. "Even though Mrs. Ragan refused to speak with us, or perhaps because of that refusal, I anticipated what her testimony might be. So, when the opportunity presented itself, I asked Parsons what the prosecution might offer *if*, and I emphasized the *if*, the lady were to testify against Mowrey. I did not represent to him that I had authority to negotiate any kind of deal, but he must have assumed that I did."

"And you permitted him to do so?" asked Sam McKinney.

"I'm afraid I did," Frank acknowledged sheepishly. "I'm not particularly proud of the implicit deception, but I felt it necessary to protect Mrs. Ragan from her own foolishness."

John Corwin had attended the by-play between the brothers McKinney as though he were a spectator at a tennis match, watching first one and then the other. Now he resumed his own agenda. "Then there was an agreement concerning Mrs. Ragan's testimony at the prior hearings?"

"Yes," answered Frank McKinney. "There was. She was unaware of it and she therefore denied it at the hearings, but there was an agreement in place."

"And?"

"The agreement was that if she were to testify against Mowrey — at preliminary, at grand jury, and at trial — any such testimony wouldn't be used against her at her own trial," answered Frank McKinney.

"That's it?"

"And that if convicted, she wouldn't swing," he finished.

Corwin nodded approvingly. "Is that in writing anywhere?"

"No. But it's solid. I have it with Ben Parsons and he's straight enough."

"Alright, let's look at it," mused John Corwin. "She's already testified at preliminary — twice. What's the deal if she refuses to testify again? Can they use any of it?"

"No," answered Frank McKinney. "They can't use it. But if they convict her anyway, they can hang her. That part of the deal would be off."

"*If* they convict her," reminded John Corwin. "They can only hang her *if* they convict her."

"My God, man," exploded Sam McKinney. "Have you read the accounts? Looked at the evidence? Have you read the testimony? It's overwhelming! The jury will convict her inside twenty minutes."

"Well, now, let's not be too sure of that," remarked John Corwin. "We do have a suicide letter in the decedent's own hand. That should be sufficient to exonerate the lady, wouldn't you agree?"

"Fabricated!" snorted Sam McKinney. "And you damn well know it, too."

"Actually, I don't," replied John Corwin equably. "And neither do you. We have no direct knowledge on the subject."

"That's true enough," acknowledged Sam McKinney. "But you'll never convince me, or let alone a jury, that it's anything but a forgery. Look at it, for Christ's sake. They — whoever — didn't even spell his name right!"

"Stress," observed John Corwin. "I should imagine that a man who finds it necessary to take his own life has been sorely tried and has been subjected to a great deal of stress. He may well have become both distraught and disoriented."

"To the point that he misspelled his own name?"

"Of course. That seems quite possible," came the pat response from John Corwin.

Sam McKinney looked into the faces of the assembled lawyers. He looked first to his brother, then to James Hart, and finally into the eyes of John Corwin. It was obvious to each man in the room that John Corwin had dominated the discussion and would ultimately dominate Mrs. Ragan's defense. And he would thereby control her destiny.

"Am I to understand, then," he asked John Corwin, "That you propose that we allow Mrs. Ragan to repudiate her prior testimony, to enter a not-guilty plea to the murder of her husband, and to thereby risk losing her own life on the gallows?"

"Please remember our earlier discussion," admonished John Corwin. "It is not our place to 'allow' or to 'permit'. It is ours only to counsel and to recommend. We must each make our separate recommendations to Mrs. Ragan and leave the issue to her own conscience. I would only ask that this be accomplished before the Grand Jury meets Monday morning. The prosecutor will want to know how to proceed."

NEITHER OF THE BROTHERS McKINNEY SLEPT well that Friday night. They had harangued one another into the small hours of the morning over their perceptions of John Corwin's expressed attitude about the defense of Mrs. Ragan. Corwin's approach to the matter was, they agreed, both arrogant and cavalier. Arrogant, in that he seemed firmly convinced that his own abundant trial skills would prove sufficient to bring off an acquittal for their self-confessed and severely compromised defendant. And cavalier, because he seemed almost reckless in his willingness to permit her to risk everything on the attempt.

On Saturday, the two brothers travelled to Troy to confer with their client. They had met together, shortly after lunch, in the small conference room just off the main cellblock on the second floor of the jailhouse. It was an accommodation provided by Sheriff Hustler, both convenient and comfortable, where their privacy could be assured.

Jane Ragan had received the McKinneys cordially and listened attentively as Sam rehearsed with her his own assessment of her predicament and the options which he considered to be available to her. He strongly recommended that she agree to testify against James Mowrey at Monday's session of the grand jury.

"You have already acknowledged your own part in the affair and the prosecutors need your testimony to indict, and thereafter to convict, Mr. Mowrey. They will clearly grant concessions in exchange for your co-operation. However," he admonished, "they must have your answer by Monday. If you do not testify at that time the grand jury will refuse to indict and Mowrey will be released."

"And," Frank McKinney appended, "in that event, we will have lost the opportunity to bargain."

Jane Ragan was indeed a fetching young woman. She had about her an aura of rustic charm, ingenuous and unpracticed, yet strongly appealing. Without seeming the least bit argumentative, she inquired of her lawyers concerning her husband's apparent suicide note. "Do you tell me then that I should take no solace in Arthur's letter?"

She looked first to Frank McKinney, then to Sam. "It seems to say that he poisoned himself. I had really expected to be released soon after it was discovered."

"No, my dear," replied Sam McKinney firmly. "It simply won't float. It's too pat, too convenient..."

"And much too obvious," added Frank McKinney, finishing his brother's pronouncement."

Jane Ragan's dark eyes darted from one brother to the other, then back again, as if in fervent entreaty. When her gaze came finally to rest on Sam McKinney's broad brow, she seemed almost to shrug in reluctant comprehension. "It won't — float," she repeated dully.

"No," echoed Sam McKinney. "It won't. The jury will swiftly recognize it to be a clumsy artifice, contrived, no doubt, by someone on your behalf.

"Worst of all," he continued, "I would expect that our production of the document as a part of your defense will profoundly affront, and thereby alienate, the jury."

Jane Ragan nodded her acceptance. "I understand," she said with an air of resignation. "I guess I had gotten my hopes up, perhaps without good reason, when the letter was discovered."

Ultimately, after further discussion and much lamentation over the unreliability of Arthur Ragan's letter, she seemed to have gotten past her disappointment. "I'm sure you're right, Mr. McKinney. You'll know best what I should do."

"Alright then," said Sam McKinney. "May we speak to the prosecutors? Tell them you will testify?"

"Mmm, yes, I suppose so ..." She seemed to hesitate. Then, "Well, maybe not just yet. I did promise Mr. Corwin that I wouldn't decide until I'd spoken with him. He sent me a note. Says he will come tomorrow. I'm sure he'll agree what should be done."

THE BROTHERS MCKINNEY WERE MORE THAN HALFWAY up the river road to Piqua before any word was exchanged. They rode in Frank's year-old rig, his big roan in harness. Frank, who was driving, seemed lost in thought, clearly pre-occupied.

When they had passed by the flour mill at Eldean, the approximate mid-point between the two towns, Troy and Piqua, Frank shifted the reins to his right hand and pivoted in his seat for a better view of his brother. Conversational lapses were unnatural to Sam McKinney and Frank had suspected he was asleep. When Sam returned his gaze, Frank affected a grimace. "You know what's going to happen, don't you?"

"I do," answered Sam. "But suppose you spell it out for me anyway."

"Alright. What's going to happen is that John Corwin will visit Mrs. Ragan, tomorrow, I think she said, and he will lead her subtly, but inexorably, to the conclusion that her husband's bogus suicide note, coupled with the skills and eloquence of her counsel, most notably those of John Corwin, will compel the jury to acquit her."

"Quite so," punctuated Sam McKinney. "That is precisely what I anticipate and our client will most certainly rise to the bait."

"Despite our best efforts to disillusion her," added Frank. "Why would he encourage her to take such a risk?"

Sam McKinney sighed heavily. "Because," he answered, "Mr. Corwin has consistently viewed our client's predicament from his own perspective rather than from hers. If the lady should, by some strange chance, be acquitted, we shall all look like champions — especially John Corwin. If, on the other hand, she is convicted, it will be Jane Ragan who will either hang or spend her life in prison. Mr. Corwin will simply return to Urbana and continue to work his other cases.

"And, of course," he continued, "None of us need suffer any embarrassment over the loss. The case has been unwinnable from the outset. Her culpability has been common knowledge throughout this part of the state."

Frank McKinney digested his brother's remarks, then asked of him, "So what do we do now? Should we withdraw as her counsel? As a protest against a course of conduct which we deem foolish?"

"No, no," chided Sam McKinney. "We cannot do that. We owe the lady our best efforts. That's an essential part of our undertaking. Whatever she decides, right or wrong, whether we agree or not, we have an affirmative duty to assist in her defense."

Excerpt from The Troy Weekly Times

Thursday, August 9, 1855

MOWREY RELEASED

James Mowrey, the supposed accomplice of Mrs. Ragan in the poisoning of her husband, is now at large — the grand jury having failed to find any bill against him. Mrs. Ragan, by advice of her counsel, neglected to appear and give her testimony against him; and of course no bill could be found without her evidence.

A true bill was found against Mrs. Ragan.

Chapter Nine

THE MIAMI COUNTY COURTHOUSE was a nearly new, thoroughly modern, and grandly imposing structure. It was the source of considerable pride to the residents of the entire county and most especially, to the residents of Troy. It was traditional Greek Revival in design and distinguished by twin ionic columns which flanked the broad main entry and extended to the full two-story height of the building. A second pair of similar but smaller columns adorned an elaborate square bell tower which stretched high above the roofline and was itself surmounted by a graceful cupola. An attractive picket fence, partly iron, partly wooden, surrounded the small courtyards on either side of the building.

No fewer than six county office-rooms opened onto the wide central hallway that ran the entire length of the first floor, while the second story contained a single judge's chamber and an enormous, high-ceilinged courtroom with a raised dais and a capacious spectators' gallery.

The courthouse building was solidly constructed, its exterior brick walls more than two feet thick and deeply footed into the earth. It was located on Main Street, in the center of town, and had been completed just a few years earlier at a cost of more than $15,000.

This, then, would be the focus of attention when the matter styled "The State of Ohio vs. Jane Elizabeth Ragan" came on for trial before the Hon. Ralph S. Hart, the older brother of defense counsel James H. Hart, at a special term of the Court of Common Pleas for Miami County.

By present-day standards, it is surprising that the involvement of the two Hart brothers, one as trial judge and the other as an attorney for the defendant, occasioned neither comment nor criticism. In any event the circumstance, at that time and place, went wholly unremarked.

Trial had been initially scheduled for early September of 1855, but had been postponed because of Mrs. Ragan's developing pregnancy and her eventual delivery of a healthy baby at the jailhouse just days before the assigned trial date. The matter was at first continued until mid-October and then ultimately set over, and a special term declared, for Wednesday, January 9th.

The fact that Mrs. Ragan's trial would be held in Troy, coupled with the vagaries of January weather in southwestern Ohio, meant that the McKinney brothers would be sorely tested just in the matter of getting to and from the courthouse each day. Two hours would have to be allowed each morning and each evening for the hitching and unhitching of the mare and for the eight-mile buggy ride over snow and ice-bound roads in each direction. They could expect to leave before daylight, return after nightfall, and to do most of their travelling in the darkness.

Because John Corwin resided so much further from Troy, it would have been wholly impractical for him to have commuted to and fro. He simply took lodgings at the finest hotel in town, the Morris House, and moved to Troy for the duration. He would not have wanted for company at the Morris House, or at any of the other local establishments, because a sizeable group of visiting news reporters, together with a few students of the human condition and a great many of the just plain curious, had descended on the community to watch the trial and had taken all the available accommodations.

All of these persons, together with what seemed to be most of the residents of Miami County, were in attendance when Judge Hart gavelled his packed and boisterous courtroom into order at the stroke of 8 o'clock on the first morning of the trial. There had existed a general skepticism within the legal community as to whether Mrs. Ragan could be tried for her husband's murder in Miami County, or, for that matter, anywhere else in southwestern Ohio. The poisoning death of Arthur Ragan, together with all of the specifics of that event, had already received such widespread publicity, both in the public press and in the common currency, that it was doubtful that an open-minded jury, or at the very least, one that was essentially uninformed, could be obtained. Pursuant to court order Sheriff Hustler had summoned an unprecedented venire of thirty-six "good and lawful men having the qualifications of electors and being householders in the county" to appear for jury duty. Events soon proved, however, that even that number of prospective jurors was insufficient. Of the original panel of thirty-six good and lawful men all but four were excused during the process of *voir dire* examination because they acknowledged that they had either read or heard of the affair *and* because they professed themselves to be unable to put aside preconceived opinions, to sit as "fair and impartial" jurors, and to decide Mrs. Ragan's guilt or innocence solely on the basis of the evidence presented in the courtroom and on the law as given by the Court.

As each successive venire was exhausted Sheriff Hustler had been required to summon another, and yet another, until both the law and the lawyers were satisfied. The process was tedious and time-consuming. By the time they had seated a mutually acceptable panel of twelve good and lawful men, they were into the second week of proceedings. The jury thus empaneled was sworn by the Clerk to "well and truly try, and a true deliverance make" of the issues between the State of Ohio and the Defendant Jane Elizabeth Ragan.

That much accomplished, the trial began in earnest. County Prosecutor Mathias H. Jones opened the case for the State. A fair, capable and precise lawyer, Jones acknowledged the State's burden to prove each and every element of the Defendant's guilt beyond a reasonable doubt. He accepted that challenge, he said, with alacrity and then proceeded to describe for the jury, specifically and meticulously, each of the compelling pieces of evidence he intended to lay before them in order to sustain the burden thrust upon him, quite properly, by the law of Ohio.

The evidence would show, he promised the twelve jurors, that Mrs. Ragan had repudiated the sacred vows of her marriage, become involved in a tawdry and illicit affair with James Mowrey, readily succumbed not only to that person's subornations, but to her own criminal nature, and willingly took the life of her husband while under the protection of his own roof. That her crime was both deliberate and premeditated would be amply demonstrated by evidence that she had purchased the poison in another community days before administering the first dose and by the considerable pains she thereafter took to secure the second dose with which to finish him off after he had seemed to be recovering. Mathias Jones assured the jury that their comprehensive examination of all the evidence would leave no doubt in their minds concerning Mrs. Ragan's guilt. He thanked the jurors for their attention, nodded to Judge Hart, and sat down. The prosecutor's opening had consumed more than two hours.

Throughout the full two hours consumed by the prosecutor's opening statement, Jane Ragan had quietly and discreetly nursed her four-month old baby. She was seated at the defense counsel table, as she had been each day since the trial began, between the McKinney brothers and directly in front of the jury box. The baby was, and would continue to be, on her breast, sleeping or suckling, the entire period of the trial.

Demurely, but tastefully, dressed in a series of dark suits and wearing a veil, Jane Ragan had maintained a keen and obvious interest in every aspect of the proceedings. Now, as Mathias Jones ticked off her sins and the separate elements of her guilt, she seemed not the least offended, but wholly captivated by every word he uttered. One might have believed her to be listening to an intriguing, but probably fictional, story about people she had never known.

John Corwin opened for the defense. From the moment of Mrs. Ragan's announced change of heart, and strategy, it had been apparent that Corwin would sit first chair for the defense team. He had already assumed the role of chief tactician and it was inevitable that the primary responsibility for the conduct of the trial would fall to him as well. And, on balance, this subtle passing of the torch was not unwelcome to James Hart or to the McKinney brothers. They had all three both encouraged and watched Mrs. Ragan make a clean breast of her affairs and acknowledge her guilt in open court on two separate occasions. They had seen recapitulations of her entire testimony in the public press and they were well-acquainted with the public awareness of her culpability. All of them, Sam McKinney in particular, would have felt less than comfortable as a leader of the charge for her total exoneration. McKinney would assist, of course, because it was his duty to do so, but he would not play the pre-eminent part in Mrs. Ragan's defense. He had already shared, along with the others, the *voir dire* examinations of prospective jurors and he would examine some of the more innocuous of the State's witnesses and otherwise participate in the trial, but he was much relieved that it would be John Corwin, rather than himself, who would carry the colors as Mrs. Ragan's standard-bearer.

In contrast to the protracted and painstakingly thorough opening statement by the prosecutor, John Corwin's response was both brief and non-specific. The evidence would show Mrs. Ragan to have been an affectionate, dutiful wife and a pillar of her church and community. It would have been impossible, he said, for a woman of her high moral character to have participated in any of the illicit and clandestine activities cited by the prosecution, let alone do any act which might have caused harm to her husband. And that unhappy gentleman, he admonished, had himself taken poison to end his life after having first prepared a note to absolve his wife. The totality of the evidence, when all was presented, would demand their verdict of acquittal.

SEVEN FULL TRIAL DAYS had been consumed by the process of selecting and qualifying the twelve-menber jury panel and by the opening statements of counsel. Presentation of the evidence did not actually begin until the second Friday of trial, January 18th.

The State, having the burden of proof, was required to go first and, to all those spectators who had paid serious attention to the preliminary hearings for James Mowrey, there were no surprises in the State's case. Assistant Prosecuting Attorney Ebenezer Parsons called and inquired of thirteen witnesses, virtually all of whom had testified before. This time, however, the examinations were more thorough and the testimony more exhaustive.

Dr. Brownell was the State's lead-off witness. At Ben Parsons' prompting he told again of his attentions to Arthur Ragan, the patient's complaints and symptoms, the course of his illness, his seeming recovery, his sudden relapse and his death. Dr. Brownell spoke of his own suspicions, his conversations with Mrs. Ragan, his post mortem examination in conjunction with Dr. Dorsey, Dr. Neff and others, performed over the objections and the pleadings of Mrs. Ragan, and his subsequent examination of the decedent's stomach and contents in Columbus in consultation with Professor Wormsley.

Ben Parsons required Dr. Brownell to elaborate fully on each aspect of his testimony, particularly with regard to his several interviews with the defendant and with reference to his own medical opinion as to the cause of Arthur Ragan's death. Dr. Brownell remained on the stand all day Friday and continued on into Monday's opening session following the weekend respite. John Corwin attempted a desultory, quibbling cross-examination shortly before noon that day, but was entirely frustrated in his efforts. Dr. Brownell had been a powerful and incriminating witness for the prosecution and his testimony was totally unassailable. Moreover, it was fully buttressed that same afternoon by the corroborating testimony of Dr. Dorsey, who had participated in the post mortem, and by Professor Wormsley, who had made the trip from Columbus to add his own scientific judgments to those of Dr. Brownell concerning the specific cause of Arthur Ragan's death. Neither John Corwin nor Frank McKinney were able to make any inroads on the testimony of the three doctors.

Hard on the heels of the medical evidence came the testimony of John Wesler, the Tippecanoe druggist who had sold arsenic to Mrs. Ragan in late March before her husband's first illness. Wesler was followed by Cornelia and Prudence Gabriel, Mrs. Sanders, and William Ashton, who told of Mrs. Ragan's unsuccessful attempt to purchase arsenic on the morning of her husband's relapse, and by Mrs. Kelly, George Kelly, Asa Ashton and Mrs. Wise, who told of Mrs. Ragan's having ultimately accomplished the purchase of five cents worth of the poison later that same morning. Mrs. Kelly and Mrs. Wise also told the jury about Arthur Ragan's relapse and their own observation that approximately half Mrs. Ragan's arsenic supply was gone that same evening.

Then came Arthur Ragan's parents, Pusey and Elizabeth Ragan, and his sister, Mary Ann Balser. Each had been with the decedent at one time or another the day of his death. They gave their several descriptions of his agonies and they spoke of his awareness that he would die. Elizabeth Ragan had been present when the defendant gave her husband chicken soup.

The final witness for the prosecution was Arthur Ragan's friend, James Tamplin. Mr. Tamplin was ultimately permitted, over objection by Mr. Corwin, to tell the jury of his final conversation with Arthur Ragan. Tamplin had been with Ragan when he died. Upon his entry into the room, he said, Ragan had taken his hand, pulled him down close and said he'd been poisoned. When Tamplin told him it was a hard thing to be poisoned by one's wife, Ragan had replied, "It is. And she isn't the only one."

Tamplin then testified that he had told Ragan that his wife had said he'd deliberately and secretly taken arsenic, Ragan had snapped, "It's a lie! Do you think I'm fool enough to poison myself?"

John Corwin's cross-examination of James Tamplin served no better purpose than to potentiate the impact of Arthur Ragan's dying declaration by requiring the witness to repeat it. Acknowledgments by the witness that Arthur Ragan had loved his wife and that she had kissed him moments before he died were unhelpful.

Mathias Jones rose to his feet, caught Judge Hart's attention and solemnly announced that the State's case-in-chief was closed, "Your Honor, the prosecution rests," he intoned.

It was January 24th, and late in the day. Judge Hart excused the jury, overruled John Corwin's perfunctory motions for directed verdict, for dismissal, and for mistrial, and adjourned for the day. The defense would begin in the morning.

Chapter Ten

IT HAD BECOME A MATTER OF ROUTINE for defense counsel, at the conclusion of each day's session, to remain behind with Mrs. Ragan until everyone else, spectators, attorneys and court personnel, had departed. Then, in the privacy afforded by the cleared courtroom, they would confer among themselves and with their client concerning the day's proceedings and developments. Afterwards, Mrs. Ragan, the baby clutched to her bosom, would be escorted by a waiting deputy to the county jailhouse across the street where she would be returned to the limited confines of the cell she had occupied since April. The lawyers would customarily adjourn their own meeting to one or another of the local taprooms for an hour or so of relaxed and convivial consultation as to all matters at hand. It was usually well after six-thirty before the McKinney brothers bid their colleagues adieu and reclaimed their buggy to begin the long, cold drive back to Piqua. James Hart and John Corwin had an easier time of it. Hart lived in Troy and Corwin could walk to his temporary residence at the Morris House in a matter of minutes.

On this particular evening, because the State had closed its case, the four defense lawyers had varied their routine in order that they might join John Corwin for dinner and for cordials in the newly-opened and elegantly-appointed dining room at the Morris House. The McKinneys had engaged a room and would stay the night.

The conclusion of the State's case-in-chief was a milestone in the progress of the trial and, for that reason if for none other, it offered an occasion for restrained observance and a mild release of tension.

It also marked a challenge and set the stage for new anxieties. The gauntlet was down. The prosecution had made a *prima facie* case in support of the proposition that Mrs. Ragan had killed her husband "with deliberate and premeditated malice." The burden would now shift to the defense to refute the matter.

"Alright, then, Jones and Parsons have done their worst," said Frank McKinney as if in benediction. "And I agree it was bad enough. But, at least, that part is over and done." He paused long enough to fork into his mouth and begin to pulverize a large chunk of well-marbled beef steak. "So now, tell me, O Wise One," he inquired of John Corwin with a twinkle, "What is the order of our proceeding?"

"The what?" asked James Hart absently.

"The program, our agenda. What's our plan of attack?" McKinney wanted to know.

"You mean, what do we do now?" asked John Corwin facetiously.

"Mmhm," acknowledged McKinney. "Something like that. The State has scored on us — rather seriously, I'd say. So, yes, what do we do now in defense of our client?"

John Corwin finished a deep draught of ale, set the tankard on the table beside his empty dinner plate and wiped his mouth roughly with a napkin.

Completely at leisure, he removed an elaborately engraved, gold cigar case from an inner pocket of his jacket. Seemingly engrossed in this new activity, he opened the case and extracted a long, black stogie. This he held to the light, rolled between his fingers and admired lovingly. Slowly and deliberately, he bit off the end, chewed the stub, lighted the cigar and inhaled deeply. Finally, almost reluctantly, he released the smoke, looked round to his colleagues and addressed the question. "You are quite right," he admitted, "in that Mrs. Ragan has been damaged somewhat. However, there was very little that we had not anticipated — because we'd already heard it before."

"Except," noted Sam McKinney, "for the testimony from James Tamplin that Ragan seemed to know his wife had poisoned him. I hadn't heard that before."

"Nor I," answered John Corwin. "And I wouldn't have expected Judge Hart to have allowed it," he added, with a disapproving glance at James Hart.

"I am neither my brother's keeper nor his mentor," said James Hart defensively. "But he's probably right. The statement would seem to qualify as a dying declaration."

"Well, right or wrong, it's in the evidence now," remarked Frank McKinney. "And the jury's heard it. We can't change that."

"Granted, that Mrs. Ragan's defense has taken on a little water," replied John Corwin. "That's to be expected. We are, however, still very much afloat and our own time has come.

"We have issued," he continued, "more than thirty subpoenas, and I expect to call virtually all of those persons as defense witnesses. They will prove up her character and the loving relationship she had with her husband.

"Add to that," he looked about the table and let a moment pass for emphasis, "the dramatic, telling effect which Mr. Ragan's handwritten letter must have on the jury. He has, in that single document, not only absolved his wife from all guilt in the matter, but he has also refuted the testimony of Mr. Tamplin."

"Is that the letter where he misspelled his own name?" asked Frank McKinney dryly.

"The same," answered John Corwin. "Whether or not it convinces, it must surely create a reasonable doubt."

"She hopes," finished Frank McKinney. "You've spoken with her. Perhaps at greater length than any of us. How does she feel about the matter?"

"She is quite confident," answered John Corwin. "She refuses to believe that the jury — any jury — will convict her in the face of her good character and the written proof of her husband's intent to poison himself."

"Truly?" asked Frank McKinney in a tone dripping with skepticism.

"She is quite adamant about it."

"So does she take the stand?" asked Frank McKinney. "Does she get up on that witness stand and tell the jury she did not kill her husband?"

"She would like nothing better," answered John Corwin. "She strongly insists on it."

"But — " began Sam McKinney laconically.

"But we cannot permit it," Corwin completed the thought. "We simply cannot let her do so."

"Whoa, now! Hold on a moment," interjected McKinney with mock chagrin. "Didn't I hear from you, just last summer, that we have no authority either to 'permit' or not to 'permit' a decision taken by our client? Did I not have to listen to a somewhat sanctimonious expatiation — from you — about our duty to abide by her instructions?"

"You did," acknowledged John Corwin evenly. "You did, indeed. But that principle applies to matters of substance, how to plead, guilty or not guilty. That sort of thing. What we are now discussing is a matter of procedure, trial tactics, and such matters lie firmly within the ambit, not only of our authority, but of our affirmative duty."

"Sounds to me," Sam McKinney groused, "like a distinction without a difference."

"Call it what you like," John Corwin responded. "The lady cannot testify. Were she to do so, she would surely hang."

Sam McKinney seemed determined to play devil's advocate. "You seem to feel very strongly about it," he remarked. Then, knowing the answer, he none the less asked, "Why is that?"

"They'll crucify her," Corwin answered softly. "If she takes the stand, the prosecutors will be entitled to use her prior statements and admissions of guilt against her, line by line, item by item. Her previous confessions will no longer be protected by the agreement with the prosecution and she will have it to wear, like sackcloth and ashes, throughout the rest of the trial.

"What's more," he continued, "if she takes the stand they'll question her about her 'swap letter'. We simply cannot allow that to happen."

"Her what?" asked Frank McKinney. "'Swap letter'? What the hell's a 'swap letter'?"

"A swap, a trade, a *quid pro quo*," answered John Corwin. "You do this for me and I'll do that for you. Surely you remember Mrs. Ragan's letter of December 6, a year ago, to Jimmy Mowrey. That's the one wherein she exhorts him to 'remove' her husband so that they might 'consummate' their passion together. If that's not an offer to 'swap' services, I don't know what else it could be. Maybe we should call it the 'Poison for Passion' letter. Whatever suits."

"I remember it," answered Frank McKinney. "I told you about it last summer, at our very first meeting."

"Of course you did," Corwin acknowledged. "And we were both very much concerned about it.

"Now then," he continued, "The State has this 'swap letter' in its arsenal. But they can't use it unless Mrs. Ragan testifies. They acknowledged that difficulty when they rested their case without attempting to get it in. That's done and the jury hasn't heard about the letter, at least not in the courtroom.

"However, if she takes the stand, she will have opened the door and the State will have every right to impeach her, not only with her prior admissions, but with the 'swap letter'. They will ask her about it, from every angle and in every sordid particular. And then, after they've beaten her over the head with it for a day or so, they'll offer it into evidence as an exhibit and it will go to the jury. They'll have it with them in the jury room to read through at leisure when they begin their deliberations."

Sam McKinney had listened, patiently and with an air of detachment, to the exchange between John Corwin and his brother. "He's right, Frank," he said, "There has never been any doubt about it. She cannot take the stand."

"Not even, I suppose, to tell the jury that she is innocent?" queried Frank.

"She announced that when she pled not guilty," said Sam McKinney. "That will have to suffice."

"The other side of the coin," said John Corwin, "is that the law will not permit the prosecution to comment on her failure to testify. It's not all we might have hoped for, but, under the circumstances, it's all we can ask."

Further discussion among the defense lawyers, over coffee, cognac and cigars, concerned the direct testimony to be elicited from the thirty-odd witnesses on tap for the ensuing sessions of court. The last of those persons to come under consideration was James Mowrey.

"Why Mowrey?" asked James Hart. "His testimony would only incriminate Mrs. Ragan." "And himself as well," came the rejoinder.

"It's a gambit," continued John Corwin. "I fully expect that he will refuse to testify on the basis of the protections contained in the Fifth Amendment. We can be very sure that the State would have already called him to testify against Mrs. Ragan if they had had any reason to believe that he would do so. I am quite confident that he has already advised the State that he would refuse to testify and that that is the reason he has not been called.

"So what we must do is to call him as a defense witness, let him take the stand and advise the jury of his refusal." Corwin almost snickered. "Then," he continued, "on final argument, we can chide the State for not calling him to corroborate their claim that Mrs. Ragan sought to induce him to kill her husband for her."

He assumed a theatrical air, "Ask yourselves, gentlemen of the jury, if all this be true, why did the State fail to call Mr. Mowrey to the stand to prove its charges against this poor woman? You will, of course, remember that it was not the prosecution, but the defense, in search of absolute truth, who compelled James Mowrey to appear at this forum. We could not force him to testify, but we certainly required him to be present, which is more than I can say of the State of Ohio."

John Corwin looked to the others for approval. He seemed almost smug.

"It's a gambit," remarked Sam McKinney to no one in particular. "Might even work."

Chapter Eleven

OVER THE COURSE OF THE NEXT FOUR DAYS, the defense called a veritable parade of witnesses to the stand. Twenty-six in number, their testimony was essentially weak and unhelpful. The first three such witnesses were persons who had visited with Arthur Ragan shortly before his death. They would only say that he appeared to be very ill and they had not seen any poison given to him. James Mowrey was summoned to the stand, protected by his own counsel, and predictably refused to testify on the grounds of potential self-incrimination.

Four witnesses, including Jane Ragan's brother-in-law, said that they had spoken with Arthur Ragan in the weeks before his illness and that he had seemed somewhat depressed. One of these people was a scrivener, a Beth Wood, who had prepared a will for Mr. Ragan. She remembered that he had come to her office on March 27th, the Tuesday preceding his death, and said that he wanted to leave all his property to his wife. She had written the will and Ragan had signed it in her presence. He had seemed "rather dejected."

A small coterie of witnesses, including members of Jane Ragan's immediate family, were called to testify concerning her character and reputation. These were relatives, friends and acquaintances who told of her having been a Sunday school teacher and a member of the church. They said that they knew of no trouble between Mrs. Ragan and her husband, that they had heard nothing against her reputation and that, as far as they were aware, she was a person of good character. Frank McKinney found this testimony to be so bland and innocuous that he felt constrained to whisper to his brother that it seemed calculated "to damn her with faint praise."

Sam McKinney signalled his agreement with a barely perceptible nod of his head, and then, because Mrs. Ragan had vacated her own chair to tend to her child's diapers, he leaned across to whisper his considered response, "If the lady is to avoid damnation, at least in this forum, her best chance is to keep her head down, remain silent, and continue to cradle, dandle and nurse her baby in full view of the jury."

John Corwin had contrived to conclude his character and reputation testimony with that of Mrs. Ragan's three sisters. Josephine Cunningham's commendations concerning the defendant's exemplary ethic and her unquestionable good name, so far as she knew, were typical of that which had already been presented. Then, beginning with Edith Cunningham Day and 13-year-old Harriet Cunningham, Corwin led the jury to the discovery and keeping of Arthur Ragan's "suicide" letter to his wife.

"I came upon it myself," said Edith Day. "We were going through Arthur's papers one afternoon last summer. My sister Harriet was helping me sort them out.

"This one paper, the letter, was in the center drawer of Arthur's desk. It was right on top of a small packet of household accounts. I'm sure it was meant to be readily found.

"I read it through, more than once, and showed it to Edith. Because we both thought it was important, we gave it to our mother for safekeeping. She said she would give it to father. He would know what best should be done with it."

Then, when her opinion was solicited by John Corwin, she volunteered, "There's never been any doubt in my mind that Arthur took his own life. That's what the letter said he intended to do, and that's what he did."

The testimony of younger sister Harriet was fully corroborative of all that Edith had said. If anything, Harriet's assurances were given with greater enthusiasm and with more certitude than Edith had provided.

"Yes," she vouched, "we absolutely found the letter — last June, it was — and we knew immediately it proved our sister to be innocent. I can't imagine why she has not been released."

Martin Cunningham had aged dramatically since his initial visit to Sam McKinney's office in April. His jaw had slackened and his physique seemed more frail than sinewy. The mottled, dark sleekness of his hair had succumbed to a disarray of stone-washed grey. Cunningham told of the rediscovery of the suicide note in the drawer where he had placed it. It was first shown to him by his wife and he had not immediately grasped its significance.

"I didn't really know what to think of it," he explained. "It hurt me to believe my son-in-law was so unhappy that he wanted to take poison. I thought maybe he was still upset over Alice's death. He'd still kept her hat in his dresser drawer.

"Anyway," he continued, "I just couldn't accept the letter for what it was. I didn't want to believe it. That he'd felt such pain — that he'd written such a letter.

"And now," he said, "I'm ashamed to say that I put the letter away, in a safe place, and I couldn't make myself think of it again until August. That's when I took it to Mr. McKinney."

Now, after another six months, Martin Cunningham's earlier misgivings had apparently resolved themselves and he seemed to have convinced himself that the note was genuine. He told the jury that he had seen his son-in-law write and was familiar with his handwriting.

"The impression in my mind," he said, "as far as I can judge, is that this is Arthur's handwriting. I know it isn't my wife's or Edie's. And I know it isn't Libby's."

Then, on cross-examination, Ben Parsons easily induced Cunningham to acknowledge that, "Yes, he spelled his name in the customary way, A-r-t-h-u-r, and no, I don't know as he made mistakes in spelling it."

In an attempt to more convincingly authenticate the suicide note, John Corwin next called a man named Harter to the stand. Mr. Harter professed himself to be a hand-writing expert of sorts, having once taught writing. He said he had examined the note and believed it to be genuine.

Matt Jones' attitude towards Mr. Harter was disdainful and his cross-examination was scathing.

Q. *Mr. Harter, how many times have you been called upon to testify as a handwriting expert?*

A. *I've never had to testify before, in any capacity.*

Q. *Alright, then, how many times have you been consulted as a handwriting expert — apart from this present matter?*

A. *I have not been previously consulted in that capacity.*

Q. *Well sir, please tell us about those capacities in which you have been professionally consulted.*

A. *I have not been previously consulted in any capacity.*

Q. *Have you taken any special training in handwriting analysis?*

A. *No sir.*

Q. *Have you personally conducted any studies or written any treatises pertaining to the subject of handwriting analysis?*

A. *No sir.*

Q. *Would it be fair, then, for me to conclude that the sum total of your credentials as a handwriting expert comes from your having taught a handful of schoolchildren to cipher — more than fifteen years ago?*

A. *Yessir. I've made no other claims.*

Q. *Now then, you've told us that you have examined this letter and that you believe it to be genuine?*

A. *Yessir.*

Q. *Please tell the jury what samples of Arthur Ragan's handwriting you used for comparison?*

A. *I had no such samples.*

Q. *None?*

A. *No sir.*

Q. *Were you sufficiently familiar, then, with Mr. Ragan's handwriting to render an opinion concerning it.*

A.   *No, sir. I am not familiar with Mr. Ragan's handwriting. I don't know that I've ever even seen it.*

Q.   *Then tell me, Mr. Harter. If you are wholly unfamiliar with Arthur Ragan's writing, and have never even seen it, how is it that you now have the arrant temerity to come into this courtroom as an "expert" and assure the jury that this highly dubious document is "genuine"?*

A.   *I only meant —*

Q.   *Perhaps we had better define your word "genuine". Tell the jury what you intended to convey.*

A.   *That's just it, sir. What I meant was that the letter appeared to me — from my limited experience — to have been written in a free and easy manner. It didn't seem to be forced, or labored, as if the writer were trying to forge someone else's writing. And I'm sure that the body of the letter and the signature were both written by the same hand.*

Q.   *It is not your testimony, then, that the letter was written by Arthur Ragan?*

A.   *Oh, no. I couldn't say that. I don't know his handwriting.*

Despite Matt Jones' effective neutralization of Mr. Harter's testimony, John Corwin stayed his course. Steadfast and unabashed, he formally requested permission from the court to read the note to the jury. After hearing the arguments of counsel, Judge Hart granted the request and Corwin read the document, sonorously and deliberately, to the twelve men in the jury box.

Then, smug in his conviction and wholly without apology, John Corwin offered Arthur Ragan's purported suicide note in evidence, as though the document mandated his client's acquittal, and the defense rested its case.

Jane Ragan had not testified. She had heeded the advice of her lawyers and had sat quietly in her place at the counsel table. She had remained steadfastly attentive to the proceedings, restrained and demure in her demeanor. She had spoken only rarely to her counsel and had not been seen to smile since the trial had begun. Her only focus, apart from the proceedings, seemed to be on the child, who alternately slept or suckled, in her arms.

Sam McKinney leaned to their client. "If you remember how to pray," he breathed, "now's the time. Matt Jones is going to tear that letter apart."

THE RULES OF TRIAL PROCEDURE are such that the prosecution has the right, after the close of the defendant's case-in-chief, to rebut evidentiary matters introduced for the first time as a part of the defendant's proofs.

And so, when trial resumed after the noon recess, Messrs. Jones and Parsons were well-prepared to contend with the claimed suicide note introduced by the defense team. They immediately recalled James Tamplin to the stand. He had already testified, as a part of the prosecution's case in chief, that Ragan had told him that he had been poisoned. Not only was Tamplin a close friend to Arthur Ragan, he said, but he had worked alongside him at a cooperage shop for the two-year period before his death. He was also the Recorder of the Temple of Honor, Ragan's lodge, and was well acquainted with his handwriting.

"I'm certainly no expert," he admitted. "But I am thoroughly familiar with Ragan's handwriting. I've seen him write a number of reports concerning Temple activities. I have a great many of these in my possession. I am also quite familiar with his signature.

"Neither the letter nor the signature look like Arthur's handwriting," he asserted.

"Is there any question in your mind about it?" asked Jones.

"I have no doubt whatever," answered Tamplin. "The first name is spelt wrong and the R is not at all the way he made it. The writing is too heavy and the whole appearance is unlike Arthur's writing. Then, too," he added, "I never knew Arthur to misspell his first name."

Arthur Ragan's sister, Mary Ann Balser, had also testified as a part of the State's case-in-chief. Now she was recalled for rebuttal and this time her testimony was devastating.

She had been present at her brother's house, after his death, along with Edith Day and Prudence Gabriel. The three of them were engaged in gathering up his papers and personal effects and she had personally examined each paper they found before putting it into a box for safe-keeping.

Matt Jones handed her the suicide note.

"I saw no such paper," she snapped. "Everything that had my brother's name on it, I gave to my father. I examined them and know what they were. Those that were Libby's I put into the box. I was very careful to get all the papers that had his name so that they might be taken care of. Every single paper was opened and read. This paper was not among them."

Concerning the question of handwriting, Mrs. Balser was yet more adamant. She knew her brother's handwriting quite well and this was not his. "Much too large and much too coarse," she said.

And, after Prudence Gabriel had confirmed Mary Ann Balser's testimony in every particular, Matt Jones produced a record book known to have been kept by Arthur Ragan in his own hand. At Jones' request Sam McKinney had to concede the book to contain true specimens of Ragan's handwriting. Then, building on that concession, Jones called another fourteen witnesses, local bankers and businessmen, to render opinions, based on their familiarity with Ragan's handwriting and on comparison of the letter with the book entries, as to the provenance of the purported suicide letter.

By the time the last such witness had been excused no person in the courtroom could have possibly believed the note to be genuine. Matt Jones had done his work well.

And suddenly, it was over. The prosecution rested its case in rebuttal and John Corwin announced that there would be no sur-rebuttal. The presentation of evidence was complete.

Judge Hart declared an adjournment for the noon recess. Closing arguments would begin promptly at one o'clock.

Chapter Twelve

THE FIRST MURDER TRIAL ever held in Miami County took place in 1816 when a young man named Armstrong was convicted of the murder of his father. Now, a full forty years later, Jane Ragan's trial for the poisoning death of her husband was only the second murder prosecution in the history of the county. That single fact, quite apart from any other consideration, would have accounted for the enormous public interest which had developed about the proceedings. The additional ingredients of infidelity, design and intrigue on the part of a mysterious and seductive young woman were sufficient to command state-wide attention to every detail and nuance of the trial.

The new and capacious county courtroom had been overfilled since trial began. All of the seats had been routinely occupied and the walls and aisles lined with standees. Other would-be spectators had waited patiently outdoors, in the January cold, in hopes of gaining entrance later in the day. The newspapers had carried regular and exhaustive accounts of the testimony and other events of the trial for the benefit of those who had been unable to attend. There was little else of interest to anyone. The pulse of the trial had quite become the pulse of the community.

It was small wonder, then, that Judge Hart's announcement that closing arguments would begin after lunch should produce such a rush of excitement. Criminal trials, in nineteenth century mid-America, were entertainment forms. They were contests, often of epic proportions, involving concepts of right and wrong, justice, vindication and retribution. They also involved much that was theatrical, dramatic, melodramatic and, sometimes, just plain trite. And the high point of the trial process, at least as an entertainment form, has ever been the closing argument.

The courtroom was packed, as were the hallways inside the courthouse building and the streets and yards outside, when Judge Hart nodded to signal counsel to begin their perorations.

Prosecuting Attorney Matt Jones went first. He was the consummate prosecutor: thorough, precise and relentless. He argued the State's case for nearly two hours, reviewing, dissecting and analyzing each piece of evidence that had been presented. He spoke of the witnesses, their demeanor, their motivations and their credibility. He talked about presumptions and inferences, that which was probable and that which was not, the burden of proof and the requirement that he prove each element of the defendant's guilt beyond a reasonable doubt. Finally and painstakingly, he showed the members of the jury that the totality of the evidence required the inexorable conclusion that Jane Ragan had, intentionally and with premeditated malice, poisoned her husband. He expressed his confidence that the jury would abide by the evidence and the law, that they would do their duty, and that they would return a verdict for conviction.

All four of the defense attorneys were permitted to address the jury. Sam McKinney spoke first, then James Hart and Frank McKinney. All of their remarks were brief in duration and general in terms. They spoke, not of the evidence, but of concepts. They spoke of the presumption of innocence and of the essence of reasonable doubt. All of them were professional in their deportment, restrained in their delivery, and respectful to the jury. Collectively, their remarks consumed less than an hour.

John Corwin was a prepossessing lawyer. His solid appearance and his easy bearing commanded respect and the resonant timber of his voice induced attention. He was equally capable of flowery oratory, stentorian rage, whispered poignancies and fervent pleas. Before he finished his argument he would have used all of these expedients. Rising purposefully from his counsel chair, he strode to the center of the room and stationed himself directly in front of the jury box. He nodded respectfully to Judge Hart, looked hard at each individual juror and began his remarks. His manner was direct and his tone conversational.

"May it please the Court, Gentlemen of the Jury: If, in the day to day workings of the law, this were an unimportant case, I should be brief in my remarks — especially after hearing the very able arguments of my colleagues for the defense. But when I reflect upon the grave accusation made by the State of Ohio against the defendant; when I consider her perilous position; when I look upon you gentlemen of the jury sitting there before high heaven, charged to determine her guilt or innocence, my soul is overwhelmed with the magnitude of our shared responsibility, and I should be a recreant to duty if I did not exert every effort to save the life of this poor, friendless, and unfortunate woman.

"Gentlemen," he said, "I have confidence in you as honorable men, as human beings, as citizens of exalted character, of refined feelings and purity of purpose. And upon that confidence, I would be willing to submit the case to your decision. True enough, you have a grave duty to perform, and I would sympathize with you because of your awesome responsibility to decide such an issue as this — so momentous and so remarkable in its character. It is one of solemn consideration, and I hope that you will discharge your duty truthfully and faithfully. I, too, feel deeply impressed with the importance of my position. Humble as it may be, I know that if I omit anything essential in this defense, in some degree, the life of this young woman is at stake.

"In examining this case, gentlemen of the jury, you will find that the whole issue depends entirely upon circumstances such as the law, truth, and humanity must condemn. I am asked to save the life of this woman, who, in her girlhood, was the pride and solace of her parents. A woman who, in her conjugal relations, was always the kind, loving and devoted wife. A woman who is now, in her bereavement, the lonely, distressed and disconsolate widow. And as I contemplate this picture, and reflect upon the mental anguish of that gray haired father, who daily visits her cell, as I recollect the mournful mother, with her bleeding heart, offering up prayers to God for the safety of her child — you must pardon me, gentlemen, for those emotions that have stirred my soul. Ah, gentlemen, there is much, at the very threshold of this case, to possess the mind, and to carry conviction to the inner conscience of any man, concerning the innocence and the purity of this defendant, and I hope that such considerations may favorably affect your final decision.

"When I look, too, around this room and see this immense auditory, when I see such a lovely array of beauty and intelligence assembled in a single forum, I sense that one great and immutable fact is established and that is, that where justice and humanity are concerned, there you will always find woman, with her heavenly presence, interested in the scene.

"And now I appeal to your consciences as men. I implore you, as fathers of families, whose conduct in this case will be a subject of future reflection for the balance of your lives, if you do not consider yourselves constrained by the testimony adduced in the progress of this trial to acquit her!

"But I must proceed to the argument."

John Corwin did indeed "proceed to the argument." And he kept at it for the remainder of that Thursday afternoon — and all day Friday — and on into Saturday. He carped and caviled over the testimony of every witness. Did Dr. Brownell misdiagnose his patient? Did Dr. Wormsley really perform all available testing procedures to determine the presence or absence of arsenic in Arthur Ragan's stomach? Should liver tests not have been performed also? How certain were the Ashton brothers about their testimony and how reliable were the children, the little Gabriel girl and young Master Kelly? Wasn't it perfectly reasonable to believe that Mrs. Ragan was troubled by rats and needed rats-bane for that purpose and none other? Could anyone truly believe this kind, loving, Christian woman to be capable of taking the life of the husband she loved so dearly?

"The witnesses all say," he reminded the twelve male jurors, "That she was invariably kind and attentive, that she was ever present and always ready to wait upon her husband during his sickness.

"She did not complain," he admonished, "though in ill health herself at the time. Yet when anything was wanting, or a duty to be performed, she was the woman to do it. Is that, gentlemen, the conduct we would expect of a murderess?"

He struck a thoughtful pose. "A philosopher has said that man is a wolf to his fellow. But I say to each of you that a man must indeed be cruel and bloodthirsty," his voice rose in righteous indignation as he glowered at the prosecutors, "who could wish to take the life of this woman or who could be malicious enough to suppose that she could have poisoned her own husband!"

John Corwin argued philosophy, human behavior, medical science and the law. He read to the jury from medical textbooks and quoted from legal authorities. He pulled no punches and forbore no theatrics in pleading Mrs. Ragan's cause. And, without the least show of embarrassment, he trotted out the all but discredited suicide letter and unashamedly insisted on its authenticity.

"To complete the establishment of the innocence of this woman, you will recollect that after Ragan's death, his letters were collected and taken to the home of Jane Ragan's father. In examining those papers, the defendant's sister found this letter and handed it to their mother who carefully preserved it."

And, concerning Mrs. Cunningham, who had been absent from the proceedings since the defense had begun its case in chief, John Corwin was less than truthful. "She has collapsed," he explained. "The strain of the state's relentless persecution of her daughter has proved too much for her psychic and emotional equilibrium. She is now lying, a helpless invalid, in the bedroom of her home. If she could have been brought into court to testify, the authenticity of the letter could have been conclusively proven.

"The father of the defendant, Mr. Cunningham, who was well acquainted with Arthur Ragan's hand, believes it to be his writing. Other witnesses have attested to the same fact."

Throughout this latest segment of his summation, John Corwin had been waving the letter about like a banner. Now he held it steady and read it, yet another time, to the jury. He made light of the misspelling of Ragan's given name. It was no more than an inadvertence, he said, upon which the State had attempted to capitalize.

Then finally, just before noon on Saturday, after nearly two full days of argument, he was finished, "Gentlemen of the jury, I am sorry that I have detained you so long, but I thought I might say something which would aid you in coming to a conclusion. Again I implore you to give this woman the benefit of the facts. If the State has not satisfied you *prima facie* of her guilt, her innocence is established. The case is now stripped of all its mystery, and you have the testimony to lead you. Let mercy and truth influence your minds in rendering a verdict. I humbly and respectfully ask of you — indeed, I beseech you — to let this poor woman, with her helpless babe, go forth — free from her cell. I submit the case."

It was the middle of the afternoon, after a liberal and restorative lunch break, when Judge Hart began to read his charge to the jury. This would be the Court's instruction concerning the issues to be decided, the law to be applied, the jury's responsibilities, and, ultimately, his own comments, guardedly neutral and noncommittal, on the evidence.

Judge Hart had been working on his charge, sporadically, after-hours and after supper, since the trial had begun nearly four weeks ago. It had been, at first, a patchwork thing of random bits and pieces, fully disjointed and lacking continuity. More recently, however, it had begun to take shape, to mature, and, finally, to crystallize into the thorough and carefully organized treatise that he wished it to be. He had extended the noon recess an extra hour in order that he might review it one more time and apply those two or three finishing touches he deemed to be essential.

Now, with the jury at full attention, he explained the elements of the crime charged in the indictment, murder in the first degree. He explained the legal concepts of "intentional", "deliberate", "premeditated" and "malice." He spoke of the presumption of innocence, the State's burden of proof, and the essence of reasonable doubt. He discussed with the jury the nature and quality of evidence, both direct and circumstantial, and the propriety of inferences which might arise or flow from that evidence.

Significantly, Judge Hart described to the jury the opposing contentions of the parties and the proofs adduced by each side to support its argument.

"The State," he reminded, "relies mainly on the following circumstances to establish the defendant's guilt: *First*, the conduct of the defendant during her husband's illness, and afterwards."

For emphasis, Judge Hart had raised the index finger of his left hand and flicked it forcefully with the middle fingers of his right hand. Now he raised the second finger and continued the count, "*Second*, that during the latter part of March she purchased, in another town, a quantity of arsenic sufficient to kill a man.

"*Third*," he produced another finger, "that only a few days later her husband was suddenly taken violently ill.

"*Fourth*," he continued, "the attending physician, Dr. Brownell, found him, in his judgment, to be suffering from poisoning and manifesting symptoms usually associated with arsenic.

"*Fifth*," the count went on. "That the following Monday after Dr. Brownell had pronounced the patient to be convalescent and out of danger, the defendant was found again seeking for arsenic under a forged note and the false pretense that it was for a Mrs. Sanders."

Now it became necessary for the judge to switch hands. "*Sixth*," he continued, using his right forefinger, "that shortly after the defendant's having procured the second supply of poison, the patient suddenly, that same day, relapsed into his original symptoms in aggravated form and died the following day.

"*Seventh*, that about half of the arsenic obtained on Monday was found to have disappeared immediately after the patient's relapse.

"*Eighth*, that upon a post mortem examination, arsenic was found in the stomach of the deceased in an amount sufficient to produce death.

"*Ninth*, the defendant's alleged uneasiness about the proposed post mortem examination and her offer of a reward to have it stopped."

Judge Hart was just about out of fingers. "And *tenth*," he counted, "the dying declarations of Arthur Ragan that he did not poison himself.

"There are other minor circumstances connected with these main facts, which the State, by its counsel, urges. Such minor circumstances are often quite as important as main facts. They may become, and often are, the natural and best support of the main, or principal, facts at issue.

"In these principal facts, and in their attending and corroborating circumstances, the State maintains it has not only a *prima facie*, but a conclusive case against the defendant."

Judge Hart lowered his hands to the papers from which he read, cleared his throat for punctuation, and addressed the defendant's case. "On the other hand," he observed, "the main grounds of the defense will be included in the following propositions: *First*," and the fingers reappeared, "that Arthur Ragan did not die of poison. *Second*, that if he did, he poisoned himself. *Third*, that the State has failed to make out a *prima facie* case against the defendant, and *Fourth*, that even if there is a *prima facie* case, the State has failed to prove the defendant's guilt beyond a reasonable doubt."

With reference to Arthur Ragan's purported suicide letter, relied upon by the defendant, Judge Hart admonished the jury sternly, "I would not do myself nor the tribunal over which I preside, justice, if I were to dismiss this branch of the case without suggesting to you that it is your duty to scrutinize this letter and the proofs by which its value as testimony is to be determined, with the utmost care. If it be a genuine letter, it would be monstrous to reject it from your deliberations. If it is false, counterfeit and forged, it would be a shame to justice to admit it. Let your deliberations on this subject be calm, careful and thorough. And that you should be exceedingly careful will be still more apparent when I inform you that if this letter turns out in your clear and undoubted judgment to be a forgery, it is not only to be dropped out of the testimony of the defense, but it also becomes liable to be seized upon by the State and marshalled among the circumstances of the defendant's guilt. Whether it may be so used will depend upon the defendant's connection with it as a counterfeit paper; whether it was her work, or written by her procurement, or prepared by her connivance, or used with her approbation and assent. The force to which it will, in any event, be entitled as evidence against her, must depend upon the sound judgment of the jury under all the circumstances, depending upon the extent to which she has probably been connected with the creation of it, and the extent to which she ought to be held liable for suffering her counsel to use it in her defense."

Judge Hart concluded his charge with instructions as to the manner of their proceeding, the election of a foreman, their consideration of the evidence, the pure expression of their separate and independent opinions, and the balloting process which should ultimately produce a verdict. And as to the verdict itself, he admonished, "If you find against the defendant, it will be your duty to ascertain in your verdict whether she is guilty of murder in the first or second degree, or of manslaughter.

"If you find in her favor, your verdict will simply be 'not guilty'."

When he had completed his formal charge, Judge Hart turned down the last of his papers, shuffled them together into a neat stack and looked to the lawyers, anticipating the perfunctory objections which would save the record for a possible appeal. Then he addressed himself informally to the jury and encouraged them to do their duty according to their collective wisdom and conscience.

Juror number one, Robert Johnson, a square, stolid-looking man, with a darkly beetled brow, received the assembled exhibits from the bailiff and led the jurors through an adjacent doorway and into the juryroom where they would conduct their deliberations. It was early evening on Saturday, February 2nd, and the sky had already begun to darken.

Chapter Thirteen

ONCE THE MATTER HAD BEEN SUBMITTED to the jury the participants could do no more — except wait. With varying degrees of patience, and in varying degrees of comfort, both players and spectators would wait. It was an intermission of indeterminate duration between the main body of the drama and the final act.

The spectators who had followed the proceedings from the gallery section of the courtroom remained inside, unwilling to yield up their seats or their standing places in the aisles or along the walls. Those less fortunate, who had followed from the hallways and stairways inside the courthouse and from the streets, walks and yards outside, remained where they were, ever watchful for the opportunity to move to the next closest station.

The principal players whose places within the arena were secure, broke away from the courtroom and settled themselves in a series of small, outlying encampments.

The defendant, Jane Ragan, had been returned to her cell at the jailhouse. Sheriff Hustler had opened the cellblock to her family and permitted them to be with her while the jury deliberated. Mrs. Cunningham, who had not really collapsed from the strain of it all, as reported by John Corwin, was the first to arrive. Now father, mother and sisters clustered about the defendant and her infant, alternately pacing the concrete flooring of the cellblock, offering such encouragement to one another as could be mustered, changing and cradling the baby as necessary, hugging themselves and each other, and wringing their hands in abject and poorly-concealed anxiety. Mrs. Hustler provided biscuits and the sheriff's first in command, Deputy Dolph, poured the coffee. Sheriff Hustler, along with his wife and deputies, kept watch from the jailhouse kitchen. Two policemen and the town constable had joined them there for warmth, coffee, conversation and speculation as to how long it might take the jury to reach a verdict.

State's attorneys Matt Jones and Ben Parsons were ensconced in the county prosecutor's office on the first floor of the courthouse building. Compared to the commotion created by the milling throngs in the hallway outside, the office provided a quiet niche for the prosecutors and their assistants. Several of the other county officials and a few of the local attorneys had found shelter there also. All of them had been caught up in the proceedings and would await the result.

Another group of local attorneys had settled themselves in the judge's chambers adjacent to the courtroom. Most of these were older and perhaps more prominent members of the profession, men who may have enjoyed special license to hobnob with the judge because of their own relative distinction at the bar. Judge Hart was the congenial host to all, and his clerk and court reporter kept the coffee warm.

The defense team was the most comfortably deployed of all the encampments. With Judge Hart's permission, they had retired to the lavish dining room at the Morris House where they treated themselves to a leisurely supper of roast fowl, wild rice and gravy, washed down with two bottles of Charlie Morris' best claret, and followed by his finest imported cigars. While all of them were properly apprehensive about the verdict, they were nonetheless in excellent fettle. They had done their work for nearly a month and were entitled to let off some steam. Whatever the outcome, win, lose or draw, they would have no apologies to make. They had done the best that could have been done under the circumstances. Besides, the decision to stand trial, and to risk everything, had, after all, been that of their client. The choice had been Mrs. Ragan's, John Corwin reassured them again, and they were bound to honor it.

Their conversation was light and easy. Stories of other trials in other courtrooms were traded around the supper table. John Corwin and Sam

McKinney had fought more wars than had the other two lawyers so it was natural that they would have more tales to trade. It was also natural that the conversation would continually and persistently revert to the issue at hand.

Whatever the circumstances of the several encampments, the single common characteristic shared by each was anxiety.

A short eternity passed until, just before midnight, the small brass bell sounded outside the jury room. They had a verdict.

Then, during the brief interval between the bailiff's notification of each of the several encampments and the reopening of court with all participants on hand, the ambient anxiety would escalate and intensify exponentially. Today would be Judgment Day in Miami County, Ohio.

"Not Guilty."

The two words, solemnly intoned by the foreman of the jury, seemed to hang there, a palpable presence suspended in mid-air like stale cigar smoke.

And if there was a reaction from the spectators in the crowded courtroom, it was slow in its development. There were no whoops, shouts or whistles. Neither were there upraised arms, cheers or applause. There was only a soft and slowly building crescendo of murmurs, indistinct and unintelligible. Disbelief and bewilderment registered on their faces and numbed their senses. The jury had broadsided them with the one verdict no one had expected.

Inside the bar, the lawyers seemed no less stunned than did the general public. Matt Jones and Ben Parsons remained seated. They stared quizzically in the direction of the jury box.

The four defense lawyers had risen with their client to receive the jury verdict. Jane Ragan was without her infant for the first time since trial began. Now she accepted the verdict, as did her lawyers, without change of expression. Frank McKinney had such an insistent roaring in his ears that he barely heard Judge Hart thank the jurors for their service and announce, "The defendant is discharged, and this court is adjourned."

Jane Elizabeth Ragan registered no emotion whatever. She regarded the activity in the courtroom with confidence and with equanimity, looked into the faces of her counsel and met their eyes. John Corwin met her gaze evenly and held fast until she smiled, formally and almost imperceptibly. Then she nodded to him once, as if in approval, straightened her back and walked regally, her head held high, her cool blue eyes looking neither to left nor right, through the crowded aisleway and out the double exit doors at the rear of the courtroom. Frank McKinney thought he detected just the slightest undulation of her hips as she passed through the doorway.

Twenty minutes later the courtroom had cleared. Judge Hart and the lawyers had congratulated one another on a job well done, they shook hands all around, and everyone had left for home. The four defense lawyers were alone in the now-deserted courtroom, gathering their books and papers. Sam McKinney looked up and found his brother Frank sitting in one of the middle seats of the jury box, head resting on forearms and leaning on the railing of the box. His shoulders heaved in a series of convulsions which he seemed totally unable to control.

"Frank," Sam probed gently. "What is it? Are you all right?"

Frank nodded his head violently, then heaved himself back into the chair. His cheeks were wet and there were great tears in his eyes. He shook with silent mirth.

"She used us, Sam," he chortled, "All of us. She had us on beautifully.

"She'd had her fun with Jimmy Mowrey, manipulated him, then poisoned her husband and laid it onto him. She'd used him up and threw him away like an old boot.

"Then we came along, all four of us, and she manipulated us shamelessly. Got us to do precisely what she wanted. Made us sell what she was selling — to the jury. And now, she's used us up too and she just a few moments ago threw us away like another old boot."

John Corwin had set his brief case onto the counsel table and approached. Frank McKinney rubbed his eyes. "John" he continued, "you took the lead in this thing, and you did a beautiful job of it. I doubt there's another lawyer in America could have done it half as well.

"But the point is, she manipulated you into doing it precisely the way you did, and now you too have gone the way of old used-up boots.

"I told Sam last spring this little gal's a piece of work, and now I think she's proved it."

John Corwin smiled at Frank McKinney's remarks, but he nonetheless demurred, "I don't know that we've been 'discarded', Frank. She didn't really take the time to thank us for our efforts, I admit that, but I'm sure she will."

"Don't think I'll wait for that, John. We've already got all the thanks we're gonna get. Didn't you watch her sashay out this courtroom like the Queen of Sheba just a little while ago?"

"Well, yes, I could scarcely have missed that act," Corwin acknowledged.

"True enough," agreed Frank McKinney, "and if you paid real close attention, you would've also noticed that, just before she hit the door, she switched her tail at us like a mare just comin' into season."

Frank McKinney looked at John Corwin, then at his brother, Sam. "She did, you know. She really did." He grinned. "The conniving, murdering, manipulating, saucy bitch."

Epilogue

THE RAGAN VERDICT OF ACQUITTAL was extremely unpopular and engendered considerable indignation. Under the circumstances, it was not possible for Mrs. Ragan to continue to reside in the area. She moved, shortly after the trial, to "the West." Several years later she was seen in Indianapolis, but, when accosted, she steadfastly denied her identity. She persisted in her denials until convinced that she had, indeed, been recognized. She ultimately coupled her abashed acknowledgment with a fervent plea that she not be exposed.

All of the lawyers who participated in the trial, save one, proceeded on to long and distinguished careers. Ben Parsons succeeded Ralph Hart as common pleas judge, Frank McKinney served two terms in Congress, James Hart returned from the Civil War a full colonel, and Scott McKinney and Mathias Jones continued to practice law for a great many years.

The single exception was John Corwin. After serving a 90-day stint as a captain of the 13th Ohio Volunteers, he returned home and died, "after a long illness," at age 43.

More than 45 years after the trial, Frank McKinney presented a paper to a meeting of the Miami County Bar Association. Included in his presentation was a reminiscence and a short reprise of the Ragan trial. John Corwin's summation to the jury, he said, was "a masterpiece of eloquence."

Book Two

• • •

Cheap Whiskey and Bad Women

Chapter One

GEORGE MITCHELL WAS ON A COLLISION COURSE with his own destiny. And, if we are to accept the essential concept of destiny, then we are bound to concede George to have been the principal victim of those self-same perverse forces, pre-ordained and immutable, which seized control of his life and led him inexorably to the unhappy culmination that uniquely distinguishes, however locally, his existence on the planet.

In the fall of 1878, George Mitchell was a sorely troubled man. He was then in the fifty-second year of his life, and he was troubled chiefly because he *had* trouble. He had *woman* trouble. And, as is usually the case, it was *his* woman who was causing the trouble.

At least she was supposed to be his woman. Had been, anyway. Alright, once she'd been Ben Stickney's woman. She'd been married to him a few years back. Anna Stickney. That was her name when George had first met her. She'd left Ben a long time ago, but she'd still carried the name. Then, after she'd come to live with George, she'd called herself Anna Mitchell. Like she was his wife. They'd never really gotten married, but same thing, they might as well have been. Everybody considered them to be husband and wife. She was sure enough his woman. Had been now for four, five years.

They had both come from the north part of Montgomery County, down around Vandalia, but they hadn't known one another there. George was some twenty years older than Anna. He'd left a wife behind when he came to Troy, in Miami County, nearly twenty-five years ago.

Anna had moved up to the Randolph Slave Settlement with her folks, Michael and Queen Coles, about fifteen years ago. She was only sixteen then and soon afterwards she had met and married Ben Stickney. That marriage had been a sporadic, desultory affair and hadn't lasted. By the time she was twenty, Anna had been single, fully liberated, and on the loose. She had been, since that time, involved in a series of brief and meaningless relationships.

For most of the time they had been together, George and Anna had gotten along well. He earned good money as a helper in John Wilson's blacksmith shop on West Main Street and she found ready employment as a domestic in the homes of some of the prominent Troy families. They didn't really have a residence of their own, but they nonetheless managed to live together in her parents' home or in the homes of friends or employers.

Anna had spent more time under different roofs than had George because every now and again he'd get all liquored up — he had a profound weakness for cheap whiskey — and become mean and abusive. On those occasions, he'd beat her up some and she'd seek refuge in the home of some other relative, friend or employer. Then, after George's current depravity had run its course, he'd be repentant, she'd forgive him, and they'd find themselves back together again.

These last six, eight months, though, their relationship had begun to deteriorate. He became more quarrelsome and she less forgiving. He became more possessive of her and she less willing to be possessed. More recently she'd gotten sassy toward him — uppity, he'd said — and she'd started to make fun of him in front of other people. Called him a used-up old man and told everybody he couldn't do it any more. Wasn't any use to her now. She'd have to find herself somebody who could do her some good.

Now they both knew none of that truck was true. He'd never had any trouble that way. He could still do what needed to be done just as good as ever. But that didn't stop her from talking the way she did. It didn't stop her from pandering to other men either. Worst part, she didn't even try to hide it from him. What she did was taunt him about it, laugh and snicker at him. She told him she'd be "gettin it" whenever, wherever and with whoever she pleased, and wasn't any of it his business either. After all, she wasn't married to him and he sure Lord didn't own her. Maybe, she'd said, he oughta find, and try to keep up with, someone his own age.

It was only recently, the past three or four weeks, he'd begun to think about killing her. Not thinking it, really. Just talk, mostly. What he'd talk about was "getting tough" with her. Like maybe what she really needed was a good hiding. And most of his talk about "whuppin'" her was just for show. Maybe she'd take it seriously and mend her ways. Or maybe some of their friends would think better of him if they were made to understand that he was in control. That was a part of it — a man oughta be able to control his woman. And if that meant he'd have to give her a good beating from time to time, then that's what a man had to do.

One time, about two weeks ago, he'd surprised her out on Ziegler's Hill with

Jake and Fanny Brown and another man named Wilkinson. When she refused to come home with him, he'd threatened her with a fence stake so she'd understand he meant business. That hadn't really had the desired effect either because she'd picked up a rock and hit him with it. She'd felt safe enough with other people around.

That might have been the first time he'd actually said anything about killing her. And he didn't really mean he intended to do anything like that. What he'd meant was that since she didn't seem to understand anything else, killing might be the only thing left to him. He'd mentioned a man up in Piqua who'd killed his woman and got by with just eight years in jail. Man named Davis. George didn't think he'd have to do any more time than Davis did. Maybe less, 'cause Anna had been asking for it. A man can only abide so much.

But he hadn't really meant he'd kill her. That was just foolish darky talk. He'd only said it, mostly, to get a reaction from somebody, anybody. Even after Monday night he still hadn't meant any real harm. It had hurt him deep. He'd said that. But he was gonna get past it. They could work it out, he and Anna, if she'd just talk with him. She needed to know how bad she'd shamed him. Then, maybe if she'd own to that, and wouldn't let it ever happen again, maybe they'd be right again.

But they'd have to find some place else to stay. They couldn't ever stay with Sublitts again, not ever. It'd just happen again. That was plain enough. And it'd happen sooner rather than later.

George and Anna Mitchell had been friends of George and Maggie Sublitts for more than a year. These past weeks they'd been staying in the Sublitts' home. There was an extra bedroom and George was happy to have a place where he and Anna could be together. But at the same time he hadn't been entirely easy about the arrangement. He knew Sublitts had harbored a strong lust for Anna and he could see she was attracted to him as well. It had looked like trouble coming. Then Monday night late, it happened. Sublitts had been drinking hard. He became abusive, fell into a torment and drove George and his own wife, Maggie, out of the house at knifepoint. Then, while those two huddled separately on the porch, he took Anna, with more than a little encouragement on her part, into the same bed she'd been occupying with George only moments before.

George Mitchell and Maggie Sublitts spent the night on the porch. Too ashamed to look at one another, or to speak, they heard the senseless murmurs and giggles of abandonment and the rhythmic slap of flesh from within the house. George Mitchell remained by the porch railing, rigid in his anger and mortification, eyes agape, until daylight. Then, without a word to Maggie, he slipped away into the forest. All his thoughts had to do with killing.

Chapter Two

OVER THE NEXT TWENTY-FOUR HOURS, George Mitchell's emotions had run an unimaginable gamut. He had flushed in shame, roared in rage, sulked in pique, cried out in anguish, whimpered in self-pity and wept uncontrollably. And though he kept close to the ground like any other wounded animal he slept not at all.

As the day wore on, so did George, and by evening he thought he'd worked through the worst of it. At least he'd gotten by the need to kill. Either of them. He came to understand that he could hate Sublitts without having to kill him. He could simply move away from him, make a life somewhere else and shut him out. A life with Anna. He finally decided he didn't even hate her despite her having encouraged Sublitts to take her. She had turned down the sheets and laid on her back for other men, he knew that. And while he hadn't liked it, he thought he could live with it. He knew he'd treated her bad too, so maybe she'd needed to get even with him the best way she could.

He'd get over the hurt, he knew that too. He'd been through it before. If he and Anna could go away together, some place where nobody knew them. They could start all over and make a new life. He'd give up drinking whiskey and she'd make him a home and be a proper wife. Maybe they could even have kids together. That'd give their marriage a purpose, give their life together some meanin'. Might be they could really get married, maybe even in a church. This time he'd see they had a home of their own. There'd be no more of stayin' one place and then another, here and there, livin' like gypsies.

He knew that life could be better than it had been, for both of them. As soon as the hurt went away, and they could get comfortable together, somewhere else, things would work out and life would be better.

He'd spent most of Tuesday wandering about the countryside lost in his thoughts and his anguish and, without knowing it, looking for Anna. He wanted to tell her what he'd decided. Let her know he wasn't angry, make her understand that they needed to go somewhere, west, maybe, and start over again. Make everything come right between them. He just needed to talk with her. To get this thing straight between them.

He knew she wouldn't stay at Sublitts. Maggie would see to that. She'd been every bit as angry and humiliated Monday night as George had been, but that sort of thing had happened to her before and she knew how to handle it. By now she'd be firmly in control of her household again. Anna would be unwelcome and George Sublitts would suffer the torments of the damned. Maggie would make him pay a hard price for his foolishness.

George Mitchell spent the whole of Tuesday night walking the Covington Pike. He was sure Anna would have stayed the night either at her mother's house or at her sister's. Her sister was married to Aaron White. Both the Coles and the Whites lived west of town in the Randolph Settlement, just off the north side of Covington Pike.

George wasn't really "lurking" in the vicinity of the two homes. He simply managed to be in the neighborhood against the chance he might get to talk with Anna in the morning when she passed through Peckham Lane on her way to Mrs. Dye's. Wednesday was the day Anna went to do Mrs. Dye's washing and she'd surely go by way of Peckham Lane.

And, after all, the only thing George wanted was to talk with her. To work things out between them. Their life together would be better.

ANNA MITCHELL'S FIRST SCREAMS rent the early morning stillness like a sharply honed axe through seasoned timber. As they were repeated, time and again, they increased in their primal stridency in a persistent crescendo of pain, rage and despair. It was as though she had known these atavistic, animal shrieks would be the last sounds she would ever make. And the waves of excruciating agony, the last physical sensations she would know.

The man, George Mitchell, strongly built and well-developed, had chased her nearly three hundred yards down Peckham Lane, all the while flailing her across the back, neck and shoulders with the heavy, machete-like blade of his homemade corn knife. Each new wound had taken its deadly toll until finally, hacked and bleeding, her undergarments perversely fallen around her ankles, she stumbled and fell face down in the lane. The next angry strokes of the corn knife severed the vertebrae of her neck and mutilated the quivering flesh of what had now become her corpse. The final unnecessary stroke, almost an afterthought, chopped off the four fingers of her right hand, releasing her grip on the pocketknife she had wielded and facilitating the removal of her rings.

He had — finally — meant to kill her after all. He'd first made that decision thirty-six hours ago in the anguish and the raw ignominy of George Sublitts' front porch, Maggie Sublitts' eyes on him, pitying, yet scornful of his shame and his weakness. A man driven, with his wife's active connivance, from his own bed.

But then he'd relented. Or thought he had. He'd convinced himself he wouldn't kill anyone. All that was necessary he'd thought was that he talk with her. And he'd tried to do that. He'd accosted her equably. "Good mornin', Anna" he'd said, as evenly as you please.

But she'd spat at him. Drawn and flashed her pocketknife in his face. "Get clear of me, you black son-of-a-bitch! I got no time for a softcock has-been like you."

And it'd all come back again, swept over him like an inexorable, angry tide. He'd had to kill her. Had to, even after he'd told himself he wouldn't. And, now that he'd done it, he was glad. "Bitch!" he snorted at the obscene mound of bloody flesh and rags in the dirt in front of him.

She had died the way he'd wanted her to die, painfully, helplessly and wild with terror. He'd wanted her to know his hurt and to feel his rage. Most of all he wanted her to realize, in the moments before she died, that she had brought it all on herself.

"Damned — black — bitch," he sobbed, dropping to his knees and grasping her shoulders. "You can't treat a man that way." He squeezed his eyes against the weak, early morning sun. "It un-mans him," he added, "And you'd got to have knowed it."

He found himself shaking the woman's lifeless body, her head dangling precariously from her savaged neck and shoulders. He forced himself to stop, realized he'd been crying, his jaw was juddering and his hands were trembling uncontrollably. He tried to stop that too. Wiping his face and eyes on his shirt sleeve, he snatched up the woman's pocketknife, prized the rings off her severed fingers, and staggered to his feet.

Standing uncertainly in the center of Peckham Lane, he looked down on the carnage he'd wrought, surveyed the surrounding woods and fields, and took stock of his situation. Then, head down and still sobbing, he skulked off into the woods. He'd have to head north if he were to have any chance to escape. If they caught him, he'd own up to what he'd done. He wasn't ashamed of it. Not a bit. It had needed to be done.

All the same, if he could get away clean, it would be a good thing.

GEORGE PECKHAM HAD HEARD ANNA'S SCREAMS, faintly and indistinctly, as he dressed and waited for his coffee water to come to a boil. Because he hadn't been sure what it was he'd heard, his investigations consisted of nothing more than a perfunctory glance out the front window of his house and down the pathway that was popularly known as Peckham Lane. Seeing nothing amiss, and hearing nothing further, he dismissed the matter and went on with his preparations for the day.

By the time he and his hired hand had set out to work in the fields that morning, George Peckham had quite forgotten the sounds he had only half-heard earlier and he was not at all prepared for what the two men would discover as they made their way down the lane towards the corn field at the east boundary of his property. Neither man had noted the small splash of fresh blood on the ground near the spot where Mitchell's knife had first struck home, nor Anna's corncob pipe where she had dropped it during the first frantic steps of her flight. They did remark her discarded shawl, and a few yards further along, her bonnet, as they walked down the pathway, but the full significance of those sightings was unappreciated until they came upon the mutilated, partially congealed obscenity that had been Anna Mitchell. It was not quite eight o'clock and no more than a handful of blowflies had yet discovered the angry wounds and open gashes in the dead woman's still-warm flesh. More would come.

First, in response to the shouts of George Peckham and Lee Hall, came more people. Then, in the natural course of events, came more blowflies. Next, as word got about, came Sheriff Dan Miller and two of his deputies. It was they who identified the victim and connected the bright spots of new blood with the woman's pipe, her shawl and her bonnet to reconstruct the course of her flight. And finally, summoned by the Sheriff, came old Doc Kitzmiller, the county coroner. He'd come all the way from Piqua and it had taken some time to get him to the scene. Dr. Beall, who had been called upon to assist in the examination, was already on hand when the coroner arrived.

Sheriff Miller lost no time in initiating his own investigation. He already knew that the dead woman was Anna Mitchell and it was obvious she had been savaged. He soon learned from onlookers at the scene that her husband had been seen lurking about the neighborhood last night and early this morning and that he had been carrying a heavy long-bladed corn knife. It seemed to be common knowledge that George and Anna had been estranged these last few days and that he had talked of killing her. Last, but scarcely least, was the fact that out of all the people from the Randolph Settlement who were on the scene that morning, George Mitchell was nowhere to be found.

The sheriff had little difficulty enlisting a cadre of volunteers, organizing them into a handful of posses with mounts and sidearms, and dispatching them in different directions to scour the countryside in search of their man. Although Mitchell was a blacksmith by trade, he didn't own a horse and was seldom seen to ride. He was thought to be afoot and was expected to be in custody before the day was out.

CHAPTER THREE

HENRY BRENARD WAS NOT A YOUNG MAN. He had spent most of his life tending crops on a small farm just south of Troy. And though he was not himself one of the Randolph people, he had spent considerable time in and about their settlements and knew all of them well. He had attended a goodly number of their revivals and prayer meetings and even more of their Saturday night socials. Time was, when he was a lot younger, he'd been set to marry one of the Randolph girls. He would have, too, but just a few days before the wedding, she'd run off with one of the boys from the Piqua settlement. Henry hadn't minded all that much. He'd said there were lots more young girls where she'd come from, and some of them were a damn sight prettier.

George Mitchell and Henry Brenard had known one another for nearly thirty years. They had first become acquainted through the Randolph community. Then, later on, when George had done some farm work on Newell Kerr's place south of town and close on to where Henry had been farming, the two men became fast friends. Many an evening, after work was done, they'd fished the waters and hunted the banks of the Great Miami River together. Other times they'd been content just to lie in the grass above the streambed and share a cold supper and a warm bottle of corn whiskey. Those occasions had generally turned out to be all-night affairs, with neither of them able to make his way back home without the benefit of both daylight and a few hours' restorative nap.

But those times had been long past. In recent years the two men had not seen each other often and although they were still friendly, the separate courses of their lives had taken them apart. Then, in the summer of '76, Henry had simply pulled up stakes, loaded everything he owned into a single wagon, and moved to Paulding County, way up in the northwest corner of the state. Of all the counties of Ohio, Paulding had the fewest number of people, the largest swamp area and the greatest number of woods and forests. Each of these features had suited Henry very well. As he had grown older he had become increasingly self-sufficient. While not quite reclusive, he was nonetheless content to get on by himself, working a small plot of ground, and was actually glad to be left alone in the small cabin he occupied on the southern edge of Paulding County's sprawling Black Swamp.

On the last Saturday of September, a few minutes before midnight and some ninety hours after he had murdered his wife, George Mitchell tapped softly on the rear window of Henry Brenard's marshland cabin. He had travelled the whole distance, more than seventy miles, on foot. And, except for that mindless, frantic first day of his flight, Wednesday, when he'd plunged and stumbled breathlessly through the brambles, woods and croplands with as much headlong haste as he could manage, he had confined his movements to the night season. Stricken, not with anything like remorse, but with the gravity of his predicament, and increasingly desperate to avoid capture, he had melded himself into the protective cover of the forest. The daylight hours, Thursday, Friday and Saturday, were spent resting and hiding in the deep woodland thickets. Once he'd sensed the presence of people about and spent most of the day napping in the hollow of an aged oak tree. The darkness was time for travel, when he picked his way through the woods and along the meanders of small streams, avoiding even the smallest of towns and settlements. It was also a time for foraging, and he had made a subsistence of green apples, wild berries, and the fallen nuts he harvested from the forest floor.

At first he had had no clear idea where he was headed. Only a vague notion that he should strike out to the north and west away from all signs of civilization and that he should get out of Miami County quickly. Then later, as he gathered his wits, he remembered that his one-time friend, Henry Brenard, had relocated in the north, up in Paulding County, and that the Auglaize River would show him the way. Having settled, then, on that considered destination, he continued on his course to the north, following, at a distance, the route of the Miami-Erie Canal to the headwaters of the Auglaize and then along that stream to the flat marshlands of Paulding County. Once he had reached the Black Swamp country he dared to approach those cabins and shacks obviously occupied by darkies and to inquire after Henry Brenard.

Henry's best friend in all the world was an old muzzle-loader, a crudely-forged, cap-and-ball smooth-barrel that represented the full extent of his inheritance from his father. Henry kept it at the ready, well-oiled and fully loaded, by the front door of his cabin. It was handy enough, in that location, to keep Henry well supplied with venison from the native white-tails and it was sure enough a comfort when someone came tapping on the back window in the dead stillness of a late Saturday night.

Henry Brenard directed his unexpected and unidentified visitor to come round to the front door — and met him there with his muzzle-loader. Then, with the first dawning of recognition, he demanded querulously, "Mitchell? Is that George Mitchell? Mitchell, what in the name of God brings you all the way up here, sneakin' 'round the swamp this time of night?"

And when George Mitchell was slow to answer, Brenard drew his own conclusions. "You in some kinda trouble, ain't that so? Trouble with the law, I kin tell. An' somebody's lookin' for you, that right?"

"Nah, I ain't in any trouble," George lied glibly. "Nobody's lookin' for me, far's I know. I just happened to be in the neighborhood. Ain't seen you in a while, thought I'd stop by."

"Yeah, you did," Brenard demurred. "Middla the damn night, five mile into the swamp, and you just happened to be in the neighborhood. This'd be like one of them Sunday mornin' social calls, right? Only you just got here 'bout ten hours early. Maybe you oughta come back 'bout noon, that'd be a lot more fittin'." Brenard made as if to close the door. "'Sides, you'd have a mite longer to get your story straight, tell me somethin' I might be inclined to b'lieve."

Mitchell blocked the door with the meaty part of his left hand. "Let me in, dammit. I'll tell you about it. It ain't such a big thing anyway."

What Mitchell told Henry Brenard later that night — the two men seated on opposite sides of Henry's kitchen table, a guttering candle and a pint jar of corn whiskey between them — was that he and another darkey man had got into a row and that "they" had got after him. So, he said, he lit out for parts north, and here, after a day or two, he was. He'd sure be obliged if he could stay a few days — he wouldn't be any trouble — and then he'd go on back home.

As it happened, he wasn't really any trouble and he stayed only until Monday morning. He left that day before daylight, without notice, thanks or goodbye to his host. And Henry Brenard's best pair of boots and his old muzzleloader went with him.

CHAPTER FOUR

THE SEARCH FOR GEORGE MITCHELL turned out to be a greater challenge than anyone might have imagined. The general expectation had been that he would be apprehended within hours after the discovery of Anna's body. It was thought that a simple black man, well-known in the area, on foot, and with only the briefest head start, should have been unable to elude the half-dozen bands of mounted men set loose in determined pursuit.

Information, both good and bad, concerning Mitchell's current whereabouts and direction of travel ran rife and Sheriff Dan Miller promptly sent out fresh hunting parties to follow each new lead as it came to his attention. Early reports had Mitchell in hiding at various locations within the county, but a thorough search of all such places failed to turn him out. The best information had it that he was headed northward towards the heavily wooded areas of Van Wert and Paulding Counties. Sheriff Miller quickly organized and led a small party of armed men to the area and scoured it thoroughly. He ultimately picked up Mitchell's track at the little town of Delphos, in Van Wert County, and followed it obliquely to Henry Brenard's swampside cabin. He arrived at Brenard's just before noon on Monday and learned that Mitchell had departed several hours earlier.

Sheriff Miller and his party remained in the area the rest of the week in a determined effort to catch his man. He had been very close, frustratingly close, but was finally unable to re-establish the trace. And though he and the local county officers continued to search the northern part of the state for the next several weeks, they were unsuccessful. There were numerous false clues and even a few arrests but no real progress was made.

And while those weeks passed and stretched into months without anything really new, the trail ran cold. As the clement temperatures and bright hues of early autumn sagged into the creeping chill and stark colors of a typical Ohio winter, Sheriff Miller had occasion to investigate a few sporadic second and third-hand reports, all unattributed, that Mitchell had been seen in Toledo, in Muncie, or in one or the other of the small towns of southern Michigan. Although the sheriff was diligent in his response to all such reports and swiftly dispatched his deputies to each of the assigned locales, nothing was discovered as to the whereabouts of the fugitive. Later still, with the advent of the thaws and slushes of springtime 1879, even those dubious and unreliable sources, rumor and gossip, dried up and it was generally assumed that Mitchell had made good his escape.

Queen Coles, Anna Mitchell's mother, had long since buried her daughter in a simple graveside ceremony. The mourning period was over and Anna's family had made their adjustments. There were new children and grandchildren to be tended and new crops to be planted. Life went on within the settlement.

Then fortuitously, or perhaps inevitably in the context of his destiny, George Mitchell was discovered. On a Saturday in July of 1879, a teenaged boy named Walter Lyons had journeyed from Troy for an extended visit with his cousins in the town of Washington Courthouse, located on Paint Creek in Fayette County. Lyons had chanced to see Mitchell on the streets of Washington Courthouse and recognized him at once. He had known Mitchell from the Troy settlement and knew he was wanted in connection with the murder. The boy quickly alerted the first law enforcement officer he could find, a Fayette County deputy sheriff named Leyda, and Leyda made an immediate arrest.

Mitchell steadfastly denied both his identity and the fact that he was wanted by the law. His name, he insisted, was John Wilson and he was a blacksmith by trade. He said he'd come over from New Holland just last February and he'd been smithing in the shop down the street ever since. Didn't believe him, they should ask Clara Johns over in New Holland. She'd vouch for him.

With an unsurprising want of inspiration, Mitchell had assumed the masquerade of his own erstwhile employer, Troy blacksmith John Wilson. And though he continued to protest, Mitchell offered no physical resistance to his arrest.

Upon further questioning at the jail, Mitchell finally acknowledged his identity. Having made that concession he then blithely inquired of Deputy Leyda what he was wanted for.

"For the murder of your wife," Leyda answered coolly.

"Murder?" demanded Mitchell with poorly feigned surprise. "I didn't 'murder' her. All I did was hit her one good lick with a club and then left her be. She wasn't hurt bad but she made so much fuss, I jus' took off."

"Why'd you hit her with a club?" queried Leyda, taking notes of his interrogation.

"She'd got herself all tangled up with another man," he answered easily. "I shoulda give her a real beatin'."

"Where did this happen?" asked Leyda.

"Back in Miami County. In a lane 'bout a mile and a half from Troy."

Leyda pushed. "Where's this 'lane' located?"

"I already tole ya that. 'Bout a mile and a half outside Troy. Out by the hydraulic."

The sheriff of Fayette County was acquainted with his Miami County counterpart, Dan Miller. He also remembered that Sheriff Miller had searched far and wide for a George Mitchell, accused wife-slayer. For that reason he was more than happy to advise, by telegraph, that he had Mitchell in custody. Would Miller arrange for transfer?

The response was immediate. "Congratulations and thanks. Chief Deputy John P. Miller will arrive Monday for pickup."

WILEY JONES HAD SPENT A GOOD PART OF HIS LIFE in the Fayette County jail. His life style consisted of a series of monthly cycles in which he worked a week, drank a week, and spent the balance of the month in jail for drunk and disorderly. He wasn't vicious, or even spiteful. It was just his way.

And, of course, Wiley would have been in residence at the jailhouse that Saturday in July when George Mitchell was locked into an adjoining cell. "Hey there, uncle," Wiley called out, "You look sober 'nuff to me. What you in here for?"

Mitchell had neither glanced in the direction of his new neighbor, nor offered any sort of greeting. Gingerly, he lowered himself onto his bunkbed, testing its reaction to his weight. Satisfied it would bear up, he stretched himself out on his back, tipped a soiled cap over his eyes, and locked hands across his beltline. He appeared to have no interest in conversation.

"Come on, uncle," persisted Wiley. "How come they put you here in jail?"

Slowly and deliberately, Mitchell lifted his cap. He glared menacingly at Wiley and dropped the cap back into place. "I knocked me a nigger man on the head with a club," he growled. "Damn near killed him too."

Wiley couldn't let it alone. "Why you wanna go do a thing like that?" he wheedled.

The cap lifted again. Another stoney glare. Then, "Son-of-a-bitch asked a whole lotta dumb questions about stuff 'wasn't none of his business." He let the cap fall back over his eyes and finished, "'Bout like you been doin'."

Wiley wasn't sure whether the man was serious or just having fun with him, but he made no more inquiries until the next day. By that time, Sunday morning, he was armed with fresh information. "Deputy Leyda, he say you been arrested for killin' your wife. That so, uncle?"

This time he found Mitchell a bit more communicative. "Nah," he drawled, I didn't kill her. I just give her a damn good whippin'. Teach her some manners."

Encouraged, Wiley pressed the matter. "They have it over here," he said skeptically, "that you cut her up."

"Didn't cut nobody," Mitchell insisted. "I hit her with a club. Happened out by the hydraulic."

"Is she dead?" asked Wiley.

Mitchell folded his arms across his chest and stared impassively out the barred window. "I hope so," he muttered.

***

MIAMI COUNTY CHIEF DEPUTY JOHN MILLER was the oldest son of Sheriff Dan Miller. He arrived at Washington Courthouse Monday evening just before dark. Then, Tuesday morning, in the presence of Deputy Leyda, he conducted his own interrogation of the prisoner. Mitchell stuck to his story. He'd only struck his wife one time, with a club, and took off for parts north. He'd gone first, he said, to Muncie and then to Paulding County.

"Why Paulding?" John Miller wanted to know. "Did you hide out with someone there?"

"Nossir. I don't know nobody in that county. It was just in the way of where I was goin'."

The questioning completed, the officers shackled Mitchell to the seat of Miller's wagon and the two men, the prisoner and his deputy, set off on the fifty mile journey back to Troy. They arrived there late in the evening and the prisoner was lodged in the Miami County jail to await further proceedings.

CHAPTER FIVE

GEORGE MITCHELL WAS INDICTED FOR FIRST DEGREE MURDER by the November session of the Miami County Grand Jury. The indictment charged — in the stilted, arcane, often ludicrous, language of the law and lawyers, that:

... George Mitchell, late of said county, on the twentyseventh day of September, in the year of our Lord one thousand eight hundred and seventy-eight, with force and arms, in said County of Miami, and State of Ohio, in and upon one Anna Stickney, otherwise called Anna Mitchell, then and there being, unlawfully, feloniously, purposely and of deliberate and premeditated malice did make an assault in a menacing manner with intent her the said Anna Stickney, otherwise called Anna Mitchell unlawfully, feloniously, purposely and of deliberate and premeditated malice to kill and murder, and with a certain knife commonly called a corn knife, which he the said George Mitchell in his right hand then and there had and held, her the said Anna Stickney, otherwise called Anna Mitchell, then and there unlawfully, feloniously, purposely, and of deliberate and premeditated malice, did strike, cut and wound, with the intent aforesaid, thereby then and there giving to the said Anna Stickney, otherwise called Anna Mitchell, in and upon the neck of her the said Anna Stickney, otherwise called Anna Mitchell, a deep cut and mortal wound, which said cut and mortal wound, severed and separated the body from the head, save only a small piece or strip of the cuticle or skin, of the neck aforesaid, of which said cut and mortal wound, she the said Anna Stickney otherwise called Anna Mitchell immediately, and instantly, then and there, died; and so the jurors aforesaid upon their oaths aforesaid, do say that the said George Mitchell her the said Anna Stickney, otherwise called Anna Mitchell, in the manner and by the means, aforesaid, unlawfully, feloniously, purposely and of deliberate and premeditated malice did then and there kill and murder contrary to the form of the statute in such case made and provided, and against the peace and dignity of the State of Ohio.

A formal plea of not guilty was entered on December 3rd, and the case came on for trial before Judge Henry H. Williams on Thursday, January 15th, 1880. The State was represented by County Prosecutor Moses B. Earnhart and by Special Assistant Alijah R. Byrkett. Appearing for the defendant were attorneys S. S. and J. F. McKinney of Piqua and J. M. Bond and H. G. Sellers of Troy.

A special panel of thirty-six veniremen had been summoned to serve as jurors. These men were separated and individually questioned, first by Judge Williams, then by the attorneys, to determine their suitability to weigh the evidence in the case and to decide the defendant's guilt or innocence fairly and impartially. Were they biased against darkies, people of color? Had any of them known Anna Mitchell? Had they read or heard anything about her murder? Were they acquainted with George Mitchell or with any of the persons who were expected to testify? Had they formed any opinions concerning the matter? Would they agree to follow the law as given by Judge Williams even if it differed from what they believed the law should be? And, of paramount importance to the prosecutor, could they return a verdict which would mandate the death penalty? The original number of veniremen was swiftly exhausted in the selection process and a second panel was drawn and pressed into service. Finally, late Thursday afternoon, a jury of twelve men, acceptable to both sides, was seated and sworn.

Opening statements of counsel were received Friday morning and then the jury was escorted by Sheriff Miller to the vicinity where Anna Mitchell had died. The purpose of this "jury view" of the scene of the crime was to better enable them to understand the evidence as it was revealed to them in the courtroom. They were not to attempt to "gather evidence", but only to become oriented to the area. Upon Judge Williams' instruction, the sheriff directed the jurors' attention to each of those separate locations where the victim's pipe, her shawl, her bonnet and her body had been found. The jurors gathered close around the sheriff and listened attentively to his descriptions. They had learned that a woman had bled out her life force onto the ground here and they were awed by the knowledge. They walked about solemnly and maintained a reverent silence as they contemplated the series of events that must have occurred at this place on a warm, bright morning not so very long ago.

After lunch and back in the courtroom the testimony began. It really didn't take very long. Moses Earnhart began the State's case by calling Dr. Kitzmiller, the county coroner, to the witness stand. After no more than a few introductory questions and answers, Dr. Kitzmiller was encouraged to summarize the circumstance of his inquest into the death of Anna Mitchell and to state his conclusions.

"It was the 27th day of September," he began. "I came down from Piqua on the Troy Pike. Then, just north of town, I turned off the road to the west and passed through a narrow strip of woods until I reached a lane. I later learned that this was called Peckham Lane. I went down the lane some two or three hundred yards and found a colored woman lying on her face. She appeared to have been about thirty years of age.

"There was a woods on the right side of the lane and an open field to the left. The body was near the edge of the woods with the head to the east or northeast. The head was almost completely severed from the body; the cervical vertebrae were cut clear through. There were a number of cuts on the head and a cut on each shoulder. One hand was nearly severed and the fingers on the other had been amputated. The woman's body was all hacked up. There were cuts on her breasts and wounds on her back along the upper trunk; there were some twelve or fifteen of those.

"Although any number of those wounds would have been sufficient to produce the woman's death, it is my opinion that the actual cause was the great cut to the neck. That blow, which severed the spinal column just two bones below the base of the brain, appears to have been delivered after she had fallen. It was a severe stroke and was made with a very sharp instrument. Because all of the cuts were both long and deep — some were clear through the collar bone — I should imagine the instrument to have been of pretty good length and of considerable weight. It was obviously wielded with great force."

Dr. S. W. Beall testified to having assisted Dr. Kitzmiller in the inquest. His testimony corroborated that of the coroner in every respect. He added his own observation that the woman's clothing was torn and her undergarments had dropped below her knees so as to prevent her from running further. She lay on the ground with her limbs drawn up and her spinal cord severed.

There was no cross-examination of either of the two doctors. Their evidence had been straightforward and incontrovertible. There was no point in challenging them.

Prosecutors Earnhart and Byrkett continued the State's case with an impressive procession of witnesses, each of whom contributed a distinctive thread or link to the cumulative mesh of circumstantial evidence that was drawn ever-tighter around the defendant. Their testimony demonstrated that George and Anna had been estranged from one another; that there was ill-feeling between them; that George had, on more than one occasion, threatened to harm or kill her; and that he had even considered the consequences to himself if he were to kill her. George Sublitts told the jury that Mitchell had said they wouldn't hang him for killing his wife, he'd probably just get a few years in the penitentiary.

Sublitts also told of Mitchell's having made himself a corn knife. It had a heavy steel blade about a foot and a half long, the overall length being about two feet. He'd made a hole in the wooden handle and put a string through it. Said it would be handy to carry about at night.

Queen Coles was much that her name implied. A darkly handsome woman with alert eyes and prominent cheekbones, she appeared almost regal in her manner and her bearing. She was the mother of Anna Mitchell.

"Anna was 'bout my height and size," she said. "Not any bigger'n that.

"I saw her last Tuesday before she was killed. I was down to Aaron White's on accounta a sick child. Aaron, he's married to my other daughter. Sometime 'tween eight and nine o'clock that evenin' Anna came to Aaron's house. She seemed excited 'bout somethin'. She also seemed scared.

"The both of us, me and Anna, stayed the night at Aaron's. We was up at daylight and she left 'fore breakfast. She started out for Peckham's Lane at sunrise. She was wearin' that shawl and that there bonnet when I seen her last. Yessir that's her pipe too. I've seen it often.

"Pretty soon after she left, I heard a sharp scream. Then, a bit later I heard a halloo, a kinda muffled scream. Then it grew quiet, and I never heard nothin' more.

"I've only knowed George Mitchell slightly. I do 'member he'd been with Anna in Peckham's Lane on days when she went to wash for Mrs. Dye. He'd a knowed she'd go there on a Wednesday."

A farmer named Benjamin Shill testified that he had seen Anna Mitchell early Wednesday morning. He'd been up early, had dug a bucket of potatoes from his fields and was returning home.

"I met Anna Mitchell at the little branch just south of the potato patch. She was walking and smoking a pipe. She was going east down the lane, I supposed she was going to Mrs. Dye's. She says 'Good morning, Mr. Shill,' and I said 'Good morning, Anna.' I recognize the shawl she was wearing. It's the one you have here. She was wearing a bonnet, but I can't say for sure it's that one.

"As I was going back by the fencerow, I heard a scream. I turned around and looked to the east. I heard someone running. It sounded like sheep. I heard several more screams. Then it grew silent. I hadn't seen anything."

The State's witnesses also showed that Mitchell had been in the vicinity the Tuesday before the murder, that he had been looking for Anna that afternoon and had been lurking about during the evening, and that he had been seen near Peckham Lane on Wednesday morning. And, on all such occasions, he had been carrying his corn knife. It was also shown that he had fled the area immediately after the murder.

Then, finally, there came the testimony concerning his arrest, his acknowledgments to Deputy Leyda and to Wiley Jones, and the incriminating fact that he still carried in his pocket, nearly a year after the murder, rings which Anna Mitchell had worn on her fingers the day she was killed.

Sam McKinney was the senior member of the defense team. He was also the most experienced and the ablest lawyer in the courtroom. Even so, his cross-examination of the State's witnesses was ineffectual. His attempts to show that the witnesses were mistaken, or that they were lying, were wholly unavailing.

Then, when the prosecution had rested its case and the burden had shifted, the defense tried vainly to show that Mitchell might have been temporarily insane when the murder was committed. The best they could do in that regard, however, was to offer the testimony of a local physician, Dr. Bower, who said that he did not regard Mitchell as of right mind, and the testimony of John Wilson, Mitchell's former employer, who said that the defendant was a bit "peculiar" and was subject to "spells." It was the weakest defense imaginable, but it was all they had. The one thing they dared not do was to put George Mitchell on the stand. He had already told a half dozen different stories to a half dozen different people, and his lawyers could not permit the prosecutors to cross-examine him about his arguments with Anna, the happenings in Peckham Lane and his precipitate flight to parts unknown immediately thereafter.

In rebuttal, the prosecution produced more than a dozen witnesses who had known the defendant intimately. Their testimony was unanimous in that he was a man of fair mind. He was uneducated, they agreed, but he was naturally smart and perfectly capable of distinguishing between right and wrong.

"Oh yes," said an acquaintance named Henry Canutt, "he woulda known what he was doin'. I talked with him about two weeks before the murder. He said he was feeling so tormented he needed to kill someone. He didn't actually say he intended to kill Anna, but he did say that the trouble with her was she didn't treat him right."

The evidence was closed Tuesday morning and both sides rested their cases. Beginning right after lunch, Alijah Byrkett spent the entire afternoon arguing the state's case to the jury. Then, on Wednesday, John Bond and Sam McKinney took their turns. They separately reviewed the evidence, assailed the credibility of the state's witnesses, and urged the jury to give their client the benefit of every reasonable doubt. The jury should be mindful, they cautioned, that the defendant's life was in their hands.

It was late in the afternoon when Judge Williams completed his instructions to the jury concerning the law and submitted the case to them for decision.

And, not more than thirty minutes later, the jury returned its verdict. It hadn't taken much time for them to find Mitchell to be "guilty of murder in the first degree."

The spectators, who had crowded the courtroom beyond its capacity since the first day of trial, received the verdict with a death-like stillness. There was no demonstration, no reaction. Only a silence that seemed almost sepulchral. The jury had made no recommendation for mercy and a death sentence was mandated by the law.

Mitchell himself showed no outward sign of emotion. He accepted the verdict stoically and made no comment to his counsel until after court had adjourned for the day. It was reported, however, that he "chatted laughingly" with the deputies when they took him back to the jail that evening.

CHAPTER SIX

SAM MCKINNEY SLEPT LATE the morning after the trial. He had remained at the courthouse Wednesday evening to confer with his colleagues and to discuss the verdict with those members of the jury who were willing to be interviewed. Then he had consoled himself with a leisurely supper at the Morris House, a cordial and a cigar, before undertaking the chilly, eight-mile buggy ride back to Piqua. It had been well after midnight before he'd gotten to bed.

He was not as young as he used to be, he reflected, and a week of trial had taken a greater toll of his energies than he had expected. He reminded himself that he was sixty-one years old and might fairly be excused for having languished overlong in a warm bed this cold winter morning.

The law office of S. S. and J. F. McKinney had long since moved from its second-floor location above Geyer's Hardware Store to a somewhat more commodious first-floor suite at the corner of Main and Ash Streets. Best of all, the new quarters were no more than a short walking distance from Sam's residence.

Frank McKinney met his older brother at the front doorway and fairly tugged him through. His manner was intense and he seemed to be mildly excited.

"There you are," he chirped. "I was about to send someone around to roust you out. Are you all right?"

"Am I what?" growled Sam. "Of course I'm all right. I've simply indulged myself with a few extra winks this morning. The trial seems to have quite worn me out."

"I'm sure it has," acknowledged Frank, helping his brother out of his overcoat.

"And, on that subject, I have a gentleman in my office who would like to speak with you."

"Oh?" queried Sam as he allowed himself to be escorted into Frank's inner chamber.

"Sam, I think you know Mr. Bain," Frank offered.

The small, worried-looking man raised himself out of the smooth, walnut armchair opposite Frank's cluttered desk.

"Why, of course I do," said Sam McKinney cordially, as much to Mr. Bain as to his brother. "How are you today, sir?" He extended his great paw and engulfed the smaller man's hand in greeting.

"The three of us have spent a great deal of courtroom time together this past week. I should have thought you had seen quite enough of Frank and I for a while," remarked Sam McKinney.

John Bain, juror number twelve, had been the foreman of the George Mitchell jury. He had departed the courthouse immediately after court was adjourned yesterday evening, and Sam had not had a chance to interview him.

"To what do we owe the pleasure, Mr. Bain?" asked Sam McKinney.

"Well, Mr. McKinney," said John Bain diffidently, "I think you know that the jury's verdict was unanimous. And it didn't take us so very long to decide the matter. We were all sure enough that Mitchell killed his wife just like Mr. Earnhart said he did.

"So what I want to tell you probably don't much matter anyway. But, the truth of it is, I think the man was entitled to a fair trial."

"That's true enough," agreed Sam McKinney.

"Well, sir, I don't know if I should be talking with you now. The judge said we wasn't to communicate with any of the lawyers."

McKinney interrupted. "You needn't be concerned on that score. Now that the trial is over you are released from that stricture. We are all at liberty to discuss the matter freely."

"I thought that might be so," John Bain seemed relieved. "Like I said, it may not make any difference now, but it'll ease my mind if I tell you. It's about one of the jurors. It happened on the second day of trial. We'd just heard the lawyers' opening statements and had gone back to the jury room for a recess. One of the other jurors looked at me straight-on and says, 'They ought to have hung that nigger when they caught him and saved the county the expense.'"

Sam McKinney looked evenly at John Bain. "You have reported a very serious offense, sir, and you have done right. Which juror made the remark?"

"It was juror number nine. James Caldwell."

"Did he make any other such comments?"

"Yes sir, he did," answered John Bain. "After we had reached our verdict yesterday evening but before it was announced, Mr. Caldwell said we should then take a vote whether to take the son-of-a-bitch out to Peckham Lane, where his wife was killed, and hang him to a tree out there."

McKinney nodded. "Did anyone else hear him say that?"

"I should think that all of the jurors would have heard. He said it to the whole group of us," answered Bain. "Since I had been elected foreman, I thought it was up to me to tell him we shouldn't be saying things like that. We were supposed to be fair-minded."

"Quite right," McKinney interjected.

"But in all honesty," continued Bain, "I'm sure it didn't make any difference. Mr. Mitchell would have been convicted anyway."

"That's probably true enough," agreed Sam McKinney. "But as you yourself have said just a moment ago, the man was entitled to a fair trial — by a fair and impartial jury." He studied his hands for just a moment, then looked across at Bain. "Would you be willing to sign an affidavit?"

THE FOLLOWING DAY, FRIDAY, JANUARY 23RD, Sam McKinney and John Bond, as attorneys for George Mitchell, filed with the court their motion for a new trial. As the basis for the motion, they assigned a number of claimed errors or irregularities which, they contended, had tainted the trial and therefore the verdict. Principal among the irregularities assigned were the remarks, and the prejudice implicit therein, of juror James K. Caldwell. The motion was supported by the sworn affidavit of John Bain.

Frank McKinney was elated at this latest wrinkle. "Well," he said as they drove back to Piqua, "That should certainly get us a new trial. We could hardly have done better than the foreman of the jury. Then, if we should succeed on the motion, perhaps Moses will accept a plea to manslaughter. I can't imagine he'll want to try the whole case again."

And when Sam McKinney didn't respond immediately, and failed to exude the same degree of enthusiasm held by Frank, the latter prompted, "You don't think Judge Williams will deny the motion, do you? He can't, can he? Not in the face of the evidence?"

"Yes," answered Sam McKinney. "He can. And I'm afraid he will."

"I don't understand," Frank remarked querulously. "On what basis can he ignore Mr. Bain's testimony?"

"Do you remember the *aliunde* rule which is applicable to jury verdicts?" asked Sam McKinney. And when Frank had looked back askance, he continued, "The *aliunde* rule is an old and well-established legal principle, obscure perhaps because the situation seldom arises. However, it is nonetheless well-founded in the law. The gist of the rule is that a jury verdict may not be impeached by the affidavit or testimony of the jurors themselves *unless* it is accompanied by evidence *aliunde*, from another, independent source, to confirm their testimony."

"But that's an impossible standard," Frank remonstrated. "How can we, or anybody else, ever produce evidence *aliunde* of juror misconduct if such misconduct occurs only in the jury room?"

"It's an extremely difficult standard," Sam McKinney conceded. "It creates a very formidable obstacle for us and for anyone else who would seek to undermine the verdict of those 'twelve just men, tried and true'."

"Then why file the motion at all?"

Sam McKinney sighed his own resignation. "We are obliged," he answered, "to file the motion asking the court to set aside the verdict and to grant the defendant a new trial. It's a part of our duty to the client.

"We are also bound to set forth, and to argue, all those reasons which might conceivably induce, or justify, the taking of such an extraordinary measure. This allegation against Mr. Caldwell may or may not be sufficient to tip the scale.

"We can only serve it up," he intoned, philosophically "And hope. It is, at the least, another arrow in our quiver."

GEORGE MITCHELL'S MOTION FOR NEW TRIAL, filed on his behalf by his attorneys, came on for hearing before Judge Williams the following Friday, January 30th. In addition to the arguments of counsel, the Court heard the testimony of John Bain, James Caldwell and other witnesses who professed to some knowledge of Caldwell's bias against the defendant.

At the end of the day Judge Williams took the matter under advisement and promised to render a decision within a few days. Counsel would be notified.

ON WEDNESDAY, FEBRUARY 4TH, all of the attorneys and the defendant George Mitchell were again present in the courtroom.

Judge Williams announced his decision on the defendant's motion for new trial. Reading from a prepared text, the judge addressed each of the claimed errors and irregularities assigned by counsel in support of the motion. One by one he disposed of, and ruled against, the defendant's contentions.

As to the alleged misconduct of Juror James Caldwell, Judge Williams first alluded to the *aliunde* rule of law explained by Sam McKinney to his brother, "I know of no course by which evidence can be introduced to support this assignment unless it be by the testimony of persons other than the jurors themselves. The testimony of jurors may not be received on a motion for a new trial to impeach their verdict by showing misconduct on the part of the jury. This rule is a wholesome one founded upon the wisest reasons of public policy and absolutely forbids the admission of such testimony."

And then, paradoxically, he proceeded to evaluate the allegation, "But this charge against Juror Caldwell is not true. Upon his oath he has denied the whole thing and re-affirmed his statement that he had formed no opinion as to the guilt or innocence of the defendant.

"Even if the charge were believed, we have nothing other than the foolish remark of one juror. No attention seems to have been given it by his fellow jurors and it does not appear to have affected the verdict or to have prejudiced the defendant."

With the motion for new trial overruled, there remained only the matter of sentencing. Judge Williams called upon the defendant to stand and then asked if he knew any reason why sentence should not be pronounced. And when none was given, the judge proceeded, "George Mitchell, it is the sentence of this Court that you be taken hence, in the custody of the sheriff, to the jail of Miami County and there kept in solitary confinement until Friday, the 28th of May, 1880, and that on said day, between the hours of twelve and two o'clock, that you shall be taken to the place of execution and hanged by the neck until you are dead."

Once again a death-like stillness prevailed within the courtroom. Once again George Mitchell exhibited no sign of emotion other than a nervous twitching and a single, almost imperceptible shudder. This time, however, while being escorted across the street to the jailhouse, he burst into tears. The only intelligible phrase he was heard to utter was, "They've put it on me, now."

CHAPTER SEVEN

THE PROCESS BY WHICH JUDGE WILLIAMS' SENTENCE would be carried out was initiated by the issuance of an official "Death Warrant." This was in the form of a court order, or writ, signed by J. W. Cruikshank as Clerk of Courts and directed to Sheriff Daniel C. Miller. The warrant simply commanded the sheriff to keep the prisoner in safe and secure custody until the day set for execution and, on that day, to "hang him by the neck until dead."

The actual logistics by which the order was to be implemented were left to the sheriff. It would be his responsibility to make it happen.

It had become the custom in the latter part of the nineteenth century that executions be held within the county in which the crime had been committed. And while there had been public hangings elsewhere in Ohio, none had yet occurred in Miami County. Sheriff Miller knew of a large and sturdy scaffold, complete with gallows, that was owned by Montgomery County and had already been used in nearby counties. He promptly made arrangements to rent the device for fifty dollars. It would be delivered and set up in the jailyard at Troy in time for the Mitchell execution.

Over the course of the next one-hundred-odd days, two separate, probably predictable and not entirely unrelated phenomena occurred. The first of these was that George Mitchell found religion. Denied, as he was, the solace of hard liquor, he fled to the comfort and consolation of his bible. And, by reason of his new-found devotion, he became, at least in the perception of his keepers, a better person. He read the scriptures daily and allotted regular times for prayer and meditation. His manner became gentle, almost amiable, and his behavior impeccable. Because of those changes and despite the order for solitary confinement, he was given free run of the cellblock. He ultimately came to be something of a jailhouse pet, fondly regarded and essentially harmless.

Condemned to die, he was ultimately deemed to be salvageable.

The second of these phenomena came in the form of a developing aura of public sympathy for the doomed man. Led by attorney John W. Morris, and assisted, most surprisingly, by former prosecuting attorney Calvin D. Wright, who had signed Mitchell's indictment, and by Clerk of Courts John W.

Cruikshank, who had signed his death warrant, the outpourings of sympathy for George Mitchell soon achieved groundswell proportions.

Fueled by statements attributed to Mitchell and circulated by the Messrs. Morris, Wright and Cruikshank the arguments ran that the killing had been motivated by "pure love" and perpetrated by a spurned and "half-crazed" swain. Another school had it to have been a matter of self-defense, done in response to Anna Mitchell's having brandished her own pocketknife and threatened him.

In early May, with the execution date fast approaching, a delegation of local dignitaries, including John Morris and Calvin Wright, journeyed to Columbus to appeal to Governor Charles Foster. In their petitions for executive clemency it was represented that there existed serious doubts as to Mitchell's guilt, that new evidence favorable to him had only recently come to light, that such new evidence would greatly mitigate his culpability or perhaps exonerate him entirely, and, finally, that he was insane at the time of the murder and should not have been held accountable.

The petitions had been artfully worded, principally by John Morris, and had been widely circulated throughout the county over a period of many weeks. After a formal presentation of the petitions to the governor, accompanied by strong arguments and fervent pleas, the members of the delegation, save only former prosecutor Calvin Wright, returned to Troy. Wright remained in Columbus the entire week to press for intervention.

On Thursday afternoon, May 13th, just fifteen days before the date established by Judge Williams for George Mitchell's execution, John Morris received a telegram from Calvin Wright. Governor Foster had agreed to grant a temporary respite. The order of execution would be suspended for one hundred days. Morris ran directly to the jail, still in shirtsleeves, to deliver the news. As soon as George Mitchell came to understand what had happened he jumped high in the air, clapped his hands and raced round and round the jailhouse corridor until, out of breath, he threw himself on his belly and patted the floor with his hands. "Praise the Lord!" he sang out, "Blessed be the name of the Lord. I been saved, I'm saved!"

The local newspaper reported Mitchell's reaction in its Thursday evening edition. It attributed those excited exclamations to Mitchell along with "other exhortations uttered up to the Being to whose presence and care he suddenly transported and consigned the soul of his mistress less than two years since."

The following day Sheriff Miller received formal notification from the Governor's office that the order of execution had been suspended by executive order until September 3rd. The purpose of the stay was to permit time for an official review. In view of the frenetic activities of the Mitchell sympathizers, the sheriff was not surprised at the circumstance. The first thing he did was to communicate with the Montgomery County Sheriff in order to reschedule the delivery of the gallows.

THE SUMMER OF 1880 WAS A PLEASANT AND IDYLLIC INTERMEZZO for George Mitchell. The warm, comfortable days of June, July and August caught him up and carried him along in their leisurely flow through the wondrous continuum of time and space. His spirits had been buoyed by his eleventh-hour reprieve and his hopes were encouraged by the activities of his sympathizers. There was an excellent chance, he was assured, that Governor Foster might be induced to commute his sentence to that of imprisonment for life, or perhaps even for some shorter period of time.

The horrific specter of the gallows having thus receded from his immediate horizons, George Mitchell passed his summer in relaxed congeniality. He was allowed to wander freely about the jailhouse and he visited with the other inmates frequently. He chatted amiably with his jailers, played sociably at cards and read quietly from his bible. He received visitors and granted interviews to his supporters and to news reporters. Even the food suited him. He ate well and he grew sleek.

He did acknowledge, during a mid-August interview, his awareness that he was still under a death sentence. "My troubles," he said, "are botherin' me a great deal." He reiterated, however, his abiding confidence that Governor Foster would spare him.

To all who asked of him, George Mitchell answered questions freely, except as to the crime for which he had been condemned. He steadfastly refused to discuss that event with anyone.

He allowed, however, that if it turned out that he must hang for his crime, he might have more to say on the subject. For the time being, he said, he would take solace in his bible.

INEVITABLY AND INEXORABLY, the reverie came to an end.

There had been no word from Governor Foster. Each of those one hundred borrowed days had begun with the confident expectation that Governor Foster would have completed his review of the Mitchell file and would that day exercise a meaningful clemency. Each of those one hundred days had ended with the knowledge that there had been no commutation. By the same token, however, there had been no denial. Thus each day's disappointments spawned the next day's hopes. And, withal, the sands began to run out for George Mitchell.

On Friday, August 27th, Col. J. H. Horton, Commander, 3rd Regiment of the Ohio National Guard received an order:

Dear Sir: It is deemed necessary that troops be in attendance for the protection of the peace at the execution of George Mitchell on the 3rd of September, 1880, between the hours of 10 a.m. and 2 p.m. o'clock, at the Miami County Jail.

You will therefore provide troops sufficient therefor, as provided by Section 7342, Statutes of Ohio.

D. C. Miller
Sheriff Miami County, O.

THEN, ON MONDAY, THE 30TH, the prisoner was transferred to an isolated and private cell on the second floor of the jailhouse. Special deputies were assigned to maintain a guard over him until the time of execution.

The death watch had begun in earnest, and the full effect of that circumstance was not lost on George Mitchell. His erstwhile confidence, more fragile than it had appeared, evanesced entirely as he was once again confronted with the stark reality of his situation.

On Wednesday, September 1st, the scaffold arrived from Montgomery County and a work crew set about assembling it in the yard just west of the jail building. The area immediately surrounding the gallows would be enclosed by a board fence eighteen feet high and tightly joined in order to shield the gallows from uninvited viewers. When completed, the enclosure would be sixty feet long and eighteen feet wide. The only access to the area within would be by way of the interior doorway of the jailhouse. George Mitchell's second story window offered the best possible view of the construction activity below.

That same evening, Sheriff Miller began to distribute the first of more than a hundred pre-printed, non-transferable tickets which would permit the holder to enter the enclosure at 11:30 Friday morning, September 3rd, for the purpose of witnessing the execution. It was the current perception that those persons who had participated in the process which led a prisoner to the gallows were thereby morally and ethically constrained to see the matter through to its grim conclusion. For that reason, the prosecutors, defense attorneys, judge and even members of the convicting jury were issued tickets. Other dignitaries, city and county officeholders and elected representatives, might also expect to receive complimentary tickets, or passes, to the execution. Finally, and perhaps inevitably, there was a sizeable contingency of persons frothingly eager for the opportunity to watch, at close hand, the exquisite anguish of a god-forsaken wretch who is put to death in public retribution for his crime.

Thursday, September 2nd, saw the beginning of an enormous influx of people who would come from the outlying areas of Miami and neighboring counties to see what they could of the prisoner and his execution. More than two thousand of these twenty-four hour immigrants would be permitted to pass through the jailhouse to look on the prisoner and to inspect the scaffold and the gallows from within the enclosure.

It was not intended as an unkindness, nor was it the product of any lack of empathy for the prisoner, that undistinguished members of the public, the common rabble, were granted controlled access to the condemned man and to the instruments of his destruction. It was simply the way of the times. If the death penalty were to operate as a deterrent to criminal activity, then it was deemed necessary that the administration of that penalty be open and conspicuous to the public view.

For his own part, George Mitchell felt no resentment towards those citizens who shuffled by his death cell, single-file, for a first and last look at the simple black man whose life was about to end. He seemed to understand their need to see him and he greeted them without bitterness or rancor. He glibly assured those who asked that he was ready to accept what came.

By the end of the day the crowd had doubled in size. Sheriff Miller called upon Town Marshall John Roney for an auxiliary police force of twenty men to assist the three companies of national guardsman in directing traffic and in keeping order. Between protesters, sympathizers and the morbidly curious, the entire town seemed to be under siege.

And then again, at the last moment, came another reprieve. A breathless telegraph operator ran to the jailhouse with an order from the governor. Without explanation, the execution was stayed for two more weeks to September 17th.

This time, however, George Mitchell's reaction was considerably less exuberant than before. After a full summer's wait for some sort of help from the governor, his hopes for salvation had very nearly evaporated. He had, these past several days, become fully resigned to his fate and was now ready to have it over and done.

Deep within himself, he recognized this latest reprieve for precisely what it was. A two week delay.

Chapter Eight

SHERIFF MILLER SHARED HIS PRISONER'S PERCEPTION that this latest reprieve would be the last. He gave orders that the scaffold and its enclosure be left in place until after the execution. He also arranged that the National Guardsman and the local police contingent report back for crowd-control duty on Thursday, the 16th. They would not be released until after the crowds had dispersed on the 17th. Once again, one hundred special admission tickets were printed and distributed.

The general expectation was that there would be no further interference from the governor and that the execution would proceed on the 17th. George Mitchell remained in his solitary cell on the second floor of the jail and the death watch continued. He spent virtually all of the last fourteen days of his life reading from his bible and meditating on the scriptures and on his own prospects for the hereafter.

On his penultimate day, Thursday, the 16th, he was permitted to receive visitors. He spent most of the afternoon with the principal supporters of his bid for executive clemency, the Messrs. Morris, Wright and Cruikshank. After those worthies had reported to him the fact that Governor Foster had refused to intervene further, Mitchell provided them with a full account of his activities in September of 1878, his provocations and his crime. His statement was taken down by John Morris, signed by Mitchell, and witnessed by Wright and by Cruikshank. It was agreed that the statement would not be released until after the execution.

The only other person to see Mitchell that day was R. H. Vandeveer, the special deputy assigned to be his keeper for the duration of the death watch. Deputy Vandeveer remained with his prisoner throughout the night. Mitchell passed the evening quietly, reading from his bible, praying, smoking his pipe and talking with Vandeveer. He seemed at peace and fully reconciled to his circumstance. "I'm not afraid," he told Vandeveer. "I done wrong and now that I see the light, I'm ready to die. This time tomorrow, I'll be in heaven."

And when Vandeveer offered to bring him one last drink of whiskey, Mitchell declined. "No, sir," he said. "I thank you kindly, but now I got this far along, I'm bound I'll go to heaven sober."

He took himself to bed at about midnight and fell instantly into a sound and dreamless sleep.

THE THREE COMPANIES OF COL. HORTON'S NATIONAL GUARDSMEN were in position long before daylight. They surrounded the jailhouse and the gallows enclosure at a distance of some twenty yards. Each man stood at the ready, with fixed bayonet, to hold back the motley and rapidly growing crowds of onlookers, some vindictive, some sympathetic and most, merely curious. There would be more than three thousand of these would-be spectators milling about before nine o'clock.

George Mitchell arose that morning at six o'clock. His brother Jim had come to town from Vandalia and was allowed to visit during breakfast. The brothers had not seen one another for a goodly number of years, but there was nonetheless an easy concourse between them. They talked of their childhood together, their early friends and favorite places, and they laughed over their pranks and childish games played with other children. And when Jim lost his self-control and dropped a swiftly disintegrating face into his open hands, George Mitchell put down his fork, reached across his plate and patted his brother's knee. "Don't cry, Jim," he soothed, "I don't fear it. It'll be over in a minute."

A GREAT DEAL OF CARE AND ATTENTION HAD BEEN GIVEN to each of the myriad details involved in a public execution. A site had been reserved, and a grave freshly dug, at nearby Vandalia where the life of George Mitchell had begun and where his father and mother were buried.

A polished rosewood coffin, finely trimmed in pink satin, had been furnished by the Messrs. Bond and Shilling, whose furniture manufactory and undertaking establishment was located on the first corner east of the jailhouse. The general intention was that George Mitchell's scheduled meeting with his maker be accomplished with all the proper trappings and that he himself be suitably groomed and made presentable for the occasion.

Carl Hammond owned and operated a barbershop on Race Street, some four or five blocks from the jail. He arrived promptly at nine o'clock, gave the prisoner a crisp, clean shave and covered his face with a warm, moist towel. Then, at nine-thirty, a full complement of new clothes arrived and the deputies helped George Mitchell into a formal black suit, coat, pants and vest, with freshly starched white shirt and collar, and a black tie. He was grandly attired, then, to receive his spiritual advisors, the Reverends Stanley, Weddel, Merritt and Miller, when they arrived just before ten o'clock.

Then, after matters pertaining to the spirit had been concluded in something under an hour's time, a proper table was set in the prisoner's cell and a last meal, of chicken and fish, was served to him. As he had done with his breakfast earlier, George Mitchell ate heartily. He was in the midst of his private luncheon when Deputy John Miller delivered a handsome bouquet of brightly colored fall flowers. There was a card that announced, very simply, that the sender was Mrs. J. W. Cruikshank. She was the wife of John W. Cruikshank, the clerk of courts who had signed George Mitchell's death warrant and who had thereafter petitioned the governor for clemency.

A few moments before noon, Sheriff Miller arrived and read the death warrant aloud. George Mitchell listened attentively to each word of the formal order, nodded his understanding and asked politely if he might talk with the prisoners in the first-floor cellblock. His request was granted and the procession which would lead to the gallows made a short detour through the cellblock. The prisoners had come to know George Mitchell through their common confinement. They had played cards and talked and joked with him. Now they gathered around, awed by their awareness that he was about to die. George Mitchell looked at them with a steady gaze. "You have all treated me well," he said, "an' I want to say, if you don't want to get in this place, don't drink whiskey, play cards or run after bad women."

He took his bible from an inner pocket, held it out to them, and continued, "Take the word of God and search it. No man who reads the bible and lives up to it will get here. I am goin' to leave you and I want you all to promise to meet me in heaven. The Lord will come into jail and save you as he has saved me."

There was no response from the gathered prisoners. One by one, they met his eyes and looked away. Some scratched an imaginary itch, others shuffled their feet, folded arms across their chests, or busied themselves in some other activity to conceal an awkward uneasiness. George Mitchell took each man by the hand, however briefly, then turned and signalled to the Sheriff that he was ready.

Their journey led through the rear doorway of the jailhouse and into the enclosed yard. As he passed the kitchen window he paused for a moment to say goodby to the sheriff's wife, whom he had come to know during his confinement, and to thank her for her many kindnesses.

The procession continued on to the north end of the enclosure where the scaffold had remained in readiness these past two weeks. The gallows itself consisted of two stout uprights which supported a crossbeam some eighteen feet above the ground. A single flight of wood steps led to a broad, square platform, surrounded by a sturdy balustrade and located directly below the crossbeam.

Flanked by his guards and watchers, George Mitchell mounted the scaffold staircase. His step was strong and firm as though he looked forward to the end of his journey.

Moments later, standing on the floor of the trap, the noose drawn snug about his neck, he spoke briefly to the crowd gathered within the yard.

A solemn, almost reverent, hush settled over the proceedings as all those gathered within and without the enclosure, and those who watched from neighboring rooftops and from the jailhouse windows, strained to catch the sound of the condemned man's voice.

The words came bravely, without tremor. He called out to some of the people he recognized in the crowd, spoke their names, and promised to meet them on the other side. He thanked Sheriff Miller and his family for their care and attention. Then, clutching his bible in both hands, he proclaimed to all who would hear him, "I been a sinner all the years of my life. An' for more than fifty-two of those years, I been unredeemed. That's why you find me here today.

"Since I come into this place, I seen the word of the Lord, an' he has forgiven my sins an' redeemed my soul.

"The law has said that I must die. You have said that I must die today. Here and now.

"I say to you that I accept your judgment an' I am ready to die. I gonna die now as a Christian. I forgive you — each and every one — and I hope to see you all again in heaven."

George Mitchell brought his bible to his breast, clasped it there tightly, nodded to the sheriff and closed his eyes. A moment later the trap was sprung and his body shot through the void into eternity.

SAM MCKINNEY HAD REFUSED to attend the execution. He had acknowledged an obligation to witness the ultimate denouement of his client's history, but simply hadn't the stomach for it. He had contented himself with the knowledge that his brother Frank had agreed to attend and to represent the both of them. After all, Frank was nine years younger than he and therefore presumably better able to withstand the ordeal.

Now, Frank McKinney had returned to their offices and given an account of the proceedings. "It was awful," he groaned. "His neck failed to break when he dropped to the end of the rope. He was still alive. Then we all waited while he strangled to death, his eyes bulging wide and his tongue protruding obscenely. All the while he dangled and jerked like a puppet on a string.

"Then, even after he'd stopped jerking and twitching, he still had a heartbeat. Doc Kitzmiller had to take his pulse four or five times at intervals before he pronounced him dead and let them cut him down."

Frank McKinney shuddered, "It was the most horrible thing I've ever seen and I'll never watch another. Justice may have been served today," he observed philosophically, "but I can't feel good about it."

EPILOGUE

GEORGE MITCHELL'S OWN ACCOUNT OF HIS CRIME, given to the Messrs. Morris, Wright and Cruikshank the day before he was hanged, was released to the Cincinnati newspapers on Saturday, September 18th. Because of the considerable media attention already accorded both the murder and the execution, the Enquirer and the Gazette published the statement, taken down and perhaps embellished by John Morris, in its entirety:

On Monday night preceding the death of Anna Mitchell I stayed at the house of Geo. Sublitt, where we had been living for some time. On that night he drove me from the bed I was occupying with my wife, and driving both his own wife and me out of the house he occupied the bed with my wife, threatening to kill both his wife and me if we offered any objections to his actions. While on the porch we heard him say to Anna that if she could get away with George (that is, me) that he would get away with Maggie, his wife, and then they could have everything their own way. I remained all night, and after breakfast the next morning left the house, and spent part of the day in chopping wood on the farm of Mr. Kerr. Knowing that Anna was coming to Troy that day, I also came, getting to Troy that evening. The object of my coming was to have a talk with her and to try to make some arrangements about some place to live other than at Geo. Sublitt's — his actions having nearly crazed me. The night was spent in walking the Covington pike. During the whole time I did not see or speak to any person. On Wednesday morning I walked up to Peckham's Lane, knowing that Anna would pass that way in going from her mother's to Henry Dye's, where she was to do some washing that day. I met her and spoke kindly to her, saying, "Good morning, Anna." She replied saying: "What do you want, you damned son of a bitch." I said, "Anna, I want to talk about some plan to live peaceably, and to get away from Sublitt's house." I was standing near her. She said: "Go away from me or I will cut your damned black guts out." I said: "This is not the way to do. I want to talk to you like a gentleman would talk to a lady." Her reply was: "I will get away with you and George will get away with Maggie," at the same time drawing a large clasp knife which she had got from me and striking at me in the most vicious manner. The blow struck me on the hand, making a severe cut on my fingers — see here are the scars, look at them — (Mitchell here exhibited his scarred fingers). At this I drew my corn knife, which I had brought with me for the purpose of cutting her mother's corn crop, and struck her a blow about the head, at the same time wresting the knife from her hands. She then ran, I following her. After running some distance she fell and I again struck her with the corn knife, how often I do not know, being so crazed with jealousy and anger as to be utterly unconscious of what I was doing. I am entirely ignorant of what I did with the corn knife. Suppose I threw it away, but when or where I do not know. The knife I took from her I carried about six weeks and finally lost it.

The editors of the local newspaper, The Miami Union, were not impressed. By way of response:

What purported to be a confession of George Mitchell, the negro wife-slaughterer, who was hanged here on the 17th, was given the public through the Cincinnati Gazette and Enquirer last Saturday. The gentlemen to whom the so-called confession was made announced with a grand flourish on the day of execution that they had in their possession a document which would cause a great sensation and convince the "cut-throats and cold-blooded brutes" who wanted Mitchell hung that they had succeeded in wrongfully hanging a man. Hence the "confession" was looked for with some interest. To say that the public was disappointed on reading the widely advertised document would be drawing it mild indeed. Some few who did not know that the confession was in point of fact only an attorney's paper prepared to influence Judge Williams to sign a paper asking the governor to commute the sentence of the *condemned man, read it with the idea it endeavored to convey that Mitchell had committed the murder partly in self-defense and partly as the result of a sudden passion, and that the murder was not one of such premeditation and malice that the laws of Ohio regard as meriting the death penalty. If we are to believe him, Mitchell was so crazed with jealousy and anger as to be utterly unconscious of what he did, and yet according to the "confession" he had the presence of mind to wrestle the clasp knife from the woman and pocket it or hold on to it during all the time he was in that ungovernable passion. About six weeks after, when he got over his passion he unfortunately lost the knife (vide "confession"). He was so crazed with anger and jealousy that he did not know what he was doing, and yet he had the coolness and presence of mind to stoop down over his victim and remove rings from her dead fingers!*

Again, the "confession" says that Mitchell was entirely ignorant of what he did with the corn cutter. He supposed he threw it away, but did not know when or where. On the other hand Mitchell told Mr. R. H. Vandeveer, his watcher at the jail, exactly what he did do with the corn knife. He detailed to him how, after the murder, he fled across one field, skulking along the fence of another, across another field and finally climbing a fence into a woods, and that as he climbed the fence he noticed blood on the corn knife and that it scared him and he "flung" it away. So minutely did Mitchell detail his flight, describing the fields, what grew in them, and their size, that Mr. Vandeveer was enabled to point out the locality where he said he threw the knife. The locality is now covered with a thick growth of weeds and briars, and as two years have passed since the occurrence, the knife is in all probability buried beneath the decayed accumulation of two years vegetation. We may say right here that Mitchell's statement to Mr. Vandeveer of the murder differs very materially from the "confession."

GEORGE MITCHELL WAS NOT ONLY THE FIRST person ever to be executed within the confines of Miami County, he was also the last. The law of Ohio was changed to require that all such executions be performed at the state penitentiary in Columbus. Thus George Mitchell has been vouchsafed the dubious distinction of being the only person ever executed in Miami County, Ohio.

Book Three
* ☾ *
More Bad Women

CHAPTER ONE

A SECOND MAJOR RIVER SYSTEM coursed through the western part of Miami County in a southerly direction and, as might be expected, a series of river towns had sprung up along its banks and shoals. The Stillwater River and its tributaries had long since carved out a wide and fertile valley through the gently rolling countryside. A string of small towns had grown, like Topsy, along the high ground on either side of the stream. Principal among these in Miami County were the hamlets of Clayton, Covington, Pleasant Hill, Ludlow Falls and West Milton.

Just after the turn of the century, the village of Covington, with a population of some 1800 souls, seemed most likely of all these small river towns to thrive and to prosper. It was situated on the high, hilly ground just east of the confluence of the Stillwater and its largest tributary, Greenville Creek. It was also located at the conjuncture of a significant number of the county's main traffic arteries. Rock Avenue ran directly through the center of town. To the west it became the Gettysburg Pike and to the east it was the Piqua Road. It was intersected on a precise perpendicular by State Route 48, which followed the River and connected the towns, one to another like a string of Indian beads. Within the town it was High Street and the intersection itself was commonly known, for obvious reasons, as the Crossroads. Then, just a few blocks to the south, an offshoot of this same High Street became the Troy-Covington Turnpike.

To the north, and no more than a stone's throw from the Crossroads, was the newly constructed depot for the Pittsburg, Columbus, Chicago and St. Louis Railroad. The railroad itself was also newly constructed. It ran parallel with Rock Avenue and also intersected State Route 48 on the perpendicular. A second railway depot was located on the southeast corner of the Crossroads and served the very considerable traffic generated by the D.C. & P. traction line, a fairly new electric railway line that made hourly runs from Dayton, through Covington, and on to Piqua. The swing through Covington created an oblique elbow in the route and the location of the stationhouse in the precise crook of the elbow accounted for its being commonly known as the Panhandle Depot.

Because of its central location at the hub of intersecting thoroughfares, it is hardly surprising that the Crossroads soon became the focal point of all meaningful activity within the village. Not only was it the epicenter for all modes of traffic — pedestrian, horse and buggy, steam railroad and electric traction line — but it was also the best place in town to laze about and watch the girls.

And, on a balmy evening in April 1907, that's precisely what was happening. Three young men, close friends, were lounging just outside the D.C. & P. depot. Two of them were seated on a short wooden bench and the third was slouched against a hitching post. Each of them nursed a murky-green bottle of warm beer. It seemed plain enough that none of them had any pressing commitments.

The third man, the one holding up the hitching post, was Johnny Bell. At five feet ten inches, he was the tallest of the three. He also appeared to be the most relaxed and self-assured member of the group. He slouched nonchalantly back against the post, allowed himself a leisurely swallow of beer and vented an appreciative belch. "Donato," he said, "what do you do with all your money?"

"No, no. *Non* Donato. Danny, O.K.?" came the reflexive correction from the dark, swarthy man at the far end of the bench. Coal-black hair, dark eyes and even, chiseled facial bones left no room for doubt that he was of Mediterranean extraction. Donato DiIulio was an Italian immigrant. He had been no more than fifteen when he left his home and family in Civaqua, Italy, to seek his fortune in America. Cleared through Ellis Island in July of 1903, not quite four years ago, he was promptly recruited to work at a coal mining camp in West Virginia.

Johnny Bell was the first person he had met at the mining camp and the two young men soon became fast friends. Johnny Bell, née Bellini, was also of Italian ancestry and his physiognomy and general appearance were unmistakably Roman. American-born of immigrant parents, he had been rapidly assimilated into the western culture. English had always been his principal tongue and he had never really learned the language of his forebears. Despite his relative unfamiliarity with Italian, he was nonetheless better able to understand and to communicate with Donato than anyone else and that circumstance engendered a sort of inter-dependency between the two. After a few arduous and soot-begrimed months on the job they became dissatisfied with coal mining and sought employment elsewhere. They soon found jobs with the Hoover-Kinnear Company, a railroad construction concern whose custom it was to move its crews from one job site to another. That process took them from West Virginia, through Pittsburg, and then, two years before, to Covington where Hoover-Kinnear was laying the final sections of the P.C.C. & St. Louis railway track. Because they were both quick-witted and physically handy, DiIulio had advanced to become a donkey engine driver and Bell had become a brakeman and a sometime watchman. By contemporary standards, they were earning a decent wage.

The P.C.C. & St. Louis project had initially brought them to Piqua and the two young men first found living quarters there. Then, as the work progressed westward into Covington, they continued to stay where they were and commuted to Covington by way of the traction line. The railroad project was now nearly complete and Hoover-Kinnear would soon move its work crews to Steubenville.

Because DiIulio had become enamored of the Village of Covington he found himself unwilling to leave. For that reason he had looked about until he found a job at the Wagner Brick & Tile plant out on the Piqua Road just east of Covington. He had just begun working there and had not yet found a place to stay within the village. Johnny Bell was less strongly attached and had elected to move with the company to Steubenville.

Despite the fact that Donato DiIulio had been in the States for the better part of four years, he had not yet learned to read or write the language. And while he could understand most of what was said to him and insisted that he be called Danny, which he believed to be the Americanized version of Donato, he nonetheless spoke English poorly and haltingly. In response to Johnny Bell's question, he stammered, "*Denaro? Il mio denaro?* Money? *Che denaro?*"

Johnny Bell knew how to make himself understood by his Italian friend. He spelled it out patiently and jingled the change in his pocket. "*Denaro!* That's right, Danny. Money. You make good money — *salario* — but you don't spend anything. What do you do with it?"

Donato frowned as he tried to grasp the sense of Johnny Bell's question. "*Mando* — ", he began. Then, "I send *denaro*, money, much money, *a la mia famiglia. In Italia. Ogni mese.*"

Johnny Bell recapitulated the answer, as much for his own purposes as for the benefit of the third member of the group, Johnny Nickel. "You send a lot of money back home. To your family in Italy. Is that what you just said?"

And when Donato nodded affirmatively, he added, "Every month?"

"*Si, ogni mese.* Much *denaro.*"

The two Johnnys knew that Danny's parents were elderly and that they lived in an impoverished area back home, in the southern part of Italy. And Johnny Bell had already known that Danny sent money to them on a regular basis. He had done so for as long as he had known him. His questioning had been essentially rhetorical.

"You know," he said slowly, "you really ought to spend just a little of your money on yourself. Have a little fun."

"Fun?" queried the Italian. "*Spasso? Divertimento?*"

"Yeah, that's it," said Johnny Bell. "Diversion. Play. You're allowed to have some fun, to enjoy life a little."

Johnny Nickel decided he should join in. "Makes sense to me, Danny," he added sagely.

"*Si,*" mused the Italian. "*Spasso,* fun." He grinned shyly. "O.K."

"What you need," observed Johnny Bell, "is a girlfriend. What's your word for girlfriend?"

"*Ragazza,*" came the eager response. "*Una ragazza. Si. Buono.*" Then, after a moment's contemplation, he began to chatter, "*Dove posso trovare una ragazza? Puo mostrarmi —* "

"Whoa now, fella," interrupted Johnny Bell. "Hold on a minute. What you're spoutin' now ain't nothin' but dago gibberish to me. Gimme a chance to catch up." And when Danny subsided, Johnny Bell continued. "I didn't understand a word you just said, but I think I've got the idea. Were you wonderin' if I might be able to fix you up with a date sometime? Is that what that was all about?"

"Date? *Una data?*" Danny struggled with the concept, then seemed to understand. "*Un appuntamento amoroso?* Ah, *si, appuntamento amoroso.*"

Both Johnnys reacted to the Italian's obvious comprehension. "Right!" whooped Johnny Nickel, thumping the Italian across the shoulders.

"That's it!" echoed Johnny Bell. "*Amoroso,* a date with *una ragazza.*" He abandoned his station at the hitching post, moved toward Danny, reached forward and boxed his ears, playfully, with open palms.

Danny stood up to fend off their combined assault and Johnny Nickel rose with him, still clapping him across the back and shoulders. In a moment the three friends were scuffling like puppies and giggling like schoolgirls. A married couple, with children in tow, smiled in amusement and moved further along the station platform to make room.

Then, as quickly as it had started, Johnny Nickel called for a truce. "Hold it," he cried and pointed down the line. "Here she comes!"

The "she" to which he referred was not, as might have been expected, "una ragazza." Of all the people milling about the depot, Johnny Nickel had been the first to catch sight of the traction line's brand-new Trolley Car 152 approaching from the east on the seven o'clock run from Piqua. The D.C. & P. had taken delivery, just a few days earlier, of two newly manufactured, cross-bench summer cars. These cars were unique in that they were equipped with wooden benches with reversible seatbacks, to afford passengers the option of facing forward or backward, and with side panels which could be removed to accommodate the weather. Because of the current warm temperatures, and perhaps to demonstrate the novelty of this latter feature, the company had placed both of its new cars, numbered 150 and 152, in service as summer cars, without the side panels and open to the weather. More than forty feet in overall length and factory-painted in deep dark red with lustrous yellow trim, the D.C. & P. trolley cars had about them an ambience that was almost carnival in nature. They were ridden quite as much for pleasure as for transportation and holiday excursions along the Overlook Route and over the falls at Ludlow were popular.

The efficient, guttural hum of steel rolling over steel mingled with the soft murmur of the electric engine, the low rubbing sound of the trolley pole against the overhead power line and the strident clang of the trolley bell, to herald the arrival of Trolley Car 152 at the Panhandle. There was an almost reverent silence among those who made up the small crowd gathered on the platform as the trolley glided into the station.

The three young friends had suspended their tussle in order to pay full attention to the arrival of the train, its myriad accoutrements and nuances, and to the debarkation of its passengers. Among the latter was an older couple, the man full-bearded and strongly-built, the woman frail and absent-looking. In attempting the single step down from the trolley, she missed her footing and fell forward. Johnny Bell, standing close by, was quick enough to reach out and break her fall. Then, after they had determined that she was uninjured, the two Johnnys and Donato helped her to her feet and handed her over to the full-bearded man. He mumbled his thanks and led the woman off towards Rock Avenue.

"Do you know those people?" asked Johnny Nickel.

"Not really," answered Johnny Bell. "I'm sure I must have seen them before, but I can't say who they are. The woman seems kinda vacant."

"She is," confirmed Johnny Nickel. "She's weak-minded. You ought to know them, though. They're the girls' parents."

"The girls?" asked Johnny Bell. "You mean Frosty and Blanche?"

"Mm-hmm," chuckled Johnny Nickel, "seein' as how you've been screwin' their daughter the past six, eight months, seems like you oughta know who they are. Matter of courtesy, so to speak."

"Courtesy?" queried Johnny Bell.

"Uh-huh, courtesy," answered Nickel with mock solemnity. "Fella oughta know who he's screwin', oughtn't he? That seems courteous to me."

"You mean you been screwin' Blanche more politely than I been screwin' Frosty, that it?" asked Johnny Bell.

"Well — " Nickel temporized. "At least I know who her parents are."

"Uh-huh. Apparently you do," answered Johnny Bell. "And you want to hope like hell they don't know who you are, or, for that matter, who your wife and kids are."

"Ouch!" cried Johnny Nickel. "I give up." Then he grinned puckishly. "I guess you're thinkin' it ain't real polite for me to be knockin' off Blanche regular and bein' married to another woman at the same time."

Donato DiIulio had heard the exchange between the two Johnnys, but had understood very little of it. He had divided his attention between the last few swallows of his warm beer and the boarding and departure of car 152 for the West Milton leg of the seven o'clock run to Dayton. He needed a moment to register that Johnny Bell's next remark was directed to him.

"Speaking of the girls," he began, "Danny, do you remember Frosty? I pointed her out to you last fall. We were sittin' right here one evening and she and her little sister walked by the station and waved to us."

Danny turned it over in his mind. "Frosty, *si*, *richiamo*," he answered haltingly, "*Carino, magnifico!*"

"Goddamit, speak English," teased Johnny Bell. "So we can understand you."

"Pretty, much pretty," Danny stammered.

"Better, much better," echoed Johnny Bell. Then, making certain he had the Italian's full attention, he explained in words and gestures that he and Johnny Nickel had a date — *un data* — with the girls for Saturday night. His girl, *ragazza*, would be Frosty and Johnny Nickel's would be her sister, Blanche. They were to meet at the post office at seven-thirty. Unhappily, Johnny Bell was moving to Steubenville that day and wouldn't be able to keep his date with Frosty. Would Danny like to go in his stead?

"*Si, vorrei fare quello, vorrei —* "

"What say?" demanded Johnny Bell sternly.

"Uh — yes, *si*, yes. I like. Much like," came the excited, albeit labored response.

CHAPTER TWO

AARON ULLERY'S TWO-STORY BRICK POST OFFICE, located on East Wright Street and around the corner from South High Street, was an ideal trysting place for the Floyd sisters and their dates for the evening. The front lobby was sure to be open until at least 8:00 o'clock and it was considerably less conspicuous than was the Panhandle depot or any of the other Crossroads establishments. It wasn't as though there was anything clandestine about the girls' activities or their relationships. They were both full adults and Frosty, who was 25 and the elder of the two, had even lived away from home for a year or so before she moved back in with her parents. But neither of them was anxious to encounter their father or one of his close friends while in company with their respective beaux. Even though Blanche pretended to believe that Johnny Nickel was unmarried, and therefore unobjectionable, they both knew that John Floyd would not be pleased to learn that his daughters were consorting with an Italian. He tended to look down on all these damn foreigners, whether first, second or some later generation, as an undesirable element of local society.

Neither of the girls was in the least disappointed to learn that Johnny Bell couldn't keep their Saturday night appointment or that he had sent a surrogate. Both of them, especially Frosty, had begun to tire of him and they were glad to make a new acquaintance.

Johnny Nickel made the explanations and relayed Johnny Bell's apologies to Frosty. Bell had left Piqua that same day, he said, and moved to Steubenville with the company. He had sent along two letters and a comb with Danny. The letters, he said, were addressed to him and the faney comb was for Frosty.

Johnny Nickel introduced Danny DiIulio to the girls, told them that he didn't speak English very well, but was nonetheless a good sport. Frosty took Danny's hand and tried to explain that her real name was Forest May, but everybody called her Frosty. She wasn't sure Danny had understood until he suddenly brightened and cried out, "*Si, il soprannome* — a nickname, *capisco!*"

"*Si, capisco, capisco!*" The girls squealed in unison. Then they all congratulated one another with laughter and gestures of achievement.

After the merriment had subsided, Johnny Nickel suggested they take an evening stroll together, *"una passeggiata,"* Danny registered quickly. It was a fine warm evening and everyone swiftly agreed.

They walked in pairs, with Johnny Nickel and Blanche preceding Danny DiIulio and Frosty Floyd. Without an apparent destination they passed down Wright Street, past Dunham's barbershop and Dick Toy's chinese laundry, down the hill to Main Street, then south to Bridge Street and across the river into West Covington and beyond. It soon became apparent that they had, indeed, a destination. After a half-hour's walk in the fading light, they arrived at a grassy meadow, next to the municipal electric plant, high above the power dam at Greenville Falls.

Each of the girls produced a picnic blanket and they spread them together in the shadow of the building, overlooking the falls. Johnny Nickel had brought a bottle of red wine and a generous slab of hogshead cheese. The two couples settled onto the girls' blankets in a small group and shared wine, cheese and conversation until after it had become fully dark. Then, as if at a signal, Blanche and Johnny Nickel moved their own little nest some twenty yards away and deeper into the shade of the power plant. This unexpected maneuver left Danny DiIulio alone and intensely uncomfortable with Frosty. He suddenly found himself wholly unnerved and at a total loss for words, in his own or any other language.

Danny had had no experience with young girls and he was enormously intimidated by this attractive, obviously self-assured young woman, some six years his senior. She was indeed attractive, with natural coloring nearly dark enough to match his own. She had smoky gray eyes above soft, high cheekbones and a full, tantalizing shape that excited the young Italian in ways he could not fully comprehend.

Danny's already profound discomfiture intensified as the moments passed and he heard the playful tittering and other private sounds emanating from the nearby darkness. He was finally and mercifully rescued from the throes of complete catatonia by Frosty herself, who moved gently, but surely, against him and pressed her hips gently, but firmly, into his groin. She took his trembling hand into her own, whispered his name, and guided him expertly through all the intimate ecstasies of the mating ritual. And though their acquaintanceship was only hours old, because she asked him to and because he truly believed it, he told her how very much he loved her. *"Molto,"* he breathed. *"Amo ti molto."*

The two couples spent most of the night ensconced in their separate bivouacs on the meadow above the power dam. Danny and Frosty consummated their new-found passion in successive encounters, interspersed with desultory conversation, declarations, promises, soft touches and fond caresses. It was during one such intermission that they agreed to be married very soon, and to go to New York City for the ceremony and for their honeymoon. Danny DiIulio was both smitten and enraptured. He had never in his life wanted anything more than to be married to this marvelous, *magnifico*, young woman.

Some time after three in the morning they gathered their clothing and blankets and set off up Range Line Road to the Floyd residence on the Gettysburg Pike just west of Covington. As they walked along the roadway, arms locked about one another's waists, Frosty explained to Danny the American tradition concerning the pre-nuptial hope chest, a store of silver and linens accumulated by a prospective bride in anticipation of her marriage. Danny DiIulio was so committed to their betrothal, and so charmed by his fiancée, his *fidanzato*, that he immediately extracted five dollars and change, all that he had, from his pocket and thrust it upon her as his own initial contribution to her hope chest. Then, when they reached the Floyd property line, yet some distance from the house, the girls took their leave. They would have to slip in quietly to avoid confrontation with their father. Before they said goodnight, Frosty and Danny renewed all their promises and protestations of mutual and undying affection. They agreed to meet again Wednesday evening, same time, same place. If he needed to see her sooner, he could come to the house any evening, but it should be after 10 o'clock so as not to disturb her parents. She and Blanche occupied the upstairs bedroom on the south side of the house. They each slept with a string tied to a toe and allowed to dangle out the window to ground level. Her string was the blue one and hung down on the right-hand side. If he were to jiggle it gently, she'd sneak down the stairs and come outside.

In the meanwhile, she said, she'd begin making plans for their wedding and start setting a few things aside for her hope chest. They could be married by fall.

CHAPTER THREE

THE NEXT THIRTY-ODD DAYS WERE THE HAPPIEST AND MOST IDYLLIC of Donato DiIulio's young life. He and Frosty were together two or three nights a week and each time they engaged in hot and lusty sexual escapades. Some nights they met at the post office and doubled with Blanche and Johnny Nickel as they had on their first date. On these occasions they went again to the meadow by the electric plant. Other times Frosty would come and visit him in Piqua and ride back home on the late trolley. And there were at least a half dozen times, in the middle of the week, when he would appear outside her window, well after dark, and pull gently on the blue toe-string. Whenever that happened Frosty would be with him in a moment. Then, quickly and furtively, they would make their way into her father's barn and enjoy a steamy, tumultuous hour of love-making in the hay mow.

And each time they met, they would reiterate their promises and reaffirm their wedding plans. Frosty would invariably report to Danny about the progress of her hope chest and he would just as consistently contribute all the money he could muster. In anticipation of their marriage, and in order to better fund the hope chest, Donato had suspended payments to his parents back home. Just for awhile. As soon as the hope chest, *la cassa speranza*, was complete, and he and Frosty were married and settled into a home of their own, he'd make up the difference. He knew his parents were needy, but he was sure they would understand. Perhaps one day he could take his new wife, and maybe even a *bambino* or two, back to the old country for a visit. It would be a *grande vacanza* for Frosty. She'd wanted him to tell her about his home in Italy, said she wanted to meet his family and to know everything about him. He could show her about and introduce her to the friends of his childhood, to his sisters, and to his parents. His mother and father, he knew, would be so proud, so *fiero*, of their grandchildren, *nipoti di nonni*, and they would certainly be *buona felice* with Frosty. She was so *bello*, so *magnifico*, they would love her from *il inizio, immediatement*.

Donato wrote to his parents often, partly to explain and to apologize for his temporary inability to send *denaro*, but mostly to describe his love and to tell of his plans to be married and to honeymoon, *fare luna di miele*, in New York, and to make a home and start a *famiglia* of his own in America.

Donato was so proud of his *ragazza*, and of their *fidanzamento*, their engagement to be married, that he seized every opportunity to speak of her, in his broken, Italian-English patois, to anyone who would listen and to point her out, when she passed through the vicinity, to anyone who would look. He regaled his co-workers at the brickyard with her praises and with his proofs of her love for him. He didn't mean it to be in the manner of boasting of a sexual conquest, but he wanted the men to know that she loved him enough to permit the ultimate intimacy. Then, too, because all his conscious thought processes were entirely occupied with dreams of his marriage with Frosty Floyd, and of a life shared with her in Paradise, his everyday conversation could scarcely have concerned anything else.

For their own part, his friends and co-workers listened to him absently, not really sharing his enthusiasm. Danny thought he understood their reaction. It was, after all, *his* enthusiasm, *entusiasmo*, not theirs. Frosty was *his ragazza*, not theirs, and the upcoming *matrimonio* would be *his* own, rather than theirs. With that recognition firmly in mind, he nonetheless prattled on shamelessly at every opportunity. And though his listeners grew weary of hearing it and found the matter increasingly and tiresomely trite, they accepted all his paeans indulgently and smiled insincere encouragements. He had it bad, they agreed, and no one of them wished to challenge his illusions or risk his disenchantment.

It was Johnny Nickel, and he only of all Donato's friends and acquaintances, who sounded a call for moderation and a caution against overcommitment.

"It's that hot Italian blood," he argued. "It's got you all locked up. Made you a slave to your own lust."

"Slave?" asked Danny, trying to follow his friend's meaning. "*Schiavo?*" he groped for comprehension. "*Di mio desiderio carnale?*" Then, when he thought he understood, he became angry.

Theirs was a true love, he insisted, *uno amore reale*. They would be married and join their lives together forever, he said, "*per sempre!*"

Johnny Nickel pleaded with Danny for perspective. "Take what's offered," he counseled, "and enjoy the gift. You don't need to pledge your life.

"Just put a few dollars in the pot from time to time, the hope chest, and enjoy the game."

And when Danny remonstrated at the metaphor, he continued, "You don't really believe you're the love of her life, do you? Do you think you're the only fella who's ever yanked on her toe-string or put money in her hope chest?"

Johnny Nickel reflected a moment, then chuckled, "Hell, I've been givin' money to Blanche for years. Only she don't call it a hope chest — since I'm already married. She calls it her nursery fund."

"Nursery fund? *Che cosa?*"

"That's in case we accidentally make a baby, a *bambino*," came the rueful response. "We don't aim to, but we could."

All such conversations between the two friends came to the same, inevitable conclusion. Danny became angry, sullen and yet more resolute than before, and Johnny Nickel relented. "Okay, okay," he would say. "I give up. Just make sure I'm invited to the wedding."

And when his capitulation had been acknowledged and his apologies accepted, he would add, "But, remember, I won't be bringing Blanche. I've got my wife to think about. Maybe I'll bring her. She's never been to New York either."

IF WE ACCEPT THE ADAGE THAT THE COURSE OF TRUE LOVE never did run smooth, then circumstance itself soon confirmed Donato's characterization of his relationship with Frosty Floyd. They began to have little tiffs, lovers' quarrels, seemingly meaningless, about a variety of inconsequential matters. If Frosty arrived first at a rendezvous, then, of course, that meant that he was late. If he were first, she complained that he was rushing her. Or perhaps, she would allow, he had simply misunderstood the agreed meeting time. He really ought to pay closer attention, she said, and he should certainly learn to speak better English. That, at least, would make him seem less like a foreigner.

It might also permit her to invite him into her home and introduce him to her father — which, to be sure, she intended to do just as soon as he had become more "Americanized".

Despite his obsessive infatuation with this provocative young woman, and his steadily increasing dependency on her, Donato nonetheless found her difficult to fathom and often times yet more difficult to please. Depending on the quality and intensity of his attentions to her, and upon the current swing of her own moods, it seemed that she alternately berated him either for his inconsideration or for his persistent fawning over her.

But, to resort to yet another adage, true love conquers all, and if there were many trivial spats between them, there were also many more good times. There was never any question that a date with Frosty, *una appuntamento amoroso*, could prove to be a very good time.

As it happened, that particular perception was shared by at least one other person. One afternoon in late April, the four of them, Donato, Johnny Nickel and the Floyd sisters, had slipped into an empty boxcar, parked on the Big Four siding, for a midday picnic of beer, bread and sardines purchased from a nearby commissary. Then, after they re-emerged from the boxcar, the man who had sold them their provisions caught Donato's eye and winked at him. When asked what he wanted, the man told Donato to bring the girls around to his place some night "for a good time." Donato became angry, first at the commissary man, then at Frosty when it developed that she wanted to stay and talk about it. When Donato remonstrated with her, she also became incensed, seized his soft cloth hat from his head and tore it to shreds. Then, as if to even things up, she tore her own hat to bits and scolded him for causing her to do so. The argument wasn't resolved until later in the day when Donato gave her three dollars and a half for a new hat.

It seemed that Frosty had something of a penchant for tearing clothing. A few days later she and Donato met at the Stillwater Bridge, sauntered purposefully into the upstream wooded area and had it off together on the riverbank. Then, while they were putting their clothing aright, Frosty broached the subject of her hope chest and Donato replied that he couldn't spare anything that day because he had only four dollars with which to get through the week. He wouldn't receive *il salario* for another three days. Frosty scowled at him darkly, thrust her hand into his pants pocket and seized the four dollars. In the process of extracting the bills she managed to tear away both the pocket and most of the front part of his pants. Twenty-three cents in small change spilled out in their brief encounter and lay on the ground between them. That would be enough, she snapped, to get him through the week. He needed to keep his priorities straight. The hope chest needed to be nourished steadily if they ever hoped to be married. She did promise to provide him with needle and thread in order that he might mend his clothing.

Early into their relationship Donato had told her that he preferred "Danny" to his given name. When he had pronounced "Donato" she had remarked that it sounded like some kind of Italian pastry and began calling him "Danny Doughnut". Knowing it to be an irritant, however, she used the name only when she was miffed at him or when she wanted to reprimand him. This was such a time.

She hovered over him while he sifted through the grass for his coins. "I should think, Mr. Danny Doughnut," she sneered, "That you could find a better job. A job that would pay more money than you're making over at the dumb brickyard.

"If you were earning a decent wage, you could already be married and living in a home of your own," she persisted, "instead of crawlin' around on your hands and knees scraping for enough coins to last till Saturday."

And then, when no answer came, "You want to be married, don't you?" And snidely, "Do you still love me, Danny Doughnut?"

Donato had already known she could be hateful. Johnny Nickel had warned him that she had a mean streak a yard wide. That's why, he said, Johnny Bell had been willing to leave her behind and move to Steubenville. Bell liked what he got from Frosty well enough, but he'd grown tired of her peevishness.

"Let her go," counseled Johnny Nickel. "I can find you another girl you'll like even better. They're all a dime a dozen, y'know."

Danny DiIulio's obsession was far too great for him to heed, or even hear, his friend's advice. He was only too willing to suffer whatever scorn or insult this exciting *inamorata* chose to heap upon him. Sooner or later, he knew, her mood would change and she would again shine on him, like the sun in summertime, with warm affection. And when that happened, as it did often, his own exhilaration was so profound that it made everything, every barb, every indignity, worthwhile.

He was so far committed that by the end of April he had taken a room at Hill House, a residence hotel in Covington, just half-a-block from the Crossroads, so that he could be nearer both to the brickyard and to his *fidanzata*. It was always his intention that his lodgment at Hill House be temporary, just until something more permanent became available. And, as things turned out, that's precisely what happened.

CHAPTER FOUR

SATURDAY NIGHT, MAY 4TH, WAS A GOOD NIGHT. Danny and Johnnie Nickel met the girls at the post office and the four of them repaired directly to the electric plant where they enjoyed an exact reprise of their first night together, complete with wine and hogshead cheese. Afterwards Danny and Frosty lingered lovingly on the riverbank, high above the falls, and re-plighted their troth to one another. Frosty acknowledged her sometime perverseness and apologized for it. It was just that she was so anxious for them to be married, she said, that she had become cranky. If she had seemed out of sorts with him, maybe even bitchy, it was only because she loved him so very much and was impatient for their wedding day.

And because he had received his *salario* that day, Danny was able to hasten the event by contributing six dollars to their hope chest. That would do very nicely, she told him. She had been hard at work these past few weeks, sewing and hemming, and had nearly completed a full set of linens with which to set up housekeeping. As soon as that was finished she could turn her attention, and her needle, to the design and creation of a proper bridal trousseau, *"una corredo da sposa"*, Danny proclaimed triumphantly when she had made him understand.

"We'll need a very special gown," she told him, "for a New York wedding. Something really elegant."

"Elegante!" he translated. *"Eccellente!"*

"You'll love the dress I have in mind," she said teasingly. "It will fit just so in all the right places. You'll be so proud, and excited, you'll have to restrain yourself during the ceremony. And then," she promised, "after all the guests have gone, you can take as long as you like peeling it off me."

When the image she had created produced a suggestive leer from Danny, Frosty shifted direction. She'd been looking just everywhere for suitable china and silverware, she told him. "But everything nice is just so terribly expensive. We'll have to save up as much money as we can if we're to be married in the fall."

DONATO DIIULIO PASSED THROUGH THE NEXT FEW DAYS in a state of euphoria. His love life was secure, their plans, *intenzione per matrimonio*, were maturing apace and all was right with his world.

He lay overlong abed Sunday morning, building air castles and spinning daydreams. He was not the least chagrined to learn that he had thereby missed the hearty breakfast that Mrs. Hill routinely laid out for her boarders at 7:00 and gathered up at 8:30. He was quite content to devote the morning first to the straightening of his room and the ordering of his meager possessions, then to the composition of a long and leisurely letter to his parents. He wanted them to know, yet again he realized, of his profound *contentezza* and he described for them, also again, the many *fascini* of his *fidanzata* and their plans to be wed in New York in the fall. He promised that the two of them would come home for a visit *prima possible*.

Later, after a light midday meal shared pleasantly with Mr. and Mrs. Hill, he walked the short block up High Street to the Crossroads and settled himself comfortably on the wooden bench in front of the traction depot. Although there had been no pre-arrangement to do so Johnnie Nickel joined him there after an hour or so and the two friends whiled away the afternoon watching the passersby, making small conversation and sipping sarsaparilla. Secretly both of them had hoped they might catch sight of the girls, but their ultimate failure to do so had not marred their serenity. For the two young men and for Donato DiIulio in particular, Sunday had proved to be an altogether pleasant day.

His euphoria continued undiminished through Monday and Tuesday and neither the rigors of his dusty chores at the brickyard nor the friendly jibes of his work crew were sufficient to disturb his reveries. He chattered to his mates like an excited Italian-American magpie and was not the least dismayed when his foreman, Henry Deeman, shook his craggy, gray head indulgently and said to them generally, "Don't mind him, boys. He don't have to make any sense. He's in love." Deeman sighed deeply, turned back to his clay, and added philosophically, "Like as not he'll get over it in a week or so and we can all get some peace and quiet."

TUESDAY, AFTER WORK, PROMISED TO BE ANOTHER FINE NIGHT for young lovers. It certainly started out well enough. The evening was pleasantly warm, the sky a deep clear blue. The two couples had met at the bridge and walked again to the electric plant. They had spread their blankets on the grass and remained together until after dark. Then Johnnie Nickel and Blanche announced that they would walk on ahead a piece and suggested that they all meet later back at the bridge.

Left to themselves in the covering darkness, and building on their tender detente of the preceding Saturday, Danny and Frosty languished easily in one another's arms on the high bluff above the falls. Their soft murmurings were barely audible against the comfortable resonance of the fresh spring torrent as it tumbled over the power dam and onto the bleak, stolid rocks below. Predictably, as the evening wore on they reacted to the romantic ambience and to each other as nature must certainly have intended. An initial tentative touch, followed by increasingly insistent caresses, soon led to an urgently-begun, though perhaps somewhat perfunctory, session of lovemaking that nonetheless left Danny gasping for breath and luxuriating privately in what he perceived to be the soft glow of sustained felicity. That which he considered their mutual exhilaration seemed, to him at least, only slightly dampened by Frosty's obvious consternation over his own reluctant admission that he could spare no more than a dollar for their hope chest. He'd do better, he promised, on Saturday after he would have received his week's *salario*. They had already agreed to meet again Saturday night and Danny expected that by then he would be able to make a substantial contribution.

It was nearly midnight when they rejoined Johnnie Nickel and Blanche at the west end of the Rock Avenue bridge. Danny had been lost in his own thoughts during the mile and a half trek from the electric plant and he had been only dimly aware of Frosty's developing, and to him inexplicable, aloofness. He had some sense that she had turned cool, even taciturn, in her demeanor towards him, but he had no idea that she had gone totally rancid in the short course of an hour's walk. For that reason, he was wholly unprepared for her gratingly strident reply to Johnnie Nickel's innocuous inquiry, "Did you two lovebirds have a nice evening?"

"Oh, yes," she snapped venomously. "We most certainly did. Good old Danny Doughnut, the incredible diddling dago, had himself a real good time. He got what he wanted — what he came for — and as far as he's concerned, everybody else can just go to hell. Isn't that right, lover boy?"

Danny DiIulio was struck dumb by the sheer vehemence of Frosty's remarks. He was able to comprehend very little of what she had said, and still less the reasons for her obvious anger, but he could scarcely have missed the fact that she was enraged about something and that that something had to do with him.

"*Che cosa?*" he asked. "*Tu sei —* "

He didn't finish the question. Before he could do so he was interrupted by Frosty's crude snarl, "Speak English, for Christsake."

And when he attempted to approach with arms outstretched and to placate, "Get away from me you cheap, guinea bastard. You've got all of me you're gonna get."

To her sister and to Johnnie Nickel, she said icily, "I'll walk on home by myself. You just see to it the son-of-a-bitch doesn't follow me."

Danny DiIulio was trying to make some kind of sense out of his fiance's sudden and indecipherable malignity. "But, but — " he stammered, "*la tua promessa —* "

"Promise?" she translated scornfully. "What promise?"

"*Il matrimonio. Nostro —* ," he groped for the English words. "Wedding," he blurted finally. "Our wedding?"

"Wedding?" she trilled. "What wedding is that? You pathetic, gibbering Italian idiot! There's not going to be any wedding. Not for you, anyway. You can't afford to get married, not to me, you can't. Do you think I'm some cheap piece of goods you can keep on your pitiful little *salario* from the brickyard?"

She shot him a final, spiteful glare, turned on her heel and strode up the pike towards her father's home atop the rise. Over her shoulder she spat a parting benediction, "Maybe you ought to ride the trolley down to Dayton some night. See what you can get there for a dollar."

IT PROVED TO BE A VERY LONG NIGHT FOR DONATO DIIULIO. He had been utterly devastated by his *fidenzata's* unexpected and unrestrained outburst and by the savage fit of dudgeon which had engendered it. He was, at once, both mystified and distressed at the show of this alarming aspect of her character, one which he had neither seen nor suspected before.

He roamed the streets and walked the rails of the traction line for most of the night, too exercised in his mind to go to bed. Just before dawn he crept to his room at Hill House, stretched out on top of his bedspread and stared sightlessly at the ceiling. His eyes failed to close and he got no rest at all.

However great his anguish and by whatever doubts he was beleaguered, it never actually occurred to him that his affair with Frosty Floyd might be over. She was upset, *stravolta* — *molta stravolta*, that much was certain. But he knew in his heart she'd get over it, *ricupera*, sooner or later. As he thought about it, in the gray hours of early morning, he managed to persuade himself that she had already regretted her tantrum and would want him to know she was sorry. He desperately needed to hold that single, surpassingly tenuous conviction, that she was truly sorry, *rincrescersi*, in order to get him through the long day at the brickyard before they could find one another again and be reconciled.

WEDNESDAY, MAY 8TH, WAS EVEN LONGER THAN THE NIGHT THAT PRECEDED IT. Donnto DiIulio trudged soddenly through his job assignments at the brickyard like a preoccupied and completely inattentive zombie. Twice he fed whole trays of uncut clay into the kiln and produced great slabs of useless bricklike material, and once he was nearly run over by a slow-moving wagon loaded down with freshly fired bricks. He resisted all efforts of his co-workers to engage him in conversation and would say only that he was feeling poorly because he hadn't slept well and that he had had a quarrel, *una disputa*, with his *ragazza*.

He followed Henry Deeman's instructions woodenly and imperfectly, rebuffed Lew Johnson's friendly overtures, neglected to eat the light lunch packed for him by Angie Hill, and somehow lasted out the day. He was sustained throughout by nothing more compelling than his own fervent need to mend the aching breach with Frosty.

After work, his activities were driven by that same single purpose. He repaired directly to his room at Hill House to make himself presentable. He washed away the by-products of his labors, sweat and brick dust, donned the only suit he owned, combed his dark hair with his hands and went down to dinner.

His next stop, after no more than a half-hearted stab at Angie Hill's evening fare, was Dunham's barbershop for a much-needed shave. Ed Reish's shop was located upstairs above the dry goods store, just a few doors down the street from Hill House, and was much closer than Dunham's, but Dunham's was right next to the post office and Donato DiIulio thought it was just possible that Frosty might have come there looking for him.

When he failed to find her at the post office, he settled into Frank Miller's open chair, drew his hand across a stubby cheek and inquired, *"La barba?"*

Then, while the barber tucked him in, applied warm lather and stropped his blade with a series of quick, deft strokes across the smooth, shiny leather, Donato DiIulio permitted both his eyes and his attention to become unfocused. He remained in a trance-like stupor throughout Frank Miller's tender ministrations and it was not until after the last of the hot moist towels had been removed from his face and neck that he became aware of the lively dialogue between the barbers and their patrons. It seemed that there was a tent show, *un carnevale*, in town, over by the river, and some of the featured performances were truly prodigious. There was a magic show, a trained dog act, a fortune-teller and a host of other attractions. The show would be in town for this day only, they said, so everyone should make a point of seeing it before it moved upstream to the next river town.

Donato DiIulio was in no frame of mind to be much intrigued by magic tricks or performing dogs, but it did occur to him that he might find Frosty there. So when he didn't see her at the Crossroads, he proceeded directly to the tent show, paid a ten-cent admission charge and entered the tent. A few minutes later he saw both girls, Blanche and Frosty, in company with their brother Millard, in front of a booth where a black-clad man was vigorously thrusting swords through a large wicker basket. Danny knew who Millard was and he also knew better than to approach the girls while they were in his presence. Frosty had told him more than once that Millard, like her father, hated all "foreigners" and especially despised Italians.

Unwilling to precipitate a confrontation, at least at that juncture, Donato kept his distance. He did follow their movements from one concession to another, hoping all the while to catch Frosty's eye. After half an hour or so, he realized that that tactic would not succeed. If she had seen him at all, and he suspected that she had, she gave no sign. His efforts temporarily frustrated, Donato DiIulio left the tent and walked to the Crossroads. At least, he reflected, he knew where she was at the moment. He hoped he'd have another chance later in the evening.

As he had expected, he found Johnny Nickel at the Crossroads. He had just come out the front door of the Panhandle Grocery, catercornered across the intersection from the traction depot. With an ice-cream cone in one hand and a bottle of soda in the other, he seemed busy indeed.

"Hi Danny," he chirped buoyantly. "Have you seen the girls?"

Donato DiIulio's flagging spirits were lifted, however slightly, by his friend's infectious cheerfulness. And, because he had heard the question many times before, he had no difficulty understanding it. "*Si,*" he said, jerking his thumb towards the riverbank. "*A la carnevale.*"

"The what? Oh, the tent show." Johnny Nickel translated. "Did you talk with them? *Parla? Parlavo?*"

Donato DiIulio shook his head. "*Le fratello,*" he stammered.

"Who?" asked Johnny Nickel. Then, "Oh, Millard. Okay. I got it."

He finished his ice cream, licked his lips. "Maybe he'll go on home after the show. I'm not goin' back in there anyway. The place is a madhouse. I was there before supper and that's enough for me."

Donato DiIulio nodded absently. Johnny Nickel continued, "Besides, I seem to remember that Frosty's kinda peeved at you, huh? What's your word? *Furiosa?*"

"*Si, furiosa, molta furiosa,*" came the response. "*Ma, pero — non capisco,*" he blurted. "I do not understand."

"Easy," said Johnny Nickel. "One of two things. Either she don't think you're payin' her enough or she's got eyes for some other guy." He spat the dregs of his soda into the dirt road. "Or both," he added. "Most likely both."

The Italian furrowed his brow in an effort at comprehension. "Payin'?" he queried. "*Non capisco.*"

"Paying. Like with money, *denaro,*" answered Johnny Nickel. "Like you was buying something. Which is exactly what you been doing. *Capisch?*"

Donato DiIulio turned away from his friend. "*Non capisco,*" he repeated. Then, "*Ha torto.* You are wrong. *Sposeremo?* We are to be married. In New York! *Lei stessa ha promette! Lei e mio fidanzata!*"

As if to punctuate his insistence, Donato DiIulio stalked coldly away. He wanted no more conversation with Johnny Nickel. He had made up his mind to return to the tent show and wait outside the exit flap. He was sure he'd get a chance to speak with her before the evening ended. He had only to bide his time.

And, as it happened, his persistence paid off. It was not what he had hoped for, but a conversation of sorts did occur. He had waited for just under an hour when the three siblings, Frosty, Blanche and Millard, left the tent and walked together towards Broadway. Donato followed a dozen yards behind. He made himself as conspicuous as he dared in order that Frosty might notice him and make some signal. They had progressed in this fashion some two blocks from the tent show when she stopped in her tracks, turned to look at him, and appeared to smile. Donato's heart literally jumped when she raised a finger and beckoned him to her.

Then, as he approached, he saw that what he had taken for a smile was more accurately a sneer. The initial elation he had felt at receiving her summons soured in his breast when he heard her acrid greeting.

"Get away from me, you dago son-of-a-bitch. And stop following me. I'm not having anything more to do with you — ever. So just get lost and leave me alone." Having said her piece, she took her brother's arm and allowed him to lead the little troup homeward.

Donato DiIulio stood frozen in both time and place, too stunned, too incredulous at her vehemence, and much too wounded by her words, to move. Their reunion had not been at all what he had anticipated.

Chapter Five

DONATO DIIULIO HAD ANOTHER HARD NIGHT. Compared to the anguish he now knew, the previous twenty-four hour period seemed an idyll.

For the second consecutive night he coursed the town streets and railway lines with no better purpose than to occupy his feet and to pass the time. His mind and his emotions were in torment. At one end of town he embraced a stout sycamore, as one might cling to a woman much beloved, and sobbed uncontrollably. An hour and a half later, and at the opposite edge of the village, he sank soundlessly to the ground, clutched obsessively to a solitary hitching post and remained there, as if in stupor, for another hour.

However poor his comprehension, he could not fail to realize that his relationship with his *fidanzata* had deteriorated to an alarming state and that he was in real danger of losing her altogether. At the same time, because of a naiveté born of his own inexperience and his unfamiliarity with the language, he did not fully understand what it was that had set her off. It was obvious, even to him, that her pique had somehow arisen out of his inability to make more meaningful contributions to their hope chest, and he wondered if she had interpreted that to mean that his own eagerness for their wedding day had flagged. Perhaps, he concluded, that was the problem. She had been clearly disdainful of the single dollar he'd been able to spare Tuesday evening despite the fact that he was left with only a little more than that amount to tide him through the next four days until payday. Surely, he thought, he ought to be able to convince her that he was doing the very best he could with what he earned.

Then, too, he reflected, she had seemed to disparage the amount of his wages from the brickyard. He had thought they paid him a very good *salario*, for an illiterate immigrant, but if Frosty thought he could do better, he was certainly willing to look for something else.

He also thought she might be angry because of his admittedly poor grasp of the language. Her waspish "Speak English, for christsake," had stung him to the quick. And, of course, she was right. He had been in America for nearly four years now and it was high time he learned to speak and write the language. He would find someone to teach him, as soon as possible. That shouldn't be too difficult. There were lots of Italians in the vicinity, most of whom spoke English fairly well.

What he needed to do, he recognized, was to make Frosty understand the true extent of his eagerness for their marriage to occur and the very great depth of his commitment, his *impegno*. He would tell her of his resolutions, to find a better-paying job and to learn to speak English like a native.

But, of course, he couldn't tell her anything if she refused to listen or to have anything to do with him. And she'd said that, that she wasn't having anything more to do with him — ever. She'd said it like she meant it. And with that recognition, whatever little solace he had allowed himself on the basis of his new resolutions dissolved again into abject despair. If she truly meant what she had said and was determined to have nothing more to do with him there would be no way he could convince her of his love and his firm resolve to deserve her affections. Without an encounter or an audience, *una udienza*, like with the Pope, he would have no opportunity to tell her any of these things. It was a stymie and he could see no way around it.

It was nearly four in the morning when he shambled up the stairs to his second-floor lodging at Hill House. He neither turned on the lights nor took off his clothes. Much too distracted for sleep, he simply collapsed on the floor by the low window to the front of the hotel. He spent the balance of the night in that location, overwrought and finally dry-eyed, gazing sightlessly at the lonely quietude of the empty street below.

✦ 6 ✦

AT 5:30 THURSDAY MORNING, impelled by nothing more than force of habit, Donato DiIulio arose from his station by the window and made an effort to pull himself together for the new day. He straightened his clothing as best he could, splashed water from a basin onto his face, patted down his hair and shuffled down the stairs to breakfast. He accepted a single poached egg and a single cup of black coffee from Mrs. Hill, picked up the lunch pail she had packed for him, and set out for the brickyard.

A block or so along the way, he stopped and sought fortification at G. C. Hooker's Saloon.

"*Medicina*," he announced to Mr. Hooker as he squeezed his eyes shut, grimaced painfully, and forced down a single shot of neat whiskey. "*Soffrendo*," he explained, "Feel bad, real bad."

Moments later, he emerged into the half-light of early dawn, encouraged by his expectations of the liquor, and walked the half-dozen blocks to the brickyard. He acted as though he really believed he could get through the day.

He didn't last the second hour. Stumbling and bumbling lethargically about the yard, pale and disheveled, he was so obviously wasted that Henry Deeman was constrained to inquire. "Are you all right, Danny?" he asked. "You don't look so good."

Danny looked blankly at his foreman, trying to process the question. Then, after a few moments, "*Non, non — malato* is," he stammered, groping for the word. "Sick," he said finally, "Feel sick."

And Deeman sent him home. "Go to bed, goddamit," he admonished. "And stay there till you're well enough to put in an honest day's work."

Donato DiIulio went home, but he would not go to bed. By the time he had regained Hill House, he knew what he had to do. Sick or well, he had to reconnect with Frosty. He had won her affections once and, if he had truly lost them, he would have to win them again. He would pay court to her, woo her, the Americans said, and he would make himself *irresistible*. Then, when he had her *attenzione*, he would tell her of his resolutions to find a better job and to learn *Inglese*. He soon managed to convince himself that he had now unlocked the puzzle and all would be well by the end of the day.

In furtherance of his renewed inspiration, Donato DiIulio washed his face and arms, changed clothes, and returned to the street. His spirits lightened by misplaced confidence, he sauntered through the town in search of a likely spot. Ultimately he took station on a wooden bench in front of the Panhandle Grocery. From that vantage point he could survey the bandstand, the traction depot and the entire Crossroads area. If Frosty were to come into town that day he would be sure to see her.

A PLAUSIBLE CASE FOR PREDESTINATION COULD BE MADE from the fact that the lady herself, in company of her younger sister, thirteen-year old Anna Floyd, appeared at the Crossroads less than two hours after Donato DiIulio's vigil commenced. Both of them appeared freshly-scrubbed and neatly dressed. Frosty, in particular, looked as though she had just stepped from the pages of a womens-wear catalogue. She was wearing a trim, white blouse, one that he had not seen before, and a dark, formal skirt. They passed directly in front of him, turned at the intersection and headed south towards the bandstand. Donato DiIulio followed and soon overtook them.

Warily, almost timidly, he asked if he might speak with Frosty and he was both surprised and ecstatic when she actually smiled at him. Although she gave no answer, she seemed at least willing to tolerate his company and to hear him out. Anna explained that they were on their way to Speelman's Gallery to have Frosty's photo taken. Then, after the two girls conferred, she announced that they had decided to take the traction to Piqua and have the photo taken at Thorne's Gallery instead. Danny could ride along, she said, if he wanted to. And, of course, he did.

In pursuance of their altered plans, the three young people reversed direction and returned to the D.C. & P. depot. When they boarded the hourly car to Piqua, Donato DiIulio was allowed to pay the fare for all three. The girls settled themselves on a cross-bench near the front of the car and Donato took the bench immediately ahead of them. Then, just moments after departure, he realized that his bench was reversible and he swung the backrest to the front so that he could sit opposite the girls. Facing them directly, he chattered animatedly in their direction. Anna, who seemed to like Donato well enough, listened to his remarks and even offered an occasional response. Frosty, by way of contrast, stared indifferently out the open car at the passing countryside. She varied that attitude only twice during the fifteen minute trip. On each of those occasions, she twisted in her seat, glanced archly over her shoulder, and affected a barely perceptible, but distinctly demure, smile. After the second of these small episodes, Donato DiIulio asked pointedly what it was that had her attention. *"Che cosa?"* he queried.

And, for the first time that day, Frosty condescended to speak to him.

Her eyes, dark and liquid, meeting his own in level exchange, she answered his question with neither embarrassment nor apology. "The tall man on the rear platform, the one with the paisley shirt. That's my new fella."

Donato DiIulio had no difficulty sorting him out. Clearly taller and apparently older than he was, the man seemed to have sensed that he was the subject of their discussion. He returned Donato's rude glare evenly, without rancor or hostility. Donato DiIulio wrested his own attention away from the interloper and brought it back to Frosty.

"*Come* — how — can — you — tell me — that?" he blurted painfully. "Just last week — *la settimana scorsa* — you promised to marry me — *sposare? Come?*"

Frosty Floyd did not deign to answer the question. She flashed him a transient, callous smirk, held it briefly, and returned her gaze, imperturbably, to the swiftly changing landscape to her right. Anna Floyd, seated beside her older sister and directly opposite the stricken Italian, felt embarrassment for Frosty's insensitivity and sympathy for Donato DiIulio's abject suffering. They completed the run to Piqua in a strained, rigid silence, looking for all the world like a collage of store mannequins. Anna and Donato stared fixedly at the same randomly selected bolt-head on the floor between them while Frosty riveted her own attention, studiously and defiantly, on the passing scenery.

Matters did not improve upon their arrival in Piqua. The three passengers debarked from the train at the Covington Avenue depot and proceeded directly to the Thorne Gallery. Although not invited to do so, Donato DiIulio followed along, at a distance of two or three paces. A single remark passed between them as they traversed the short distance to the photographic studio. In what seemed a needless and wholly perverse attempt to further wound her rejected swain, Frosty pointed to a disreputable-looking residence hotel and boasted of having spent two nights there with his good friend Johnny Nickel. "He was absolutely insatiable," she pronounced maliciously. "He just couldn't get enough of me."

Donato DiIulio flushed with jealousy, humiliation and other emotions too complex and too painful for description. Frosty knew she had scored on him and hastened to pursue her advantage. "We didn't leave the room for two whole days," she taunted. "I couldn't walk right for more 'n a week afterwards."

They arrived directly at the Thorne studio, but Donato was not allowed inside. "You can just wait on the porch until we've finished," she said imperiously. "Or go on home. We really don't care."

And, of course, he waited. For more than an hour he waited. Then, after the photographic session had been completed, and the girls emerged from the studio, they retraced their route back to the Covington Avenue depot, caught the three o'clock traction car and rode homeward to Covington in an estranged, starchy silence. Donato DiIulio was permitted to pay the fares for the girls as a condition of their company. The tall, older man, Frosty's "new fella," made the return trip also. He remained, again, on the rear platform and did not approach, but Donato saw that he and Frosty exchanged a series of suggestive leers at one another.

UPON THE ARRIVAL OF THE BLIGHTED COTERIE at the Covington depot the next series of events transpired very swiftly. Because Donato DiIulio had not yet been permitted to state his case properly, to tell Frosty about his new resolutions, and to make a fervent plea for reconciliation, and because he had a desperate need to do so, he begged to be allowed to escort the girls to their home.

"Not on your life, Danny Doughnut," snapped Frosty. "I've already told you it's over, and I meant it."

Then, when she and Anna started to walk out Rock Avenue towards their home and Donato attempted to follow, she turned towards him and hissed vehemently, "Stop right there or I'll call the constable. Better yet, I'll sic my father on you. He hates all you dago bastards." She stamped her foot imperiously and added, "And so do I. Just go away and leave me alone."

Donato DiIulio was wounded by Frosty's outburst. He backed away from her, then turned towards Hill House and took a few tentative steps in that direction. He stopped, looked around as if to reorient himself as to time and place, and shook his head with new determination.

Of a sudden, he altered course, cut to his right at the half-block, ran through a short alley to Main Street, went right again and reached Rock Avenue just behind the girls. There were three of them now. Frosty and Anna had somehow encountered and joined forces with their eleven-year old sister, Maude, who was also on her way to their home beyond the west edge of town.

Donato DiIulio approached from behind and timorously spoke the name of his *fidanzata*. She swivelled around just long enough to spit wetly in his direction. "Keep away from me, you greasy, guinea son-of-a-bitch," she growled, and turned her footsteps back towards her home.

Donato DiIulio somehow produced a small pistol, aimed it at her back and fired two quick shots into her body at point blank range. They would be together, "*insieme*," he sobbed brokenly, "*per sempre!*"

He next placed the pistol to his own right temple and fired a third bullet into his brain. When that shot was not instantly fatal, and he found himself still standing — incredibly and perhaps instinctively — he jammed the muzzle of the gun into his mouth and fired again. The last two shots were fired in the space of an instant and Donato DiIulio collapsed on the sidewalk. Frosty Floyd remained upright for a few seconds, then tottered uncertainly and fell heavily to the ground less than three feet from her prostrate assailant.

Daniel Minnich saw the whole thing. A drayman, he had been operating a hoisting machine and was loading building materials at the Panhandle freight depot. His attention had been attracted by the first of the four shots and by the screams of the two younger sisters. He and two members of his work crew were the first to reach Frosty and he directed other new arrivals to move her onto the grass in Mrs. Cauffer's front yard. It proved an unnecessary kindness. She died, wide-eyed and wordless, within minutes.

When Constable Harvey Hake arrived there was little to be done. Frosty Floyd's ruined body was already cooling under a sheet provided by Mrs. Cauffer. The two sisters, Anna and Maude, both hysterical, were being comforted by residents of the neighborhood, and Donato DiIulio was crumpled in a pool of bright new blood in the middle of the concrete sidewalk.

Daniel Minnich had already collected the pistol. It had apparently dropped from the hand of Donato DiIulio and was found at his right side. Minnich handed the weapon to the constable. "It's a .32 caliber Colt," he said needlessly. "Holds five shells. There's four of 'em spent and one live. I put it back on safe."

Constable Hake enlisted Minnich's crew to help restrain the gathering crowds and to keep the scene clear of intruders. He dispatched a neighborhood boy to summon the coroner and set about the task of reconstructing the event from the accounts being circulated among those gathered around Mrs. Cauffer's yard. There was little enough disagreement about what had happened, but virtually everyone wanted to speak of it.

Then, after another half hour or so, Dr. Charles Gaines, the county coroner, arrived on the scene. He examined the body of Frosty Floyd first, noted two entry wounds and considerable powder burns on her back, and pronounced her dead. He gave instructions that she be taken to the Whitmer Brothers Furniture and Undertaking establishment around the corner on High Street. "I 'spect that's where her dad will want her to be," he offered. "I think Whitmers have buried some of the Floyd people 'fore now."

He glanced in the direction of Sue Cauffer who was holding and ministering to the sobbing younger sisters. "Somebody tell Sue Ann I'll be wanting her to help take the girls home. Soon's I'm done here." He shook his gray head ruefully. "I don't much want to be the one to break this to John and

Lucy Floyd, but it's got to be done. Tell Sue Ann I'll be obliged for her help."

The coroner knelt to examine Donato DiIulio, but did not pronounce him for the very good reason that he was not yet dead. "He will be shortly," he allowed. "Actually, he's dead already, but it'll be awhile longer 'fore his system figures it out."

Harvey Hake was new to this killing business. Nothing like it had ever happened before. At least not in the five years he'd been constable. He wanted guidance. "What'll we do with him?" he asked the coroner.

Doc Gaines stroked his chin thoughtfully. "Well," he said, "it seems pretty clear he caused this mess. So, I guess you might's well haul his sorry ass over to your jailhouse and wait him out. He can die there 'bout as well as anywhere else."

"O.K., Doc," answered Hake. "I'll send for you when he stops breathing. These damn immigrants ain't nothin' but trouble."

CHAPTER SIX

WALTER D. JONES HAD BEEN JUDGE of the Common Pleas Court for Miami County since before the turn of the century. Literally. He had been appointed by Governor Bushnell, in 1899, to complete the unexpired term of his predecessor, Judge Theodore Sullivan, who had himself been elevated to the Circuit Court of Appeals.

In the fall of 1907 Walter D. Jones was in the fifty-first year of his life and the ninth year of his judgeship. He had already been twice re-elected by the voters and would soon stand unopposed for an unprecedented third four-year term. In the entire history of the county only two men, Ebenezer Parsons and Calvin D. Wright, at ten years apiece, had occupied the position longer than he had already. Judge Jones would ultimately serve as Common Pleas Judge until 1937, an incumbency far surpassing that of any other person to hold the office.

Above all else, Judge Jones was the consummate jurist. He was the son of Mathias H. Jones, one of the preeminent lawyers in southern Ohio. Matt Jones had been the lead prosecutor in the highly-publicized murder trial of Elizabeth Jane Ragan back in 1856 and had himself practiced law in the county for more than sixty years.

Walter D. Jones had fallen in love with the law at an early age and the resultant affair had flourished and matured under his father's tutelage. The two men, father and son, had practiced together in partnership for more than twenty years before the governor's appointment. That event had come at an opportune time for both. Matt Jones was well past his seventieth birthday and was already in process of winding down his practice. And, by reason of that circumstance, Walter found himself ready to accept the challenge to become a member of the judiciary. Both father and son were saddened to mark the end of their long-term partnership, but they were consoled and gratified by the fact that their professional association had been culminated by Walter's summons to the bench.

The judgeship of Walter D. Jones was distinguished not only by the length of its tenure, but by the quality of its jurisprudence. A learned and compassionate man, Judge Jones was considered to be fair-minded, practical and approachable. He had swiftly won and long since enjoyed the respect and admiration of both the lawyers who appeared before him and the county personnel whose official duties and activities meshed with his own. He was, in sum, a highly regarded and most excellent judge of the Court of Common Pleas.

It would not have been possible for Judge Jones to have remained unaware, even in a judicial sense, of the May 9th shooting death of pretty Forest May Floyd by an illiterate Italian immigrant. That tragic event had been, at least through the early part of the summer, the principal, if not the only, topic of conversation throughout the southern part of the state. There had certainly been no dearth of media attention. All the regional newspapers had accorded the story full-bannered and prominently displayed front page coverage. In their understandable haste to get it into print the reporters filed, and the newspapers published, accounts that were garbled and inaccurate as to details. It seemed that no one could identify, spell or even pronounce the name of the assassin, nor agree as to the given name of the victim. Nonetheless, the fact of a homicide, committed by an "Eye-talian" immigrant against a pretty, young, local girl, was widely circulated. That which was accurately reported was that feelings had run high within the community, and had he not been already mortally wounded by his own hand, the perpetrator would have been swiftly and unceremoniously hanged from the nearest stout tree.

That which had genuinely surprised everybody, Doc Gaines included, was that the Italian did not die. He had been left for dead, lying on a narrow, blood-soaked cot at the village jailhouse. Bound hand and foot with heavy leather straps and bandaged no better than necessary to thwart the botflies that swarmed about his head seeking access to the blood and brain tissue that oozed persistently through his open gunshot wounds, he was a singularly unappetizing sight. And though he may have been "left for dead" in the strict sense of the word, he certainly received a great deal of attention, not for his wounds, but for his circumstance. Because of the enormity of his crime and the ignominy of his condition, Constable Harvey Hake had somehow deemed it to be appropriate to allow him to become a public spectacle. He threw open the doors of his jailhouse and organized a parade of souvenir-viewers, gawkers and other morbidly curious souls, permitting each to look on, and try to speak with, his prisoner. It was a continuous procession that had lasted all night Thursday and for most of Friday before Sheriff Gibson arrived and put a stop to it.

For his own part, the Italian had lapsed in and out of consciousness throughout the night. He had been aware of his "visitors" and even spoke to some. He had seemed terrified of them, afraid he might be tortured, and his standard response to their questions had been that he couldn't remember. "*Non ricordando,*" he insisted repeatedly when asked, time and again, how it was he could have done such a foul thing.

No one could have been more dismayed than he when Friday morning came and he was still alive. He had profoundly wanted to be dead, had done all that he could to make himself dead, and yet he was not. When Dr. Gaines examined him that morning and pronounced that he just might survive two gunshot wounds to the head, the Italian had cried. He had also begged his jailers for a knife, *un coltello,* in order that he might complete the job.

Mercifully, the spectacle had ended that afternoon when Sheriff Gibson arrived with an ambulance, claimed the prisoner and removed him to the county jail in Troy. There he had received proper medical attention and eventually recovered. Although he had been initially and temporarily blinded in one eye, even that condition soon resolved itself and he seemed as good as new.

ALTHOUGH IT WOULD NEVER BE GENERALLY KNOWN, it was Judge Jones who had orchestrated the Italian's delivery from Harvey Hake's sideshow establishment. As soon as word of the prisoner's treatment had reached him, he had summoned Sheriff Gibson and suggested to him, in terms too compelling to be ignored, that the ends of justice might be better served if the prisoner were removed from public exhibition and established in the county jail to await developments.

"He will either die or he will survive," Judge Jones had pronounced as though he had uttered a profundity. "If he is to die, he should be allowed to do so with dignity, out of the public view, and away from the unfeeling taunts of the common rabble. If he survives, he will doubtless be charged and tried for his crime. That course, also, should proceed with dignity and with all the constitutional protections to which an accused is entitled in these United States. In either case, it will not do to suffer him to remain any longer in Constable Hake's custody."

ALTHOUGH NO-ONE HAD EVER EXPECTED the Italian to live through the day, police routine nonetheless required that a criminal charge be filed. And, if he were to be kept in custody — there was really nothing else to do with him — it was necessary that such a filing be accomplished forthwith.

Thus it happened that on Friday, May 10th, Doctor Charles Gaines, in his capacity as county coroner, filed with Covington Mayor R. F. Albery his sworn statement formally charging that, on the preceding day and in the Village of Covington, County of Miami and State of Ohio:

... one Donato DiIulio did willfully, purposely and of deliberate and premeditated malice kill and murder one Forest Floyd, then and there being, by then and there shooting the said Forest Floyd in and upon the back, in the dorsal region, near the shoulder blade, with a rifle of the revolver kind.

THE CORONER'S AFFIDAVIT WAS LOGGED as Complaint No. 154 on the Criminal Docket of the Mayor's Court and a warrant was promptly issued to Constable Hake commanding that he immediately "take the body" of the said Donato DiIulio and keep him in custody until the further order of the court. That directive was, of course, rather easily performed since DiIulio's bleeding, apparently moribund body was already located, and on display, at the constable's village jail.

Apart from the transfer of the prisoner that same day to the county jailhouse and to Sheriff Gibson's custody, there were no further proceedings in the matter until mid-summer. Then, when DiIulio failed to die and actually began to recover, the legal machinery designed to bring him to trial was reengaged and set into motion. A preliminary hearing in Mayor Albery's Court was scheduled for August 15th and subpoenas issued for witnesses. The purpose of the hearing was, of course, to determine whether a crime had been committed and whether there was probable cause to believe that the defendant, Donato DiIulio, had committed it. If, after hearing, such a determination were made the defendant would be bound to appear before the Common Pleas Court for further proceedings.

As it happened, Donato DiIulio did not appear for preliminary hearing. Upon advice from Sheriff Gibson and Deputy George Landry, DiIulio made his mark, an X, to a document wherein he waived his entitlement to a preliminary hearing and consented to be bound over to the Court of Common Pleas. The fact that the defendant had signed away these rights didn't really matter. The hearing would have been, in his case, a needless formality, a meaningless procedural step in the inexorable progression to trial.

SOME FIFTY-THREE DAYS LATER, the Miami County Grand Jury convened to consider and to act upon those pending criminal charges submitted to them by the Prosecuting Attorney. On October 9th, the Grand Jury returned, and the Prosecutor filed with the Court, an indictment charging, in the stilted, sometimes ludicrous language of the law, that:

... Donato DiIulio late of said County, on the 9th day of May in the year of our Lord one thousand nine hundred and seven, with force and arms, in said County of Miami and State of Ohio, in and upon one, Forest Floyd, then and there being, did unlawfully, purposely and of deliberate and premeditated malice, make an assault in a menacing manner, with intent her, the said Forest Floyd, unlawfully, purposely and of deliberate and premeditated malice, to kill and murder; and that the said Donato DiIulio, a certain revolver then and there charged with gunpowder and leaden bullets, which said revolver, he, the said Donato DiIulio, then and there in his right hand had and held, then and there, unlawfully, purposely and of deliberate and premeditated malice, did discharge and shoot off to, against and upon the said Forest Floyd, with the intent aforesaid, and that the said Donato DiIulio, with the leaden bullets aforesaid, out of the revolver aforesaid by force of the gunpowder aforesaid, by the said Donato DiIulio then and there discharged and shot off as aforesaid, her, the said Forest Floyd, one bullet entering the body an inch and a half between the shoulder blade and the backbone, going entirely through the body and lodged just beneath the skin in the left breast, and the other entering the body about one or, one and a half inches to the left of the seventh cervical

vertebrae, passed entirely through the body coming out just above the clavicle, or collar bone, of her the said Forest Floyd, then and there, unlawfully, purposely and of deliberate and premeditated malice, did strike, penetrate, and wound, with the intent aforesaid, thereby then and there given to her, the said Forest Floyd, with the leaden bullets aforesaid, so as aforesaid discharged and shot out of the revolver aforesaid, by the said Donato DiIulio, one entering the body about an inch and a half between the shoulder blade and the backbone, going entirely through the body and lodged just beneath the skin, in the left breast, the other entering the body about one or one and a half inches to the left of the seventh cervical vertebrae, passed entirely through the body, coming out just above the clavicle or collar bone, of her the said Forest Floyd, both being mortal wounds, described as aforesaid, of which said mortal wounds, she, the said Forest Floyd, then and there died, and so the jurors aforesaid, upon their oaths and affirmations aforesaid, do say that the said Donato DiIulio him, the said Forest Floyd, in the manner and by the means aforesaid unlawfully, purposely and of deliberate and premeditated malice, did kill and murder ... contrary to the form of the statute in such case made and provided, and against the peace and dignity of the State of Ohio.

The legal effect of the indictment, or True Bill, was that the defendant, Donato DiIulio, had now been formally charged, by the State of Ohio, with murder in the first degree. If convicted he would be put to death — unless, and only unless — the jury were to make a specific recommendation for mercy. In that case he would be imprisoned for the rest of his life. There were no other alternatives.

Simultaneous with the filing of the indictment, properly signed by A. B. Campbell as Prosecuting Attorney, the Clerk of Courts issued a *capias* to the sheriff commanding him to immediately take and safely keep the Defendant Donato DiIulio and to have his body before the Court on Monday, October 14th, to answer to the crime charged. Once again, the official directive was easily accomplished. The defendant was still in jail, the strongly recuperating and moderately unwilling guest of Sheriff Gibson.

The tedious process of framing the issues for trial was essentially completed with the event of the defendant's formal arraignment on October 14th. True to his own very specific charge Sheriff Gibson duly presented the body of Donato DiIulio before the Court. That done, he addressed the bench and respectfully requested leave to approach.

"By all means," answered Judge Walter D. Jones. He looked to the prosecutor's counsel table. "Mr. Campbell. You'd better come along, too."

The three men huddled together across the bench and around the small desk where Renna Spitler, the official court stenographer, sat in readiness. She would record their whispered colloquy in her unique brand of shorthand in the same manner as she did everything else that transpired while court was in session.

Ralph Gibson was a strong, hearty man just shy of his thirty-third birthday and characterized by an innate friendliness. Although still in his first term as county sheriff, and very much in awe of the distinguished Judge Jones, he was not at all timid about expressing himself directly when the situation required.

"Your Honor," he observed, including Prosecutor Campbell into the conversation, "I think you gotta problem with this here defendant. He's Eye-talian, you know. He can't speak but a word or two of English and he can't understand any more'n he can speak.

"You're gonna ask him how he pleads to this indictment and he ain't gonna have any idea what it is you're askin' him."

Judge Jones nodded his acknowledgment, looked to Alva Campbell, and raised an eyebrow. "Mr. Prosecutor?"

"That's my understanding too, Your Honor," said Alva Campbell. "Do we know anyone who can make him understand?" He had addressed the question to Judge Jones, but looked to the Sheriff for an answer.

"Maybe," said Sheriff Gibson slowly. "He and Deputy Landry have got kinda friendly these past few months. I don't know how it works. DiIulio doesn't know much English and George can't speak Italian, but somehow or other they seem to understand one another pretty well. Seems like it's worth a try."

And that's what they did. Judge Jones explained the indictment in general terms to Donato DiIulio and to Deputy Landry, and then Landry and DiIulio chattered between themselves in a highly personalized, bastard form of Italo-American gibberish, punctuated by seemingly incomprehensible gesticulations. Ultimately, and laboriously, they got through the matter and the event was memorialized by the journalization of an entry, reciting that:

This day came A. B. Campbell, Prosecuting Attorney, on behalf of the State of Ohio, and the defendant, being present in his own proper person and in custody of the Sheriff, waived the reading of the indictment and for plea to said indictment says that he is not guilty as charged therein.

Said defendant thereupon requests the Court to assign counsel for him, and the Court, upon being satisfied that the defendant is in indigent circumstances and unable to employ counsel appoints W. A. Haines, Esq. to defend said defendant.

The order was predicated upon Judge Jones' adamant refusal to accept the defendant's open acknowledgment that he had done the deed and upon the court's insistence that an attorney be appointed to protect the defendant's rights.

CHAPTER SEVEN

THE FORMAL ARRAIGNMENT OF DONATO DIIULIO on the charge of first degree murder had taken place in the high-ceiled, capacious common pleas courtroom located on the third floor of the new Miami County courthouse. Although it had been completed and placed in service some twenty years earlier, in 1887, the building was still generally referred to as the "new" courthouse. It was, quite properly, the source of considerable civic pride and had been widely pronounced to be one of the most impressive such structures in the nation.

Situated at the precise center of a full city block, completely enisled by a low stone wall and surrounded by a broad, gently terraced lawn, the building was, and still is, an imposing and megalithic edifice of quarried stone symmetrically described by tall Tuscan columns, wide staircases, and porticoed entrances and ultimately surmounted by a cast iron capitoline dome and a full pantheon of bronze-like statuary. The architecture, an inventive admixture of the classic Roman and Greek orders, was effectively conceived to invest the new courthouse with an aura of grandeur and majesty suitable for the dispensation of justice at the county level.

The interior aspects of the building were no less ornate than those of its facade. The floors, walls and cornices were richly caparisoned with mosaics, friezes and bas relief. Above the third floor atrium a vaulted ceiling of stained glass was supported by four pillars from which emerge, in high relief, eight sculptured masques, each representative of an historic ethnic.

The courtroom itself had been appointed in a manner aptly calculated to achieve a stately and dignified ambience. The walls and doorways were of burnished black walnut, as were the two counsel tables, the jury box and the massive elevated bench at the front of the room. Two rolltop desks of differing sizes were stationed along the left side of the room for use by the clerk and the bailiff. The two-tiered jury box was against the opposite wall, beneath the calendar clock, and was suitably equipped at either end with gleaming brass gaboons for the convenience of the lawyers during trial. Lighting was provided by elaborate, perhaps even gaudy, brass chandeliers suspended from the twenty-foot high ceiling. This august and sedately panelled sanctum, then, would be the venue for the trial of Donato DiIulio when the matter came on before the court next spring.

The private chambers of Judge Walter D. Jones were located across the hall from the courtroom and consisted of two large rooms, an anteroom shared by the court bailiff and the judge's secretary-receptionist, and an inner office occupied by the judge himself. This room was furnished with matching rolltops at opposite corners, a library-type table, the judge's desk, swivel chair and three matching armchairs, all of polished white oak and strong construction.

In the late afternoon of the day of Donato DiIulio's arraignment Judge Jones chatted amiably with his single visitor. They had already covered the weather, the progress of the high school football season and the local political situation. After a momentary lull in their conversation, Judge Jones seemed to shift gears. He put on his reading glasses and opened a manila file folder which lay at the center of his desk. "I had suggested to Brooks Johnson that he send word that I would like to see you," he began. "I assume that he did so."

And when he received a nod in acknowledgment, he asked a question, "Did he say why?"

"No, your Honor, he didn't. I probably didn't give him a chance. I'd stopped by the clerk's office to file some papers. When I saw Brooks I asked about his little girl, that'd be Persis. Then, of course, he asked about my two little ones, Mildred and Helen, and pretty soon we were both jabbering away like a couple of magpies. I doubt if either of us heard much of what the other one said. Just as I walked out the door, he told me you wanted to speak with me."

At age thirty-eight, William A. Haines was already one of the leading criminal defense lawyers in the county. Although he had had no formal legal education, he had read law with several of the more prominent local lawyers and had been admitted to practice some twelve years earlier. He had been around long enough, and was savvy enough, to recognize that a summons to the Judge's chambers, passed along by Brooks Johnson, could not be lightly ignored. The Clerk of Courts was the most respected and influential elected official in the county. If Judge Jones had seen fit to use the Clerk's chief deputy as the messenger, the matter was likely to be one of considerable importance.

"We had that Italian fellow, DiIulio, in for arraignment this morning," Judge Jones began. "You'll remember he's the immigrant laborer who's accused of shooting his girlfriend last spring — May, I think it was. Happened over in Covington."

"Yessir," said Haines. "I remember reading about it. Seems like feelings ran pretty high there for awhile. There was even talk about organizing a lynch party."

"There was," acknowledged Judge Jones. "But the plan to do so never materialized. Everyone believed he was going to die anyway so there'd be no point."

"And of course," Haines finished the thought, "he didn't die."

"That's right," answered Judge Jones dryly. "No thanks due to modern medical science, he didn't die. In fact, when I saw him in court this morning, he looked stronger and healthier than you or I."

W. A. Haines looked askance. "You said 'No thanks due...' Was he not treated appropriately?"

"Appropriately?" growled Judge Jones with a petulance that surprised Haines. "Hell, he wasn't treated at all. At least, not in the beginning. The only thing they really did was to wrap his head with gauze so they wouldn't have to look at his gunshot wounds, then change the wrappings from time to time when the flies got bad. The man just simply got better all by himself."

"You mean he seems to have healed over in spite of the benign administration of twentieth century medical inattention?" asked Haines wryly.

"Precisely," confirmed Judge Jones. "And," he continued, "were that not sufficient to do him in, Constable Hake held him out for public inspection — like a three-headed dog — until Sheriff Gibson rescued him and brought him over here.

"The point is that whatever this poor devil has done, or not done, he was not accorded, at least initially, that fair and impartial treatment to which an accused is entitled under our system of laws."

"Yessir," Haines agreed equably. "That seems clear enough." He could see where the conversation was headed. And, having no objection, he was content to allow it to develop at the judge's pace.

Judge Jones affected a rueful grimace. "Alright, then," he conceded, "what's done is done and we can't change it. We can't rectify earlier deficiencies.

"What we *can* do," he added, "what we *must* do — is try to make the system work better in the future."

Judge Jones sipped from a water glass, set his jaw and cleared his throat as if to lend emphasis to what he was about to say. "I am determined that this man, DiIulio, receive that treatment prescribed by the law, fair and impartial, from this day forward. That's why I sent for you.

"You have made quite a name for yourself as defense counsel and I consider that reputation to be well-deserved. I have been impressed with your courtroom work and with your persistent dedication to the best interests of your clients."

Although Haines assayed a self-deprecating gesture, Judge Jones waved off the anticipated interruption. "Let me finish," he growled. "It's because of your reputation and because of those demonstrated talents — that I want you to defend this man, DiIulio. Your appearance on his behalf will signify this court's intention that he be accorded every safeguard and that his rights be properly protected.

"I have already signed an order appointing you as his counsel. I am hopeful that you will accept the assignment."

Bill Haines appeared to consider. A small, wiry man, no more than six inches above five feet in height and weighing something less than ten stone, he seemed an unlikely colossus. And though his personal destiny would ultimately enable him to bestride his profession like the Apollo at Rhodes, it would be many years before he finally achieved that pinnacle.

At the instant bank and shoal of time, he eased his slight frame from the white oak armchair and walked lightly to the window overlooking the massive stone jailhouse on the other side of Plum street. From that vantage point he seemed to survey the activity and scenery below, all the while lost in thoughts of his own. His expression was entirely inscrutable. His finely chiselled facial features, high, prominent cheekbones and burnt umber complexion suggested a predominantely Anglo-Saxon ancestry greatly enriched by the merest splash of the local Shawnee.

A full ten minutes elapsed before Bill Haines turned his attention back to the judge. "Has a trial date been established?"

"Not yet," came the response. "I thought it best to consult with counsel."

"I would need some time to prepare," Haines mused thoughtfully.

"Granted," said the judge. "You can have whatever time you need. It will be a difficult case."

Haines nodded as though satisfied on that score. Then, as if working his way through a checklist, he moved to another item. "I have the impression, from the newspaper accounts, that this fellow speaks no English?" It was a question. "And, of course, I cannot speak Italian."

"Granted," replied the judge. "We will need an interpreter."

"We may need *two* interpreters," asserted Haines. "One for me, and one for the Court."

Judge Jones raised an eyebrow. It was an inquiry.

"I would anticipate," Haines continued, "that *my* interpreter would attend and participate in all my interviews with the defendant in order to enable us to understand one another. The interpreter would thereby become privy to all attorney-client communications. Clearly all such exchanges are protected. We cannot permit a scenario in which the prosecutor might then compel the interpreter to testify, in his own persona, as to matters he has learned in the process of translating conversations between myself and the defendant."

"You're quite right," agreed Judge Jones. "I confess I had not yet thought the thing through to its conclusion."

A pause ensued, during which each man appeared to weigh the matter. Judge Jones tapped the butt end of his pencil lightly on his desk blotter for a moment, then continued thoughtfully. "Tell you what let's do. You make some inquiries. Find an interpreter in whom you have confidence and retain his services on behalf of the defendant. I will order that his fees and costs be paid from county funds, but it will be specifically articulated in the order that he be *your* interpreter, a part of your defense team, and that he may not be questioned — by either side — except as to his translations.

"We can reserve, for the time being, the issue as to whether he may be used to interpret the defendant's testimony at trial. We can leave that question to your judgment. It might even happen that you will not wish the defendant to testify at all — in which case, of course, there would be nothing to be translated to the jury."

He looked to the defense attorney for acceptance of his proposal. Haines' sharp bright eyes were deep-set under beetled black brows and a full head of straight, coal-black hair, cropped short and combed forward. They were locked onto a random spot on the wall behind the judge's swivel chair and just above his shoulder.

"Will that work?" asked Judge Jones.

"It'll do," replied Haines thoughtfully.

The judge continued, "You haven't told me that you would accept the assignment. I assume, however, from our discussions, that you will do so."

He waited for a nod from Haines, then, "It will not be an easy task. Not only is the offense charged a capital crime, but the manner of its commission appears to have been both heinous and cowardly — two shots into the back of a defenseless young woman. Mr. Campbell has already announced his intention to seek the death penalty. And, as you remarked earlier, public sentiment runs high against the defendant, an untutored, apparently unregenerate, Italian immigrant. We both know of the strong and prevalent resentment of all our immigrant laborers, especially those Italian. I'm sure you've seen some of Walt Thomas' editorial comments in the Union concerning these 'undesirable aliens', he calls them. I've been at considerable pains to induce Walter to defer any further editorial remarks until this DiIulio matter has been resolved."

"How're you betting on that one?" asked Haines.

"I'm not," answered Judge Jones. "But I am hoping."

"In any event, you must know that your representation of this defendant is likely to bring you more censure and criticism than credit. It will not be a popular cause."

Bill Haines affected a painful move. "None of my causes, or for that matter my defendants, are popular. I'm used to it. My job is not to win public approbation — my job is to win. I may not always get it done, but it's not for want of trying.

"Certainly I accept the defense of this DiIulio. It really doesn't matter to me whether he's Italian, Mongolian, or some kind of striped-ass ape. He's entitled to a defense, the best defense the law will permit, and I'm more than ready to do my part."

He smiled wryly. "I know that sounded a little pompous, but I'll certainly do what I can. From all I hear, and from what you've told me, I guess it might prove to be a bit of challenge."

Judge Jones returned the smile and offered his hand. "Indeed," he said, "It may turn out to be a very difficult challenge."

CHAPTER EIGHT

"You don't mean to say you're actually going to defend him, do you? That awful person?" Blanche Bausman Haines affected a look of extreme distaste, as though she had just swallowed an ample dose of castor oil. An alert, attractive woman, she was nearly thirteen years younger than her husband. She had been barely eighteen when she had married W. A. Haines in the spring of 1900. In the early years of their marriage, because he considered her to be quite young and perhaps a little silly, and because she had been born on the twenty-fifth of December, Haines was wont to refer to her fondly as his Christmas goose. Now, at twenty-five, she had matured comfortably into her role as wife, mother and member of the local social hierarchy.

Having posed the question, more rhetorical than interrogatory in nature, Blanche allowed no time for an answer before rushing ahead with an astonishing volubility, "One of the members of my literary club, a woman who lives in Covington, has actually seen him. It was last spring, right after he'd killed that poor girl. Her husband took her to the jailhouse and made her look in on him. Practically the whole town did so. Anyway, she says he seemed very like one of Mr. Swift's 'yahoos', more animal than human. He was very dirty and disheveled; and horribly bloody, with rags wrapped round his head. And he just lay there, groaning and snorting like a wounded boar, wild and untamed.

"They say he's one of those immigrant laborers, Italian, that's what he is, an uncivilized, uneducated brute. A wop, they call them. He can't speak a word of English. He just grunts and gestures, like some kind of African Hottentot." She paused to catch her breath, and to consider her simile. Satisfied, she forged ahead. "He actually looks like one, too.

"And he killed this lovely young girl, just shot her with a revolver," Blanche ran on, "in the back — twice — and in broad daylight.

"Surely you don't intend to become his lawyer," she argued peevishly.

Haines waited to see if his wife had quite finished. "Judge Jones made a point of asking me to do so," he said soberly. "And I've agreed. It's my job, Blanche. It's what I do."

"It will be such an embarrassment," she pouted. "For both of us."

Bill Haines wrapped his arm around his young wife, squeezed her shoulder and smiled. "Now you are being a goose, aren't you, Love? We both know where lies my duty — to the court, to my profession, and most especially, to the defendant." This time he paused before completing the thought. "The poor immigrant bastard."

She made a reluctant grimace of resignation. She had known how it would end. "I know," she conceded, "but I don't have to like it. Most people won't even understand it. They'll think you're taking his case out of sheer perversity."

AFTER HE HAD LEFT JUDGE JONES THAT AFTERNOON, and before he had gone home for supper, Bill Haines had dropped by *The Miami Union* office for a visit with its editor and publisher. Walter S. Thomas, who was also a practicing attorney, snorted disdainfully when he learned of Haines' intention to defend the Italian. He did agree, however, at Haines' insistence and because he was a fair man, to withhold further editorial comment on "the immigrant problem" and on the DiIulio case until after the trial. Then, grudgingly, he helped the lawyer root through the Union's old newspaper files and clippings and to retrieve copies of the several accounts of the shooting death of Forest May Floyd.

Later in the day, supper over with, the girls put to bed and Blanche occupied with her needlepoint, Haines repaired to the small room, just off the living room, which he used as a study. He spent the evening poring over the Union accounts, chronologically arranged and spread across the surface of his desk like a thin covering of opaque snow, all the while making copious notes on the lined pages of a fresh legal pad which he had posited on the desk-leaf to his right.

Long after Blanche had retired, read a bit, and gone to sleep, Haines folded his newspapers, filed away his notes and crept into bed beside her. He was satisfied that he had learned, processed and catalogued all the information that had been reported. However garbled or inaccurate the reportage may have been, it provided a point of departure. It was as good a starting point as any.

Bill Haines had been born on a farm in Staunton Township just outside of Troy and was raised, there and elsewhere, pretty much as a farm boy. He had acquired early on, and would continue for a lifetime, the habit of rising early in the morning. Tuesday, October 15th, was no exception. Up at 5:30, he had scrubbed, shaved, eaten a light breakfast of fresh fruit, and was on his way before daylight. The first order of business was to unlock the small utility shed behind the house and to wheel out his new safety bicycle. It was a Colonel Pope special with coaster brake and pneumatic tires, the latest and best model money could buy, and it was a real beauty. Lovingly he wiped away the accumulated dust with a soft cloth, oiled the chain, and adjusted the seat before setting out on the seven mile journey to Covington. He wanted to visit the scene of the crime, orient himself to the locale, talk with some of the people and get a feel for the local climate. The exercise, he knew, would better enable him to place in context the information he had gleaned from the *Miami Union* accounts.

Pedaling along at a leisurely pace, he made the trip in less than forty minutes. The early morning traffic was light and the turnpike was a good one. Haines had long been an enthusiastic cyclist and he was in top physical condition. However lean and diminutive he appeared, he was also trim, sinewy and keenly honed by regular application. The fact that he held the all-time record for the annual nine-mile road race from Troy to nearby Pleasant Hill was the source of considerable pride for him. He had accomplished that feat in twenty-seven minutes some eleven years earlier, at age 27, and no one had bettered his mark since.

As a part of his self-imposed orientation course, Haines first cruised all of the village streets, alleys and byways, then repeated the process until he had achieved a comfortable conversancy with the entire community. He next retraced the routes of all the principals as described in the newspaper accounts. He made a point of locating, identifying and interviewing each of the witnesses mentioned in the accounts, and then, finally, he simply visited each business establishment and spoke with anyone and everyone who was willing to talk about the Italian, the Floyd girl and the tragedy they had combined to produce. Many of his overtures were rebuffed and he met with more than a little scorn and derision from the mostly partisan townspeople, but he also gained some insight, won a few concessions and established a modicum of local rapport. In the end, he was satisfied. He knew, from the outset, that the process would have to be repeated, probably more than once, before he would be ready for trial. He had not yet communicated with his client, this man DiIulio. After he had come to appreciate the defendant's version of the episode, together with all its attendant circumstances and subtle nuances, he would undoubtedly need to revisit the vicinity and its people in order to test the several histories of the event he had heard, and those he expected to hear, against the reality.

BILL HAINES MADE A SLIGHT DETOUR TOWARDS THE END OF HIS RETURN trip to Troy. Perhaps a mile or so west of town he swung right onto the Washington Pike. Then ten minutes later he took a left onto the Newton Pike and continued onto McKaig Road after it branched off to the left and toward the town. None of these back roads were paved and their surfaces were not as smooth and easy as the Covington Pike, but the route took him directly past his mother's home at the near edge of town. And while the pedaling was more difficult, it was now late afternoon on a cool day in October and he was glad for the greater exertion.

Elizabeth Haines had been a widow for more years than she had been married. She had broken up housekeeping and moved off the farm after her husband, Theodore, had died back in the seventies. Because she had been a frail young woman and was unequal to the task of raising her eleven-year-old daughter and five-year-old son, it was arranged that her own mother, Anna Brown Hedges, would take the children into her home at the old Shawnee settlement in Gallatin County, Illinois. The town itself, appropriately named Shawneetown, had been founded by the charismatic warrior chieftain, Tecumseh, on the west bank of the Ohio River, just below its confluence with the Wabash. For each of the next four years, the young William Haines attended school for three months and helped on the Hedges farm the remaining nine months. Then, at age nine, he was bound out to a neighboring farmer, a man named Felix Bryant. The promise was that if he would stay on with Mr. Bryant until he was twenty-one he would be released from bondage and given a good plow horse and a bridle. To his way of thinking, the game had seemed scarcely worth the candle, and, at age sixteen, the boy ran away. Clearly bright and energetic, he was able to educate himself well enough to land a teaching position at a one-room log schoolhouse in nearby Equality, Illinois. It wasn't really much of a job. The Equality school district was both primitive and impoverished. The schoolhouse windows were not of glass, but of pig bladders, and the pay for the barely educated young teacher was abysmally low in amount.

But while he taught, he also studied, and after a succession of such meager teaching jobs and a few years of study at Southern Normal University, he ultimately achieved both a proper teaching certificate and a full-fledged college education.

During the period of his indenture to Mr. Bryant, and thereafter as a runaway, Haines had been something of an exile, from his family as well as from his bond for servitude. Nonetheless he had remained in touch with Grandma Hedges. By 1890, her husband had died and she had moved back to Troy to be near her daughter. Later that same year, at age twenty-one, the young Bill Haines came to Troy to visit his mother and grandmother. And there he remained. He supported himself by teaching and he read the law with Walter Thomas and with several of the other established attorneys of the town. Then, more than twelve years before, in 1895, he had been properly certified and admitted to practice law in the State of Ohio.

By 1907, his grandmother was no longer alive. His mother, Elizabeth Haines, was living by herself in the small frame residence on McKaig Road. She seemed less frail in her sixties than she had in her thirties. It was as though the years had toughened her, strengthened her mettle as if by crucible. Diminutive in physical stature, her physiognomy left no doubt as to the mold from which her son's sharply chiselled features had been cast. Snapping eyes, sunk deep behind high prominent cheekbones, bespoke a keen intelligence only slightly daunted by a lifetime of quintessential adversity. Her obvious composure attested to the fact that she had made her compromises and had achieved an inner serenity. Long straight hair, still dark in her seventh decade, and a dark, rich complexion combined to confirm the common ancestry she shared with her mother and then, in turn, passed on to her son.

Bill Haines made a point of visiting his mother on a semi-regular, sometime basis. It offered the chance to assure himself of her well-being and to keep her abreast of his own activities. She reciprocated his attentions by her own willingness to set out for him the occasional impromptu snack, usually something from her garden, and by her wholly unfeigned and abiding interest in his career in general and, in the particular, in some of his more challenging cases.

He was unwilling, so late in the day, to accept the full supper she had offered to prepare. Blanche would be not at all pleased if he were to spoil his supper with her. Reminding himself, however, that he had had nothing since breakfast, he felt no compunction at consuming the four ripe apples from the bowl set in the center of his mother's table. While he munched his way through her small store of apples he told her what little he knew of the DiIulio matter. Not surprisingly, she already knew nearly as much as he did. She was an avid reader of the local newspapers and was quite conversant with all that which had been reported. And while she recognized the existence of a strong bias against the defendant, not only because of the nature of the crime with which he was charged, but also because of his Italian extraction and his status as an illiterate and uncommunicative immigrant, she herself felt no prejudice whatever. That fact may or may not have been the product of her own heritage.

"I know that you will devote your entire attention and the benefit of all your skills to the interests of your client. Whatever kind of monster he may be, or seem to be, and whatever kind of atrocity he may have done, I'm sure there is something decent that can be said for him," she admonished. "After all," she chided playfully, "he is some mother's son."

"Which translates," Haines interrupted, "to mean that he is a genuine human being and is therefore entitled to be heard and to be fairly and vigorously defended?"

"More than that," she rejoined. "He is entitled to be treated as a *helpless* and *forsaken* human being. They say he doesn't speak or understand English and that he is essentially ignorant of our ways. That makes him helpless. What's more is the fact that he is thousands of miles removed from his family and has been entirely abandoned by those whom he had considered to be his friends. He is most certainly forsaken," she concluded pedantically.

"But you would not be expected to realize these things," she allowed a sly smile. "You're not a mother, are you?"

CHAPTER NINE

THE FOLLOWING MORNING, A FEW MINUTES PAST EIGHT, Nellie Gibson stood at the massive sink along the far wall of the kitchen wing of the jailhouse complex. Her arms were immersed to the elbows in grey soapy water as she alternately washed and scoured the serving tins, cups, utensils, pots and pans that made up the only remaining traces of the institutional breakfast just completed by the twenty-odd inmates of the Miami County jail. A slight young girl, still in her teens, stood by her side and dried each item as it was rinsed and handed over to her. Standing in the open doorway to the reception area, and filling it completely, was Nellie's husband who was nearing the end of the second year of his first four-year term as county sheriff. Ralph Gibson was a big man, tall, wide and impressively constructed. He possessed an innate strength, both physical and intellectual, which had been indurated by years of work in the railroad yards before entering the county political scene. Less than six weeks shy of his thirty-third birthday, he had a full head of dark hair, a broad, open face and a friendly, gregarious manner.

"Mornin', Mr. Haines," he bellowed effusively when the lawyer entered the anteroom. "You're too late for breakfast, but we've got plenty of coffee. And muffins, too. How 'bout a blueberry muffin? They're fresh this morning. Nellie made about twice what the prisoners could eat and she's got a whole tin of 'em left over."

"No, thank you, Sheriff," answered Haines. "I finished breakfast more than an hour ago and I couldn't eat another thing. The coffee sounds good, though. I'd be glad for a cup of that."

He allowed himself to be led into the kitchen and seated at the rectangular table where the sheriff, his wife and staff took their meals. Gibson waved off his wife's offer to do the honors and poured two mugs of steaming coffee from the large pot on the stove. He placed one of the mugs in front of the lawyer and sat himself down, across the corner of the table, with the other.

"Looks like another fine day," he offered. "We'd best enjoy them while we can. Winter'll be comin' on soon enough."

"You're absolutely right," agreed Haines. "We're having a gorgeous fall season. Every day has been a treat."

The two men tested their coffee, still too hot to drink. Haines surveyed the room, smiled at Nellie and nodded to the girl. He looked back to the sheriff.

"Well sir," said the latter, "I know we've got a good reputation for coffee, and the price is right, but I'll be much surprised if that's the only thing that brought you over here this morning." A knowing twinkle appeared in his eye. "I heard Judge Jones asked you to defend this DiIulio fella." And when Haines raised his mug in confirmation, Gibson asked, "Are you gonna do it?"

"Yes," Haines answered. "I am."

"Good," pronounced the sheriff. "The poor bastard needs all the help he can get."

"And," Haines interrupted. "You bloody well knew I intended to accept his defense. Otherwise I wouldn't be over here scalding my tongue on your coffee."

"Yeah," conceded the sheriff. "I guess I did have that figured out. All the same, I'm real glad you're gonna try to help him.

"He doesn't really have much workin' for him. He can't speak English and he's got no family, no friends, leastwise, as far's we know. He's been here more'n five months and he hasn't had a single visitor. No one."

"Wait a minute, Sheriff," Haines interrupted again. "He's got to have a mother. I have it on the best possible authority that everyone has to have a mother."

"Well, yeah, maybe he does," said the sheriff. "But we ain't seen her around here. I s'pose his parents, if he's got any, are over in the old country. Italy, I guess. He hasn't written to anybody, far's we know. And he's not got but one or two letters in all the time he's been here. They were from somewhere in Italy, no place I've ever heard of. It's none of my business, but I'm sure he's never answered them.

"So, if he does have a mother, or maybe even a father, I don't s'pose they'd have any idea the kinda fix he's in."

"I'll talk to him about it," said Haines. "His family, whoever they are, ought to know. They surely won't like it much, but they'll need to know."

"That ain't gonna be as easy's you think," continued the sheriff. "Remember, he don't speaka da English."

Haines nodded. "So I understand. Somehow or other, though, we'll have to get past that." He finished his coffee, set his mug down decisively and pushed back his chair. "Maybe if I go on up to the conference room you'd have someone bring him along?"

"Do better'n that," answered Sheriff Gibson. "Let's us go get him."

Gibson set down his own empty mug, stood and led Haines from the kitchen, through the reception area and into the lock-up. With a polished brass key the length of his own bearlike paw, he opened the thick, heavy outer door that gave into the impregnable, eight foot square, security cage that surrounded the entrance to the cellblock. Once both men were inside the cage, he closed and locked the outer door, then turned and approached the solid, steel door that provided the only access to the jail itself. A sliding panel, also of steel, covered a small barred opening in the door, just at eye level. Sheriff Gibson slid the panel to the right and surveyed the interior of the cellblock. A series of two-man cells were located along the perimeter and surrounded the open bullpen area in the center of the enclosure. All of the prisoners save one appeared to be confined within the cells. The single exception was the Italian, DiIulio, who was seated at the more remote of the two picnic-style, wooden tables in the center of the bullpen. Directly across the table was another man, this one wearing the sheriff's department uniform and insignia. Both men, elbows on the table and foreheads supported by open hands, stared intently at the red and black checkerboard on the tabletop midway between them.

Sheriff Gibson stepped aside to permit Haines a view through the barred window. "That's your man," he said. "He can't speak English and George can't speak Italian, but somehow or other they manage to communicate. I can't imagine how he did it, but George found a way to teach him draughts. Now they have a game or two a couple times a day. George says he caught on real quick and plays pretty good, so he must not be too stupid.

"Anyway, they seem to get along pretty well. George kinda took a shine to him and DiIulio seems to like him well enough. One thing, he seems to trust him, and that makes my job easier."

Gibson inserted a second brass key into the lock of the inner metal door, swung it open and invited Haines to enter the cellblock. "You go on in. Everybody's accounted for and I'll watch from here. Ask George to introduce you to your client, then bring him out, and we'll put you in the conference room."

Bill Haines felt no apprehension whatever as he entered the bullpen area and made his way toward the two men seated at the far table. He had been here before. In fact, he had a passing acquaintance with some of the inmates and they exchanged greetings as he passed down the center of the open room.

"Hi, Mr. Haines," cried one. "You gonna do the Eyetalian?"

And another called out facetiously, "Gee, Mr. Haines, I didn't expect to see you here. What'd they get you for?"

Haines' only response was to smile and bob his head amiably in recognition and acknowledgment. Then he came upon a short pudgy man with a twinkling eye and a scraggly unkempt beard. He knew this fellow rather better than the others because he had twice defended him for chicken-thievery. Once, in fact, he had even secured an acquittal by showing that the chickens in question, while admittedly stolen, had been stolen from someone other than the complaining witness. Whether or not he had been fairly entitled to the verdict, he had enjoyed more than a few bantering exchanges with his client.

When he saw the man in jail again, Haines could not resist a remark. "Well, well," he said. "If it isn't old Roscoe Hensnatch! What latest fowl deed brings you back into this fowl habitation?"

And when Roscoe, whose name was certainly not "Hensnatch", made a disapproving grimace, Haines pressed on shamelessly. Appearing to consider the possibilities, he simply mused, "Some sort of fowl play, I'd imagine."

Roscoe seemed desperate to change the subject, or at least to spike the punning. "Mr. Haines, you ain't gonna try to defend the Eyetalian, are ya?"

"Yes, I am," replied Haines. "Why do you ask me that? If I've defended you for stealing chickens, it must be obvious that I'm willing to do 'most anything and that I'll stick at virtually nothing."

"Yeah, I know that, Mr. Haines," came the rejoinder. "But even you can't win this one. Your guy's a goner."

Haines paused in front of Roscoe's cell to complete the dialogue. "Oh?" he asked, with raised eyebrow. "How's that?"

"Plain as the nose on your face," answered Roscoe. "Jury won't have a choice. They gotta convict him. He's gonna get the chair."

"Maybe you'd better explain it to me." Haines was becoming impatient. "I'm a little thick this morning."

Roscoe was eager to oblige. Smug and pedantic, he spelled it out. "Well, y' see, they was only two whores in the whole town of Covington." He drew himself to his full height and folded his arms in judgment. "And he killed one of 'em."

"So?" asked the lawyer.

"Why, think about it, Mr. Haines. Just think on it a minute. They ain't twelve men in the county would let a man wipe out half the whores in Covington and then live to tell about it. It's hard on the whole town. Takes most of the fun outa life for the young fellas and puts a terrible strain on all the honest women.

"It's just intolerable, Mr. Haines. Intolerable. They gotta cook him for it. There ain't no other way."

Bill Haines shook his head in mock consternation. "For one incredible moment, Roscoe, I believed you might have had a serious, rational thought. It seems I was mistaken."

LESS THAN THIRTY MINUTES LATER they were together in the conference room located on the second floor of the jail complex. It was just the two of them, the lawyer and the defendant, and they were strangers to one another. In the eyes of each man the other was a quantum whose value was wholly untested.

They had been formally introduced, of course, but that could account for only so much. When Haines had finally reached the far end of the bullpen, he had paused behind Deputy George Landry and pretended to watch the game. He had also intended to use the opportunity to study the Italian. That chance was cut short, however, because as soon as he had sensed the lawyer's presence, Landry moved his pieces rapidly and ended the game with a quick series of captures. Then he jumped to his feet, greeted Haines deferentially and attempted to introduce the lawyer to the prisoner by use of a highly stylized system of signs and syllables that was wholly unintelligible to Haines and appeared to be only minimally comprehensible to the prisoner. He patted the lawyer gently on the shoulder, smiled reassuringly to DiIulio and placed the latter's hand into that of the lawyer. He had tried to convey the sense that this man was a friend who could be trusted.

Sheriff Gibson had acted as gatekeeper when Deputy Landry conducted the two men out of the cellblock, up the stairs and into the private conference room. In the course of that short journey, Haines had asked Landry what he knew about DiIulio's family.

"Oh, he's got a family, alright," Landry had assured. "He's got a mother, a father, and maybe even a sister. But he won't talk about them. He's not gotten but two letters since he's been here. Both came from Italy. He read them, cried for a while, then tore them into little pieces and flushed them. He doesn't want his people to know he's in any kind of trouble. Says he'd rather they thought he was dead. So he won't write and he refuses to let anyone else send word to them."

Bill Haines and Donato DiIulio surveyed one another across the small table in the windowless, locked and closely guarded room that was reserved for conferences between the prisoners and their lawyers. The interview, thus far, had not gone very well. Communication of any sort seemed virtually impossible and Haines found the attempt to be both futile and stultifying.

Thumping the center of his own chest with his fingertips, he tried again. "I — me, mio — Haines," he stammered, "lawyer, attorney."

DiIulio attended studiously, but was unable to comprehend. He had never heard the word *lawyer* in any language. He knew that *attorno* referred to something that was close at hand, nearby. So he grinned, perhaps foolishly, to signify that he was very well aware that the other man, Haines, was indeed in close proximity.

"*Si,*" he nodded. "*Capisco,*" he assured although he had not understood at all.

Building upon that which he mistakenly believed to be a conversational entree, Haines repeated his chest-thumping gesture and forged ahead. "I — mio, Haines — "

And the Italian grinned broadly, bobbed his head and pointed to Haines. "*Si. Tu, Hanes,*" he acknowledged.

"have been asked by the court to act as your attorney"

Now the Italian was confused. He understood that a court, *una corte,* was *nearby.* He could see the courthouse from the barred window of his cell. It was just across the street. And he thought he knew the word "asked," what an *ascia* was, but what did an *axe* have to do with anything? He held up his hands, palms outward, to signal an interruption, then made a chopping gesture and raised both eyebrows in mute inquiry.

Bill Haines shook his head ruefully. This was not going to work. He felt sure they could eventually learn to communicate on some rudimentary level. Others had done so. The Italian had learned, here in America, to drive the railroad donkey engines, to bake bricks and to provide for his daily subsistence. He had even managed to make friends and to establish a romantic relationship with the Floyd girl.

However, it was painfully obvious that the two men would be wholly unable to engage in any kind of meaningful dialogue concerning the crime with which DiIulio had been charged, the subtleties of his relationship with the dead girl, his justifications and expectations, and finally but scarcely least, the exceedingly complex and esoteric legal concepts which would come into play in a prosecution for first degree murder. Thus it was that after a few more equally feckless conversational gambits, Haines raised a forefinger in the universal pantomime for "hold it right there, I have a better idea."

He pushed back his chair, rose to his feet and stabbed his chest a final time. "I'll be back," he said. "Later. I'll return another day."

This time, the Italian understood him. "*Ritorno,*" he repeated. "*Tu ritornereste?*"

"*Si,*" answered Haines, offering his hand. "I will '*ritorno*'. Soon."

THAT EVENING, OVER SUPPER, BILL HAINES CONFESSED to Blanche his utter frustration over his initial interview with his client. "In all my life," he admitted, "I've never felt so completely helpless, so totally ineffectual."

"Why are you surprised?" asked Blanche archly. "You knew his limitations. And your own as well. The two of you have no common language. How could you possibly expect to communicate?"

The concession came slowly, and reluctantly. "I know," he said grudgingly. He set down his suspended soupspoon and dropped his forearms to the table. "I know. I guess I'd hoped he might have had some little conversancy with English. He's been in this country, and functioned fairly well, for several years now.

"And," he continued, "perhaps we will eventually come to understand one another better. One thing, however, is very certain. The need for an interpreter, someone who can translate and clarify, is absolutely imperative." Then, after a moment's reflection, he added, "And immediate. This morning's fiasco has confirmed both the need and the urgency."

"Didn't you tell me that Judge Jones had already agreed to provide an interpreter?"

"Not quite, Blanche, not quite," answered Bill Haines. He had picked up his resting soupspoon and was sipping still-warm chicken soup from the blue willow bowl which rested, in its turn, on a spotless, white china service plate. "What he said was that an interpreter would be provided at county expense — but it's my job to locate and to retain him.

"I wonder," he mused aloud, "where such a person might be found. A teaching center? A university? Surely Ohio State has a Romance Language Department."

"I should certainly think so," Blanche answered. "And if they haven't anyone, they can probably suggest where else you might look."

The matter of finding and engaging a suitable person to act as an interpreter carried them through dinner and beyond. Then, over coffee, Bill Haines told his wife of having encountered his former client, Roscoe "Hensnatch" at the county jail. And, because he had been amused by their morning exchange, he repeated Roscoe's waggish remarks and his dire assessment of the Italian's predicament. Blanche snorted rudely. She was not at all amused.

"What a terrible thing to say," she railed. "It's certainly not funny and it's a callous, despicable slander of that poor, dead girl. It's also a wicked slander against her sister," she added, "whose name, I believe, is also Blanche. My friends from Covington all report that both sisters were lovely, and perfectly proper young women."

Haines set his jaw, averted his eyes and patiently waited out the storm. When he was satisfied that the torrent had subsided, he spelled it out for her, "Doesn't really matter, Blanche, whether it's true or false. The only hope this boy has, this DiIulio, is for me to convince a twelve-man jury that the Floyd girl was a rotten, scheming, conniving slut, that she was an evil, depraved predator, and that, just maybe, she might have deserved exactly what she got. If I can do that, if I can make them understand, however subliminally, that he did what he did out of anguish rather than malice, then I just might be able to save his life."

Blanche was still truculent. "And the girl's reputation?"

"Doesn't matter, Blanche. My job is to save his life." He folded his napkin, prepared to leave the table. "But if it's any comfort to you, I think Roscoe was right about it. The girl did not have a very savory reputation."

CHAPTER TEN

BILL HAINES DID NOT FIND HIS INTERPRETER at Ohio State University, nor at any of the other colleges or universities to which he applied. To be sure, they all had Romance language departments, but he found no one there who was willing or able to help him to confer meaningfully with his client and to participate in his defense. That which Haines did find, in the cloistered towers of academia, was sympathy for his predicament and, more helpfully, a number of valuable suggestions as to where he might look for assistance. That bit of guidance, not surprisingly, took him eventually to the Italian consulate in Cincinnati.

He had telephoned ahead, stated his business and made an appointment. Then, on a crisp morning, the first Monday in November, he had taken the train to Cincinnati and a cab to the consular offices on Vine Street. He was politely received by a slight young man, obviously Italian, who took his professional card and escorted him into the private chamber of Charles S. Ginocchio, Royal Italian Consular Agent for the Cincinnati area.

As if in studied contrast to his clerk, the man himself appeared to be within a few years of Haines' own age and seemed also to have been freshly molded from seasoned old-world clay. A sturdy, robust-looking man, he was at least two inches taller and twenty-five pounds heavier than Haines. His full head of wavy dark hair was complemented by an abundant continental-style mustache and alert blue eyes appraised his visitor from behind efficient wire-rimmed eyeglasses. The fluid grace with which he moved was only slightly impaired by an inconvenient artificial limb. He had lost his lower left leg in a childhood accident, but he managed to get about on a wooden prosthesis so well that his disability was almost unnoticeable. Now he approached his visitor from alongside an ancient ornate desk and took his hand warmly. He laughed easily when Haines stumbled over the pronunciation of his name.

"It's really easier than you'd think," he said lightly. "Most people want to pronounce it *Gin-oke-io*, like Pinocchio, Gepetto's wooden puppet. And except for the first letter, both names are spelled *and* pronounced — at least by Italians — precisely the same. It's *Gin-'notch-io*."

"And, of course," offered Haines, "It's also *Pin-'notch-io* and an entire generation of American children have perpetuated the error."

"True enough," acknowledged the consul, "but it doesn't matter a whit. It's a delightful story, however you pronounce it. I'm sure Mr. Collodi wouldn't mind that the name has been Americanized."

He invited his guest into an armchair and seated himself in another on the visitors' side of the desk. Strong, thick hands rested easily on the handle of the polished ebony walking stick set upright between his legs.

"You've had a fair morning's journey, the B & O, I presume. I trust it was not too difficult?" he asked.

"No, no, not at all," replied Haines. "It was actually quite pleasant. Good, clear weather, engaging scenery. I was glad for the opportunity."

"You've told me something of your circumstance," said the consul, alluding to their earlier telephone conversation. "If you'd be good enough to elaborate a bit on those basic facts, perhaps I can be of assistance."

Bill Haines accepted the invitation with more than a little alacrity. He spoke for nearly two hours and told of everything he had learned concerning the immigrant, Donato DiIulio, his relationship with the Floyd woman, the events of the homicide, the status of the pending criminal proceedings, and finally his own frustrating and unproductive interview with his client. "What I need," he said, "more than anything in the world, is someone who can translate from English to Italian, and vice versa, in order that I can communicate with my client and prepare for trial. And then, when the matter comes on for trial, probably next spring, I'll need that same someone, hopefully, to act as an interpreter so that the defendant, the judge, the lawyers and, most importantly, the jury, will be able to understand one another."

He paused and looked expectantly at Ginocchio. He had anticipated either a barrage of pointed interrogatories or, in the alternative, a pained display of official disinterest. The Italian consul, however, had listened well and comprehended all that Haines had expressed. He had no questions, only a rueful comment.

"It's a damnable shame," he lamented. "So many of these young people, many of whom are no more than children, come to this country to seek a better life. Innocents all, they come in droves. Bright-eyed and full of hope, yet totally unprepared for what they must surely encounter, they forsake the comfortable security of home and family, travel thousands of miles to this brave 'New World,' and come almost inexorably to grief, disappointment and disaster."

He shook his head sadly. "Italy, particularly in the south, is blighted and impoverished. We can scarcely fault these young people for wanting to escape their situation and to seize upon the promise of prosperity that America represents. But we need to help them. We need to educate them. We must somehow better prepare them for the enormous differences in custom, language and culture that lie in wait, almost in ambush, for them.

"Unhappily, however, the Italian government has not been able to provide this needed assistance. I don't know that it ever can. It's just such a terrible shame. These are good people. They're young, they're bright, they're ambitious. They are among Italy's finest sons and daughters." Ginocchio drew himself up short. He hadn't meant to sermonize. With a sigh, he concluded, "And so very many of them are being simply and tragically wasted."

In a gesture of apology, he placed his hand on the sleeve of Haines' jacket. "I'm sorry, sir, I've digressed from the subject. You were telling me of your need for an interpreter?"

"Yessir," Haines interjected. "I was. Do you know of such a person? Someone on your staff? An official translator of documents? Perhaps a correspondent?"

Ginocchio returned an ingenuous smile and emitted a deprecating chuckle. "I wish I could tell you, Mr. Haines, that this office were as abundantly staffed and as globally involved in business and governmental matters as most people imagine. Unhappily, we are neither. Our staff consists of the clerk who received you this morning, and myself. The nature and press of our business is such that my own position is that of an unpaid, part-time volunteer.

"The point, of course, is that we do not have official translators, interpreters or correspondents. Nor," he added ruefully, "do I know of any such people."

Bill Haines' disappointment was, at once, both manifest and profound. His search had brought him to this place and now it seemed to have ended here. "Do you have any suggestions?" he asked. "I'm fresh out of ideas."

A moment grew between them, during which Ginocchio appeared to consider. Finally, in a sympathetic tone, he answered. "Well sir, I've never been involved in anything like this, and I've never acted as an official interpreter, but if you think it might help, I'd certainly be willing to try."

"To translate? To interpret?" asked Haines with obvious incredulity. "To come to Troy? First, to consult and then to attend the trial? Is that something you could do?"

The Italian consul affected a wry grimace. "You've told me this man's life is at stake. I can try."

"It would entail a rather substantial commitment of time." warned Haines before Ginocchio waved him off.

"Time is not a problem for me," he explained. "I think I mentioned earlier that my duties here at the consulate are essentially part-time and are rendered on a voluntary basis. I do have a job just down the street a bit at the Union Savings Bank. They've been very liberal and have pretty much permitted me to set my own hours. I have no reason to doubt that both my employers will accommodate. I can certainly be available, in Troy or elsewhere, whenever you need me."

Throughout their brief acquaintanceship Bill Haines had assumed that Ginocchio, because of his situation as consul for the Italian government, had at least some conversancy with the language of his employer. Perhaps, he thought, it was the language of his antecedents. The man, though fully American in both speech and mannerism, seemed to be of Italian extraction. And, perhaps also, he had studied the language of his forbears in college.

"May I presume," he assayed, "That you are reasonably fluent in Italian? The idiom, the several dialects?"

Ginocchio chuckled amiably. "You need have no apprehensions on that score, Mr. Haines. My Italian is probably better than is my English. It's certainly better than that which is taught at our universities." He made an indulgent smile. "But then, most of our language professors are not really Italian, are they?"

"And you are?" asked Haines with interest.

"Actually," replied Ginocchio, "I have dual citizenship. I am American-born, right here in Cincinnati, of Italian parents. They, too, like your DiIulio, had emigrated to the promised land.

"Then, when I was three years old, we all returned to Italy. I was educated there. I took my elementary and preparatory training under the tutelage of the Catholic order of the Falesian Fathers. Ultimately, I graduated from the Falesian College at Alessio. That would have been in '91.

"In the meanwhile, my father had died, so after my graduation my mother and I came back to the States. We've been here in Cincinnati, or Newport, rather, ever since.

"And so," he concluded, "Italian has been the language of my childhood and my so-called 'formative years.' I grew up with it."

"Excellent," cried Haines. "You appear to be the very person I've been seeking." He rose, and the two men sealed their agreement with a handshake.

"I expect there will be considerable advantage to me in all this," added Ginocchio casually.

And Haines, mistaking his meaning, hastened to assure, "Your fees and expenses will be a matter to be determined by the Court."

"No, no," Ginocchio demurred. "I didn't mean a financial advantage. I meant that the experience will doubtless contribute to my own education. You see, sir, I also have a license to practice law."

"Truly?" asked an incredulous Haines. "In Ohio?"

"Yes, sir. I received a Bachelor of Laws from the Salmon P. Chase College of Law here in Cincinnati just last spring and then on June 10th," he looked at the calendar behind his desk, "not quite six months ago, I was admitted to practice."

Haines was amazed. "Well I'll be damned," was all he could say.

Ginocchio raised a finger. "Remember, sir, that I said only that I have a license. I have, as yet, no practical experience whatever. I will regard my involvement with your case as a rare, and most fortuitous, opportunity to learn something about trial practice in the real world."

MONDAY WAS LIVER-AND-ONIONS NIGHT in the Haines household and the lawyer brought a hearty appetite to the supper table. His lunch that day had consisted only of two ripe apples which he had purchased at the B & O depot in Cincinnati and devoured on the return trip to Troy. He was so excited over having chanced upon Charles Ginocchio that the three-hour trip had seemed no more than a brief excursion through the pleasant countryside.

"I can scarcely believe my incredible good fortune," he said to Blanche as soon as she had served his dinner and sat down at the opposite end of their polished walnut dinner table. "Mr. Ginocchio strikes me as a really fine young man, Italian-American, who speaks both Italian and English as though he were native to both lands — and, for what more it's worth, he also has a law degree and is admitted to practice in Ohio."

Blanche looked momentarily askance. "Surely you're not going to take him on as co-counsel. Are you?"

"No, no, my dear," he answered. "I'll handle the lawyering. I'll not want any help in that department. But the fact that this man Ginocchio has been schooled in the law is nonetheless a definite plus. His legal training will better enable him to understand the subtleties and the legal ramifications of the proceedings. His grasp of the fine points and the technical distinctions of the law will inevitably redound to my client's benefit."

He ran on in this vein for nearly an hour. Finally, as Blanche was gathering up the dishes and preparing his coffee, he put the cap on it. "Best of all," he pronounced, "the man actually seems to care about the plight of this poor bastard, DiIulio. He appears, at least at this point, to empathize with him and with his troubles. He says he feels a need, maybe even an obligation, to become involved."

Blanche Haines did not fully share her husband's enthusiasm about locating such a suitable interpreter. Nor, for that matter, was she particularly sympathetic to her husband's cause, which she perceived to be the provision of a murder defense for the untamed, untutored, nearly sub-human, Italian immigrant. He had, after all, cruelly and coldly slaughtered one of their own, a truly lovely and innocent American girl whose only crime had been that of befriending the upstart foreigner. To her credit, however, she knew better than to express her reservations. That way lay domestic warfare, a battle she could not win and did not wish to provoke.

She understood her husband's commitment to his client's cause, his zeal to defend even the unpopular defendant in an exceptionally high-profile case. She recognized, approved and even applauded his dedication and his strong sense of duty, but she did not share it. She simply kept her own counsel and avoided the controversy.

"So," she asked, "What happens next with your Mr. Ginocchio? Where do you go from here?"

"He'll be here Thursday, this Thursday, and the two of us will interview DiIulio together," answered Haines. "Can you believe it? He actually apologized because he couldn't be here sooner."

"Well, then," said Blanche, feigning an interest she did not feel. "Perhaps we should ask him to come by for dinner."

"Mm-hmm," agreed Haines. "Perhaps we should. Especially since he'll be here anyway. I've already arranged for him to stay with us overnite. We'll be talking with DiIulio Thursday and Friday. And on subsequent occasions as well. I have a great deal to learn about my case — and my client."

CHAPTER ELEVEN

THE BUSINESS OF AN OHIO COMMON PLEAS COURT is conducted over the course of three separate, four-month terms of court which begin respectively, on the first Monday of January, May and September in each year and continue until the succeeding term begins. There was once an expectation, unrealistic at best, that those cases initiated within a given term would be completed before the term ended. What happened most often was that those cases still on the docket at the end of term were simply "carried over" for disposition during the next term of court. However, adherence to tradition generally required that a special order be entered in each pending case to formalize the carryover procedure.

The indictment charging Donato DiIulio with murder in the first degree had been returned by the Grand Jury and filed with the court on October 9th, during the September term of court. Although no one really expected the matter to be disposed of within term, it was nonetheless necessary to address the matter of carryover before the year, and the September term, would expire.

Thus it was that in December 1907, defense counsel W. A. Haines and prosecuting attorney A. B. Campbell had been summoned into Judge Jones' chambers. The three men were well known to one another. Their professional activities had brought them into frequent contact over the years. By that same token, a mutual respect and an easy cordiality had developed among them. Alva Campbell was the youngest of the three. At age 31, he was already midway through his second term as county prosecutor. An extroverted, gregarious man with florid complexion and a stout, not yet pudgy, physique, he made friends readily and was enormously popular. He would seek the death penalty for Donato DiIulio, not from any sense of vindictiveness or moral outrage, but because it was his clear duty to do so. The law commanded it and he must therefore insist upon it. It was as simple as that.

They had already gotten through the pleasantries. Both of the lawyers had young daughters and they had spoken of their own preparations for the Christmas season and their children's conditioned and impatient excitement over the holiday.

Judge Jones tapped the closed manila file which lay on the center of his desk. "Alright, gentlemen," he began, "what about this DiIulio matter? Can we set it for trial?"

The two lawyers looked to one another, each inviting the other to make the first response. It was Campbell who spoke. "I can be ready most any time, your Honor. My case is easy.

"However," he continued, "I'm sure Bill has had his hands full just trying to communicate with his client. I have no wish to push him."

"I appreciate that, Alva," replied Judge Jones. "I have already promised Bill that he could have all the time he needed to prepare for trial. I assured him of that when he agreed to take the case. I also promised him an interpreter and I think you've agreed to that also."

"I have indeed, your Honor. This case could not possibly be tried without one," said Campbell.

Judge Jones looked to Haines. "Well, Bill, how's that fellow working out? Pinocchio, is it?"

"Ginocchio, your Honor," answered Haines. "With a G."

"Oh, good," injected Campbell facetiously. "I'd hate to have to watch an entire jury focus on the man's nose throughout a week of trial."

"They can watch it if they want," said Jones, "but I don't imagine it will grow very much. From what little I've heard about him, his reputation seems to be impeccable."

"I'm sure it is," replied Campbell. "I've met the man. Bill brought him by one day and introduced him. I've also made some inquiries of my own. Everyone speaks very highly of him."

Bill Haines shifted his attention from one to the other to ensure that it was his turn. "And," he said, "by way of response to your question, Judge, Mr. Ginocchio is indeed working out very well. He, and he alone, has enabled the defendant and me to understand each other fully. He has made a great many trips to Troy — three hours each way — just so that I might confer with my client. The best part of the mix is that he and the defendant seem to have developed a kind of friendship, a genuine rapport, and that, I believe, will eventually build into a willingness to trust. A willingness, that is, on the part of DiIulio to trust Ginocchio, and ultimately, and perhaps by extension, a willingness to trust me.

"When that happens, and I think it will very soon, I will be in a position to offer a meaningful defense to the charges lodged by the Grand Jury. I expect that I can be ready for trial by the end of February."

Judge Jones flipped through his calendar. "It looks as though the first Monday in March is the 2nd. Will that do?"

"Suits me," said Campbell.

"That's fine," answered Haines.

During the latter part of their conversation, Judge Jones had been scribbling on a plain sheet of paper. He handed the completed document across the desk and invited the lawyers to examine what he had written. "I've prepared an order. If it looks alright to you, I'll send it over to Brooks for filing."

The two lawyers reviewed two handwritten sentences:

On application of the defendant this case is continued until the next term of this Court. By agreement between counsel for defendant and the prosecuting attorney, this case is assigned for trial on Monday March 2nd, 1908.

"I think that says it," said Campbell.

"Done," acknowledged Haines, returning the order to the Judge.

Then, as the lawyers made ready to leave, Judge Jones raised an admonitory finger. "Just one more item," he cautioned.

"I have already filed an order appointing this man Ginocchio as official interpreter for the purpose of this trial. His fees and charges will be taxed as a part of the costs of the proceedings. I think you've already agreed to that." He paused long enough for each of the lawyers to confirm his prior consent.

"We are also aware that this same Mr. Ginocchio has been assisting Bill in his discussions with his client. I consider that participation by Mr. Ginocchio to be quite essential to Mr. DiIulio's defense and therefore entirely appropriate from a legal standpoint."

After both lawyers had nodded agreement, he continued. "I recognize, however, that an argument might be made that since Mr. Ginocchio's official position here is that of court-appointed interpreter his participation in discussions between the accused and his lawyer could vitiate confidentiality. Following that argument, it is conceivable that Mr. Ginocchio could himself be called as a witness and required to testify concerning matters which should properly be protected by the privilege."

A. B. Campbell took the point, but declined to assert the advantage. "I accept the potential, your Honor, but I would not think of pressing the issue. It wouldn't be fair."

"Precisely," pronounced Judge Jones. "I was quite confident that you would see it that way. I simply wanted to articulate the problem and to solicit an understanding — from both of you — that Mr. Ginocchio is to be considered, at all times during the trial, as an officer of the court and that he may not be called upon to disclose, or to confirm, any matter communicated between the defendant and his counsel."

"That's eminently fair, your Honor," said Haines.

"Agreed," Campbell confirmed.

Judge Jones rose from his swivel chair to escort the lawyers to the door. "Thank you, gentlemen. Your professionalism does you credit."

ON THURSDAY, JANUARY 23RD, 1908, A. B. CAMPBELL, in his capacity as prosecuting attorney, filed a formal praecipe with the Clerk of Courts directing him to draw a special venire of 36 names from the county jury wheel.

In response to that directive, and in accordance with time-honored procedures mandated by law, the clerk, whose name was J. H. Landis, produced a large, lottery-type wheel perhaps 40 inches in diameter and mounted in an upright position on a rigid wooden stanchion. The wheel was equipped, around its circumference, with small slots wherein had been placed individual slips of paper, each of which contained the name of a person who was both a resident and an elector of the county. The names in the slots had been selected by lot and certified to the clerk by the county jury commissioners from a special roster of resident electors which had been compiled and kept current by the jury commissioners.

Then, in the presence of a small coterie of assembled witnesses, Sheriff Ralph Gibson spun the wheel and the clerk drew a name from the slot indicated by a pointer. The process was repeated 36 times until a special panel, or venire, of that number of persons had been selected. A formal record of the proceeding was entered on the docket and a writ issued to the sheriff requiring him to serve each of the veniremen with a summons to appear for service as a prospective juror on March 2nd, 1908.

And, on February 21st, Sheriff Gibson was ordered to serve the first of some 99 subpoenas to compel the attendance of witnesses at trial. Sheriff's fees of ten cents for each witness served and eight cents for each of the 1033 miles traveled came to $9.90 and $82.64 respectively, and those amounts were ultimately charged as costs in the case.

OVER THE THREE AND A HALF MONTH PERIOD from mid-November of 1907 through the end of February 1908 Bill Haines had made regular and frequent appearances at the county jailhouse to visit with Donato DiIulio. On most such occasions, especially those early on, he was accompanied by Charles Ginocchio. Eventually there came a time, well into their relationship, when Haines and DiIulio could manage, on a painfully primitive level, to exchange small bits of uncomplicated information and to make known their simple requests of one another, but it was never easy. The language barrier between them was almost insuperable.

Ginocchio and DiIulio, by contrast, discovered an immediate inter-personal symbiosis. Upon the occasion of their first meeting Bill Haines had enlisted Deputy Landry to assist in making introductions; however, it quickly became apparent that Landry's assistance and the necessity for introductions was quite unnecessary. Ginocchio had simply extended both arms in the universal gesture of friendship for the prisoner, spoken to him in Italian and explained his mission, and the two men were swiftly locked in the warm embrace of a shared kinship. Within moments they had begun to prate and chatter like a pair of playful chipmunks cavorting in the bright sunshine of a pleasant summer afternoon. It was as though Ginocchio's presence had breached a dam of stoic reserve and released a swollen stream of animated volubility. A veritable host of repressed emotions, questions and pronouncements had seemed to spring forth in a continuous monologue, punctuated only by Ginocchio's sympathetic responses and attentive encouragements. The net result was, of course, that that first encounter between lawyer, client and interpreter had been more social than professional and their most notable accomplishment had been that the three of them became easy and confident together.

Then, as the winter progressed and the trial date approached, their successive sessions together became better focused and increasingly productive. Ginocchio, because of his own training in the law, was able to explain to DiIulio, in Italian, the nature of the American legal process, the significance of a trial, the issues to be tried, the principal elements of Ohio's adversary system of justice, the respective roles of the lawyers, the court and the officers, and the potential penalties that could be imposed in the event of a conviction. If the verdict was for murder in the first degree, the death penalty was mandatory unless the jury were to recommend mercy, in which case the sentence would be life imprisonment. If the verdict was for murder in the second degree, the sentence would also be life imprisonment, and if manslaughter, the sentence would be one to twenty years in the Ohio State Penitentiary at Columbus.

DiIulio really didn't understand what he perceived to be the state's unnatural and inordinate interest in his having killed Frosty Floyd. He had thought the whole affair to have been a private matter between the two of them, a lover's quarrel, so to speak. He had also thought — childlike — that the quarrel was over, it had ended with her death, but however that matter came down, he was adamant in his insistence that he preferred the death penalty to life imprisonment. He would rather be executed than penned up for the rest of his life like a despised, forsaken bird in an iron cage. *"Morire,"* he protested stubbornly. *"Preferirei morire."*

Bill Haines made the most of his opportunities to learn about the defendant DiIulio, his orientation, attitudes, level of intelligence, and his hopes, fears and motivations. Through his many intimate interviews with his client, made possible through Ginocchio's resourceful assistance, he came to understand the nature and quality of DiIulio's relationship with the girl, all that had transpired between them and, in the end, why the defendant had struck down the woman whom he had loved and so fervently wished to marry.

And in the process, and perhaps inevitably, he also came to feel a sympathy and an empathy for the defendant, who was, he reflected, more properly a young boy than a young man.

During each of his sessions with his client, Bill Haines took copious notes. He noted the names of probable witnesses, those potentially hostile as well as those presumed to be friendly, the identity of persons, dates and places involved in the short sordid saga that had begun and ended three-quarters of a year before. Then, between sessions, he revisited the people, the events and the localities entered on his notes in order to confirm, or to clarify, his own understanding of all that had happened between the two young lovers during their brief courtship last spring.

As the winter wore on, Bill Haines persevered. All his time and attention were devoted to the cause of his client. He did not need reminding that his client's life was at stake and he was too conscientious to yield it up by default. Diligence, to the point of doggedness, was Bill Haines' long suit.

ON THE SATURDAY BEFORE TRIAL, just as Blanche began to lay out their supper, Bill Haines locked the brass clasps on his worn leather briefcase. Inside, in an ordered series of manila folders, were his trial materials. They included an abbreviated dossier on each of the thirty-six veniremen who had been summoned for jury duty, a compendium of legal briefs and citations concerning the specific issues which would be presented for decision, a series of files for each of the ninety-nine witnesses who had been subpoenaed for trial, and a large tablet of foolscap replete with notes and memoranda to guide him through the proceedings.

"*Sono pronto*," he pronounced sonorously.

"What?" asked Blanche. "Did you just ask me to hurry up with supper?"

"Well, I might have," acknowledged Haines with a sly smile. "I'm sure it sounded that way.

"What I intended was '*sono pronto*' and I think that means 'I am ready.' In Italian, I mean. I'll have to ask Gino," he said, referring to Ginocchio.

"Do you mean that you're ready for supper or ready for trial?"

"For trial," he answered blandly. "I'm ready for supper also, but it has required only a few hours to build an appetite. It's taken months to prepare for trial."

"I know you've worked very hard and I've no doubt that you're well-prepared," conceded Blanche. "I think you know I haven't felt a great deal of sympathy for your Mr. DiIulio, but I do wish you well. Whatever happens to your client, I want you to win. Because I know you care so very much."

Bill Haines squeezed his young wife about the shoulders. "Thank you, dear. That's nice of you to say so. I don't really mind the work. It's not really work at all. It's a challenge, a contest with enormous stakes, and it's the sort of thing I most enjoy."

He sat down at the table, winked at his daughter Mildred, and changed tack, "But I've been most grateful for the 'supernumerary' day. I don't think I could have done without it."

Blanche looked at him sharply. "Whatever are you talking about? A 'super' what?"

"Today, Blanche," he explained with yet another wink at Mildred. "This is the 29th of February. It's a twenty-four hour gift. If this were not a leap year, I would have had less time to get ready for trial.

"And God knows I've needed every day," he added in benediction.

CHAPTER TWELVE

IT TOOK ALL DAY MONDAY, March 2nd, to select a jury.

They began at nine and by 11:30 the initial panel of thirty-six veniremen had been exhausted. Most of those summoned were excused on grounds that they were opposed to capital punishment or because they had read of the case in the newspapers and had already formed opinions about the guilt or innocence of the defendant. Others acknowledged that they had strong feelings about the "immigrant problem" and a particular bias against Italians.

Judge Jones directed Sheriff Gibson to scour the courthouse and its environs, seize as many able-bodied, sentient human beings as he could lay hands upon, and deliver them to the courtroom for jury duty.

The process resumed at 1:15 and the lawyers spent most of the afternoon working their way through the small group of prospects plucked up and presented by the sheriff. By four o'clock they had finished their *voir dire* examinations and announced themselves satisfied with the panel. Brooks

Johnson administered an oath to the twelve men in the jury box. Each of them raised his hand and solemnly swore that he would "well and truly try, and true deliverance make" of the case between the State of Ohio and the Defendant Donato DiIulio.

As soon as the members of the jury had resumed their seats, Bill Haines rose to his feet and moved the Court for a jury view of the scene of the alleged event, "Not for the purpose of engaging in any investigation or gathering evidence," he assured, "but merely to enable the jury to better understand the evidence as presented from the witness stand."

Judge Jones promptly denied the motion. "With respect to counsel, I do not perceive the factual issues to be sufficiently complex as to require a view. Let's proceed to opening statements."

"Exception, Your Honor," intoned Bill Haines to preserve the question for possible review by an appellate court.

"Noted," responded Judge Jones automatically before turning his attention to the prosecutor. "Mr. Campbell, you may begin."

Alva Campbell was ready. He already had the indictment in his hand. This was the original indictment, the one filed with the court and bearing the seal of the clerk. A copy would not suffice. It was necessary that he exhibit, and read, the original to the jury.

And he did. He drew himself to his full height, strode to the jury box, showed them the document, explained what it was, and read it to them verbatim. Every tortured, stilted and painfully redundant word and every convoluted, arcane and needlessly prolix sentence of the document he read in sepulchral, sonorous tones. Then, having made his obeisance to the procedural form, he told them what the case was about.

It was about murder, he said. Premeditated, deliberate, cold-blooded, and unmitigated. Murder in the first degree. The indictment which had been returned by the Grand Jury, made up of other Miami County citizens, charged it and he, acting on behalf of the State of Ohio, would prove it.

"The defendant," he told them, "is an illiterate Italian immigrant. He speaks no word of English. He came to this country to make money so that he could live well and so that he could send American dollars back home to Italy. And, after several years of moving from one place to another, each time changing jobs to get more money, he somehow found his way to this county, to Covington, Ohio. He came to Miami County three years ago, in 1905, and he's stayed here ever since. He came and he stayed because the pay is good and the living is easy.

Another reason he stayed is that he was well-received and well-treated, perhaps too well, by the good people of Covington. So well, in fact, was he treated by the locals that he very soon insinuated himself into the acquaintanceship of one of the town's fairest and most eligible young maidens. This was Miss Forest May Floyd, the 25-year-old daughter of Mr. and Mrs. John Floyd, a distinguished elderly couple, who live just west of Covington on the Gettysburg Pike. Miss Floyd was a kind and compassionate young woman who apparently befriended the defendant despite his perversely willful ignorance of the language and customs of the country in which he had lived and worked for nearly four years.

"The evidence will show, gentlemen, that in her generous and considerate willingness to accept the defendant into her acquaintanceship, the lovely Miss Floyd effectively sealed her own doom.

"No sooner had the defendant," Alva Campbell turned to point an outstretched arm and finger, "this man DiIulio, achieved Miss Floyd's acceptance than he began to press for more. With a shocking disregard for propriety, he repeatedly attempted to force his attentions on her. Then, after she had repulsed his unwelcome advances, the defendant became obsessed with his illicit quest and began, first to pursue and afterwards to stalk this innocent young woman as she went about her daily business. She, who had initially been the reluctant object of the defendant's affections, next became his fearful prey, and would ultimately become the victim of his unnatural yearnings and his savage depravity."

Without having intended to do so, Alva Campbell had permitted himself to become caught up in his own rhetoric. His indignation over the defendant's wanton villainy was both righteous and genuine and he had allowed it free reign. Now he found himself on the very balls of his feet, towering over the jury, his emotions and his voice having risen in an awesome stentorian crescendo.

He paused a long moment, looked into the faces of the twelve men in the box, and waited for his words to register. Satisfied, he withdrew towards the center of the courtroom, regained something of his former composure and continued in a level, modulated tone, "Gentlemen of the jury, the State will prove to you that on Thursday, May 9th, 1907, the Defendant, Donato DiIulio, spent the entire day dogging the footsteps of his victim, Forest May Floyd. He accosted her and her younger sister, Anna Floyd, in Covington, intruded himself into their company, accompanied them to Piqua and back, demanded to walk them home, and upon their refusal, followed them anyway. All of these things he did, in spite of the fact that the girls had offered him no slightest encouragement and had repeatedly asked him to leave. Then, when they finally tried to run away from him, the defendant, Donato DiIulio, drew a .32-caliber revolver from his pocket and shot Forest May — not once, but twice — in the back. She died within minutes, her death having been directly and proximately produced by the two gunshot wounds.

"The evidence will show that the defendant killed Miss Floyd deliberately and with premeditated malice and that he was, at all times, fully aware of the nature and quality of his actions. He was quite sane and he was not under the influence of any compulsion or delusion.

"In sum, gentlemen, the State will prove to you, beyond a reasonable doubt, each and every one of the allegations contained in the indictment. And when the evidence is all in, and the Court has instructed you in the law, your duty will be clear and your verdict inexorable. That verdict will find the defendant DiIulio guilty of murder in the first degree and will expressly withhold any recommendation for mercy. He is entitled to no more mercy than he himself has shown his victim."

Alva Campbell held to his station in the center of the courtroom long enough to assess the effect of his remarks on the individual jurors. He established momentary eye contact with Davis Martindale in the front row, third seat from the left. Martindale, a good-sized man with ruddy features, had been the first juror to be seated in the case. He was a farmer, resided in Staunton Township, and was a staunch advocate for capital punishment. Campbell fully expected that Martindale would be elected foreman of the jury.

The prosecutor completed his survey of the jurors, gave an almost imperceptible nod to Judge Jones, and strode purposefully back to his chair at the plaintiff's counsel table, the one nearest to the jury box.

Judge Jones waited patiently and respectfully for Alva Campbell to resume his seat, arrange his papers and settle himself into a properly attentive attitude. He allowed an additional, albeit unhurried, second to pass before turning his attention to the defense side of the arena.

"Mr. Haines," he called out, "you may address the jury."

"Thank you, Your Honor," responded Bill Haines as he rose to his feet. "I can be very brief."

Stepping away from the counsel table with an athletic grace, he moved his lean frame lithely and directly to the midpoint of the low balustrade that separated the jury section from the balance of the courtroom. His bearing was relaxed, his aspect candid. He allowed himself a swift, but thorough and incisive, appraisal of his jury.

"Afternoon, gentlemen," he began affably. "Does everybody remember about the six blind men — from Indostan, I think — who went to see the elephant?

"Because they were blind, they couldn't really see him at all, but they thought they might learn about him by touch and by feel. And, of course, they did. Each of them learned something, but none of them quite got it right. One fellow felt the elephant's leg and pronounced him to be like a tree. Another touched his trunk and declared him to be like a snake. Each of them explored a different aspect of the elephant and drew a different conclusion as to what an elephant really was. Seems like another one had got hold of his tail and decided the elephant was really pretty much like a rope.

"Point is, each of them was correct as to what he had observed, but none of them had the slightest idea what an elephant really was. The information they had gathered, separately and collectively, was both incomplete and out of context.

"It's an old story, been around a long time. You could probably even call it a legend. But, however old and trite it may be, it still has *vitality* and it's directly relevant to what you just heard from the prosecuting attorney.

"Now, Mr. Campbell is an able lawyer and an exceptionally honorable man. He spent a little time here this afternoon telling you precisely what it was he expected the evidence to show, and I'm very certain he was both honest and sincere about everything he said. Mr. Campbell is most honorable.

"But he didn't get it quite right either. Like the blind men from Indostan, he couldn't tell you the whole story because he doesn't yet know the whole of it. He hasn't had the opportunity to examine the other, and very contradictory, aspects of the elephant.

"And that's not Mr. Campbell's fault. Y'see, there were only two people who ever knew all there was to know about what happened over in Covington last spring. One of them, tragically, is dead, and the other hasn't been able to tell about it because he can't speak our language. It's been a total lockout. None of them — the people who needed to know — have been able to unravel this thing. Coroner Gaines, Constable Hake, Sheriff Gibson, Mr. Campbell, even the members of the grand jury who returned the indictment — none of them have been able to come by sufficient information to fully understand why it was this young woman had to die on the streets of Covington last May.

"You gentlemen, before this case is over, will hear the full story. I will bring to you, in this courtroom, the key which will end the lockout. That key will appear to you in the person of Mr. Charles Ginocchio who is the Royal Consular Agent of the Italian government. Mr. Ginocchio speaks both Italian and English fluently and will act as an official interpreter in this case. It is important for you to know that he is here as an officer of the court, partial to neither side, so that you, as jurors, can hear the defendant's story from his own lips.

"I have no doubt, gentlemen of the jury, that when the evidence is all in, specifically including the testimony of the defendant, fairly and impartially translated, and this case has been completed, you will have seen the entire elephant. You will be in possession of all the facts. And, thus armed, you will understand — and appreciate — that the defendant, Donato DiIulio, had no conscious ability to prevent the death of this vile and unprincipled young woman. The evidence will show that she herself was the architect of her own destiny, that it was her own venal and dissolute conduct that set in motion those predictable, immutable forces which led inevitably and inexorably to her own tragic demise, and that this pathetic, childlike defendant was powerless to withstand or to interrupt the relentless press of those forces and to stay his own hand.

"You will learn, these next few days, of a double tragedy. You will learn that the death of the wanton Miss Floyd is no greater tragedy than is the concomitant destruction of the life and the immortal soul of this youthful and fatally naive defendant.

"And when all is said and done, gentlemen, I am certain that your verdict will be that the defendant is not guilty by reason of temporary, emotional insanity."

CHARLES GINOCCHIO HAD TAKEN ROOMS AT THE TROY HOTEL and would remain in town for the duration of the trial. He had sat through the day's session of court as a spectator rather than as a participant. He had been assigned a table alongside the north window-wall of the courtroom, inside the bar, but away from the center of the arena. His presence was necessary in order that he might keep the defendant apprised of the proceedings. This he could do only belatedly and imperfectly because the proceedings could not be continuously interrupted in order to permit him to translate directly each question and answer during the jury selection process or each of the remarks of counsel in their opening statements to the jury. It had been arranged that he would monitor those activities, as well as the testimony of the witnesses, make such notes as he felt necessary, and then visit the defendant each evening and acquaint him with what had transpired during the day.

It was nearly eight o'clock, well after suppertime, when he arrived at the jail to review the Monday proceedings. Sheriff Gibson escorted him into the bullpen, where he found DiIulio in the midst of a game of draughts with Deputy Landry. The Italian seemed to have the better part of the game so Ginocchio was content to wait and to watch the game to its conclusion. They chatted briefly, in a unique form of pidgin English loosely comprehended by all three, until DiIulio had clinched his victory.

A few moments later, it was just the two of them, DiIulio and Ginocchio, in the second-floor conference room. Ginocchio had explained the process by which the jury had been selected and had synopsized the opening statements of the lawyers. He had braced himself for DiIulio's anticipated reaction.

"*Matto!*" he exploded. "*Pazzo? Non sono matto! Che cosa?*" His jawline took on an unaccustomed rigidity. "*No, non sono matto,*" he declared.

"*Conosco,*" Ginocchio assured in his most conciliatory manner, "I know. *Conosco.*" Then, in easy conversational Italian he explained that Mr. Haines had not intended to convey that he was insane, a lunatic. He had simply meant the jury to understand that he couldn't help himself, that the impulse to kill Frosty had been irresistible, and that, for that reason, he should not be held accountable. Temporary insanity, *follia temporanea*, he explained, was a legal concept. It was, most importantly, a legitimate defense to a first degree murder charge. Mr. Haines, he said, was a very good lawyer and was working quite diligently in his behalf.

"*Sì,*" answered DiIulio dully, his anxieties somewhat mollified by Ginocchio. "*Capisco.*"

CHAPTER THIRTEEN

THE SPECTATORS' SECTION OF JUDGE JONES' COURTROOM was no less elegantly appointed than was that area "within the bar." Separated from the trial arena by a low walnut balustrade similar to that which surrounded the jury box, the spectators' gallery was enormous. It was equipped with row after row, phalanxes actually, of rigid armchairs, each of which were separately constructed of wrought iron and white oak, solidly bolted to one another as well as to the floor. Standing room along the exterior walls and in the aisleways between the individual brackets of the permanent seating units enabled the gallery to accommodate nearly two hundred spectators.

There were at least that many in attendance when court convened at nine o'clock on Tuesday morning for the second day of trial. There was even a small contingent of Italian immigrant laborers, some of whom had a rudimentary conversancy with the English language and could therefore hope to comprehend some part of the proceedings. The trial had engendered considerable interest throughout the county and it was generally known that the testimony would begin this morning. The jury had been selected and opening statements completed. The trial, the actual presentation of the evidence, could now begin in earnest.

"Call your first witness," commanded Judge Jones of Alva Campbell after having gaveled the assemblage into order.

"Thank you, your Honor," replied Campbell. "The State calls Mr. H. J. Walker to the stand."

H. J. Walker was the county surveyor. He had no knowledge of any of the events involved in the trial and, were it not for the stringent requirements of the formal rules of evidence, his testimony would have been entirely superfluous. As it was, he had prepared a map, or sketch, of the murder scene for use at trial. If the map were to be used, the rules required that the maker appear in court and identify it as an exhibit. His testimony was entirely perfunctory, not in the least controversial, and there was no cross-examination.

Alva Campbell's next witness was John Floyd. He was a rough-hewn, solid-looking man whose stern features and dark piercing eyes were only partially attenuated by a full, heavy beard of mottled black and gray color. In response to Campbell's questioning, he told the jury he lived a mile west of Covington on the Gettysburg Pike. He was 59 years old and his wife, who was feeble-minded, was 56. She wouldn't be able to come to court. The two of them were the parents of Forest May Floyd. She was only 25 years old when she died, he said. She would have been 26 in August.

"Last time I saw Forrie May alive was at lunch that day, May 9th. She and her sister Anna had ate early so's they could go to town and have their pictures taken. Didn't see her again 'till the undertaker brought her home to bury."

"Were you acquainted with the defendant Donato DiIulio?" asked Campbell.

"No, sir. Never laid eyes on him," Floyd answered curtly. "Never even heard tell of him 'till he killed my daughter."

When Bill Haines asked, on cross-examination, if he knew any of his daughter's beaux, he said, "Not by name, I didn't. There wasn't anybody she was real serious about. Same with Blanche. Neither one of them had a steady fella."

"Did they receive company in your home?" asked Haines.

"Yeah, they did sometimes. Not often, but sometimes on a Sunday afternoon."

"Did you know any of them?" persisted Haines.

"Not by name, I didn't. Only by sight. Like I said, there wasn't that many and they wasn't there that often."

"And you said you never heard of Donato DiIulio?"

"That's right. Not before he done what he did."

"Might you have heard him referred to as 'Danny'?"

"Never did," Floyd answered sharply.

"Do you know a Johnny Nickel?" asked Haines.

"Know the name. I think he lives there in Covington."

"Did he ever keep company with your daughter? Either of them?"

"Better not have. I believe he's married," came the answer.

"Johnny Bell? Or maybe Johnny Bellini?" asked Haines evenly. "Ever hear a name like that?"

"No, I haven't. Not ever."

"Mr. Floyd," Haines pressed, "is it possible that any of these people, Johnny Nickel, Johnny Bell, Johnny Bellini or Danny DiIulio, were ever in your home as company for either or both of your daughters?"

John Floyd was becoming angry, both visibly and understandably. "No, it's not possible. I'd 'a known Nickel and I'm tellin' you he wasn't ever there. And them other names all sound Eyetalian, and we never had no Eyetalians in our home. Not ever."

"Thank you, sir," said Bill Haines. "I only needed to be sure. I assure you I have intended no affront."

Haines stood motionless in the center of the courtroom. Eyes fixed narrowly on a random point on the wall just above Judge Jones' head, he searched for the most sensitive, least offensive, way to phrase his next series of questions. However odious the task, it was necessary for him to inquire.

"Mr. Floyd," he asked blandly, "did Forest May speak to you, at any time during the last months of her life, of an engagement to marry?"

"Of course not," came the off-balance answer. "She was never engaged to anybody. I've already told you she didn't even have a steady fella."

"And if she had been engaged to marry someone," Haines continued relentlessly, "you'd expect to have known about it, wouldn't you?"

"Yes, I would've," came the clipped, indignant response.

"Just one more question, sir, and I'll let you go," assured Haines. "To the best of your knowledge, was your daughter Forest May Floyd ever engaged to marry the defendant Donato DiIulio?"

"That's ridiculous!" spat the witness defiantly. "Far's I know she didn't even know the man. Even if she had, she wouldn'ta wanted to marry the likes of him."

"Yes, I'm quite sure you're right, sir," conceded Bill Haines. "I truly do not believe your daughter ever intended to marry the likes of Donato DiIulio. I apologize for the question."

✦ ☾ ✦

THE TESTIMONY OF ANNA FLOYD, the victim's younger sister, had been eagerly awaited by all those who followed the progress of the trial. Onlookers in the spectators' gallery, news reporters at their assigned press tables within the bar, and members of the general public who learned of each day's court proceedings by word of mouth or by means of printed reports, all were attuned to the fact that Anna Floyd had spent most of the day of the homicide in the company of both her sister and the defendant Donato DiIulio, and that she was the principal witness to the killing.

Alva Campbell asked that she be sworn, then gently led her through the preliminaries. A pretty girl, newly-turned fourteen, she seemed relaxed and wholly unintimidated by her circumstance.

She remembered that May 9th had been a Thursday. She and Frosty had gone to town, to Speelman's Gallery, to have Frosty's photograph taken. It was her best recollection that they had first seen DiIulio at the Italian store near the Crossroads and that he had followed them when they turned onto High Street towards Speelman's. He caught up with them very quickly and said he wanted to talk with Frosty. Anna said she told him they were going to Speelman's and the three of them chatted briefly. In the course of that conversation, she said, they decided that Frosty should have her picture taken at Thorne's Gallery in Piqua. Frosty thought Mr. Thorne was a better photographer than Mr. Speelman.

When DiIulio asked if he could go with them, Anna said he might, and they walked together back to the traction depot and caught the noon car to Piqua. Once there, he followed them as they walked from the Piqua depot to Thorne's, waited outside while the photograph was made, and then returned with them to the depot. The three of them rode back to Covington on the three o'clock car. Upon arrival, Frosty refused to permit DiIulio to go home with them. She said she would tell her father if he insisted. DiIulio became quite agitated and said he didn't care if she did, he wasn't afraid of any of them.

The two girls began walking towards their home, she said, and the Italian remained behind. They soon met their little sister, Maude, who was also on her way home, and the three of them walked together out Rock Avenue. When they got to the Main Street intersection they saw DiIulio coming towards them again. He grasped at Frosty's arm and she started to run away. DiIulio pulled a revolver out of his hip pocket and shot at her twice. She fell to the ground a few feet away and then DiIulio shot himself as well. Anna ran to where her sister had fallen, sank to her knees and watched her sister die. Forest May spoke no last words, only blinked her eyes and shuddered. It was over in a matter of minutes.

Bill Haines' approach to Anna Floyd was both sympathetic and cautious. Despite her easy presence on the witness stand, he suspected that she might yet give way to emotion. She had just described an experience which must certainly have been harrowing for a young girl. She had been required to relive a terrifying chain of events which had culminated in the death of her sister. If she were to break down, or if he were to be seen as badgering her, his client's cause would suffer irreparable harm. He would content himself with a benign, uncritical examination, ask only the easy questions, and take what he could get. He knew her testimony had been truthful and he couldn't change the facts.

Who were the other members of her family? How long had they lived in the Covington area? Where did she go to school? What was her grade level? And did she like school? These were among Haines' opening lines of inquiry. Calculated more to place the witness at ease than to elicit information, they seemed to achieve their intended effect. Anna Floyd came to regard Bill Haines as an interested, somewhat avuncular examiner rather than an advocate for her sister's slayer.

Moving unobtrusively toward the heart of the matter, Haines asked her genially, "Did you know this man, this DiIulio, before that day?"

"No, not really," she answered, then added, "I mean I knew who he was, but I didn't really know him."

"And how was it that you knew who he was?"

"From my sisters. Frosty and Blanche. I'd heard them talking about him. And Frosty had pointed him out to me once."

"When they talked about him," Bill Haines wanted to know, "what did they say?"

"Oh, I don't remember. Only that he was an Italian and couldn't speak English. I think they said he worked at the brickyard."

"Anything else?"

"Well, I know Frosty used to like him well enough. Sometimes, after everybody was asleep, she'd sneak outside and see him."

"I don't understand," Haines feigned ignorance, "After everyone was asleep, how would she know he was outside? By pre-arrangement? Did he tap on the window?"

"Well, something like that. Sometimes they would have made a date, like maybe the day before. Then, other times, he's just show up, late at night, and call her out."

"How did he do that?" asked Haines, "Did they have some sort of signal?"

"Yes. It was a string. It was tied around her toe, the big one, and it hung out the window and down almost to the ground. If the Italian wanted to see her, all he had to do was jiggle the string."

"That's clever," marvelled Haines. "Whose idea was that, the Italian's?"

"Oh, no. Frosty had used it for years. Lots of fellas knew about it. Blanche had one, too. They said it was like a bellcord in a hotel. You know, pull for service — whatever that means. One time, a couple of years ago, one of the railroad workers pulled too hard, really yanked on it, and Frosty got mad. She said he almost ripped her toe off."

Bill Haines turned away from the witness and sauntered back to the defense counsel table. Seemingly lost in thought, he allowed time for the full import of Anna's disclosures to settle on the twelve men in the jury box. Regaining his place at the table, he leafed through his pad of foolscap as though undecided what direction his next line of questioning should take.

After another moment or so, he seemed ready to continue.

"Anna," he asked mildly, "do you understand Italian?"

"Oh, no," she answered quickly. "It all sounds like gibberish to me."

"That's fair enough," said Haines, "but I gathered from some of your answers to Mr. Campbell's questions that you were privy to several of your sister's conversations with the defendant that day, like where the photographs were to be taken, whether he might accompany you, things like that. How would you know what it was they spoke of?"

"Oh, that was pretty easy," she replied conversationally. "A lot of it was sign language and finger-pointing, you know, gestures and expressions. Danny, that's what she called him, knew a few words of English and Frosty was usually able to pick up a word or two of Italian. She always seemed to know what he was trying to say. And then she told me what it was they'd talked about."

"But most of what you knew of their conversations, you learned from Frosty, is that right?"

"Mmm-hmm," answered Anna. "Pretty much all of it. He could only speak a word or so of English and I couldn't understand a bit of Italian, so except for some of their gestures, I was totally at sea. But Frosty explained what it was he wanted."

"And what was that?" asked Haines.

"She said he'd somehow become obsessed with her and she didn't know how to make him let her alone. Frosty was a really attractive woman and she always had a lot of fellas around, but this was different. She told me that he'd got it into his head she was going to marry him and it looked as though he meant to follow her around like a love-sick puppy until she did. She just couldn't seem to get rid of him."

"Do you know whether your sister ever gave him any reason to believe she might be willing to marry him?"

"Oh, no, she'd never do that," came the quick response. "She didn't even particularly like Italian boys. She called them guineas — or wops. She'd spent time with this DiIulio and she seemed to like him alright, at least, at first, but she would never have agreed to marry him. That idea could only come out of his own imagination. It was like he was just totally smitten — or maybe even crazy."

Bill Haines seemed satisfied with Anna's answer, made a note on his pad, and changed tack again.

"On the day Frosty was killed, had she encouraged Mr. DiIulio to believe she might have cared for him?"

"Oh, no, just the opposite," Anna insisted. "In fact she made it plain she didn't want him around. She only agreed that he go with us to Piqua on condition he pay the fare for all of us. And then she wouldn't talk with him or even look at him the whole day.

"Finally, when he insisted on walking home with us, she told him to go away or she'd tell our father. She called him names and said she never wanted to see him again. I don't think he could have been very much encouraged."

"And after he shot her," Haines asked, "and then shot himself, did either of them say anything?"

Anna bit her lower lip, collected herself quickly, and answered. "Frosty never said another word to anyone. She just stood there for what seemed a very long time, holding on to Mrs. Cauffer's fence. He screamed something in Italian — I don't have any idea what it was — then shot himself. Twice. He shot himself twice, in the head, before he fell. The second time, I think, he actually put the gun in his mouth. He fell down straightaway. Then, Frosty's legs gave way and she fell, too. He went down first. Neither of them said anything after that. Frosty died and Danny was unconscious.

"I thought he was dead, too, but it seems I was mistaken."

ALVA CAMPBELL PRESENTED TWO MORE EYE-WITNESS ACCOUNTS of the shooting. Little Maude Floyd, the youngest of the four sisters, was only twelve when she saw her sister die in Mrs. Cauffer's front yard. She said she had no sooner met with and joined her sisters on Rock Avenue than the Italian had begun shooting. She heard the first shot, looked back and saw Forest May clinging to Mrs. Cauffer's fence, then she saw the Italian shoot her again and she watched her sister fall to the ground. She remembered that the Italian shot himself also, but couldn't be sure whether it was before or after Forest May had fallen down.

Daniel Minnich had been operating a hoisting machine at the freight depot on Rock Avenue and was only about ten feet away from the participants. He'd heard a shot, then a scream, and he turned in time to see DiIulio shoot again. Then he shot himself and fell immediately to the ground. He watched Forest May hold herself to the fence another moment or two and then he saw her collapse. On crossexamination he said he remembered hearing a total of four shots, two and two. He and his men went to the scene. They turned the Italian onto his back, believed him to be dead, and turned their attentions to the girl. She was still alive and he had her moved onto the grass at Mrs. Cauffer's. She died a few minutes later.

By agreement of counsel, a .32-caliber colt revolver loaded with five cartridges was offered into evidence. It was stipulated that four of the cartridges were spent and the fifth was live. Daniel Minnich identified the revolver as the one he had taken from DiIulio's side.

Although Alva Campbell had subpoenaed no fewer than fifty potential witnesses, he called only thirteen more, for a total of eighteen, to testify at trial. And for the most part, the testimony of those additional witnesses was either perfunctory or cumulative or both. To the casual observer much of it must also have seemed tedious and superfluous.

Dr. Gaines testified concerning his examination of the body of Forest May Floyd. He described the wounds he had observed, spoke in terms of the point of entry and the course of the projectiles, both had passed through the body near the heart, and expressed the opinion that either of the wounds would have caused the victim's death.

Dr. Gaines also described the Italian's self-inflicted wounds, the worst of which was produced by a bullet having traveled through both lobes of his brain. A second bullet had entered just under his lip and, due to its course, had not done a great deal of damage.

One man, Henry Deeman, and two women, a Mrs. Eberenze and a Mrs. Weaver, had each ridden on the same traction car to Piqua as had the defendant and the two

Floyd sisters. They all agreed that the defendant was smiling and teasing Forest May, but that she seemed sullen and angry. Deeman was a co-worker with DiIulio at the brickyard and had been curious as to why he wasn't working that day.

The D.C.& P. conductor, Louis Fisher, remembered that the Italian had paid the fare for all three. He had also noticed that Forest May seemed to be exchanging coquettish glances with a tall man who stood alone on the rear platform.

The photographer, T. R. Thorne, testified that the Italian had waited outside his Piqua studio all the while he worked on the girl's photograph.

Thomas Hill, the proprietor of Hill House, and his wife, Angie, were next. Mr. Hill had found the defendant a job at the Wagner Tile Company. He said that DiIulio had left a revolver with him for a time, but had called for it on Monday before the shooting. Mrs. Hill testified only that the defendant had taken no breakfast that day. On cross-examination Mr. Hill admitted that he had believed DiIulio to be either crazy or in deep trouble all the time he had boarded at Hill House.

And G. C. Hooker told of having served DiIulio a single shot of whiskey at five in the morning. Some of the spectators began to grow restless and they wondered about the value of such evidentiary matters.

The interest of the most jaded of the spectators was galvanized, however, at the appearance of the victim's sister, Blanche Floyd, on the witness stand. Although she had not been an eyewitness to the shooting, it was generally credited that she alone was privy to the true nature of her sister's relationship with the Italian. It was known, after all, that she and Johnny Nickel had often doubled with Frosty and her Italian friend DiIulio.

Except that she lied. She did not know DiIulio at all, she said. In fact, she persisted, she had never even seen him until the night before her sister's murder. On that evening she and Frosty had been together at a tent show and a John Nickel, whom she knew only slightly, had pointed him out to her. Nickel had warned the two girls that the Italian seemed to be following them. Parenthetically, she appended, she'd never heard of anyone named Johnny Bell either.

Bill Haines was unable to shake her story. She was adamant in her insistence that she had never met DiIulio, and had never seen or heard of him before that night, and had certainly never been in his company. And, she added, if anyone had said otherwise, they were clearly mistaken.

Johnny Nickel followed his paramour to the stand and confirmed her denials. He'd been married for twelve years, had three children, and barely knew any of the Floyd girls. He knew the Italian only by sight, but he had seen him following the Floyd sisters at the tent show. Concerned, he said, he made it his business to follow the Italian awhile to be sure his own perception was correct and then he told Blanche about it.

And no, in response to Bill Haines' questioning, he had never had an affair with Blanche or been out with her. He was happily married and would never think of such a thing. Did he know Johnny Bell? Only slightly. No, he'd never been anywhere in company of Blanche Floyd, Forest Floyd, Donato DiIulio, Johnny Bell, or any of them. He had only become concerned for the two girls when he saw the Italian acting strangely at the tent show. He had satisfied himself that the Italian was indeed following them and had warned Blanche about it. That was the extent of his involvement with any of them.

Millard Floyd, older brother to the Floyd sisters, seemed to corroborate Nickel's testimony when he told the jury that Blanche and Frosty had asked him to escort them home from the tent show that night. They had told him that someone, maybe an Italian, was following them and they were afraid.

Alva Campbell's final witness was truly superfluous and very nearly irrelevant. Lewis Johnson testified that he had worked with DiIulio at the brickyard. DiIulio had told him, in his pidgin English, that he had a girl friend and that the two of them were not getting along well. At least, Johnson conceded, that's what he had understood the Italian to have said.

And, on that piddling note, Alva Campbell gathered his notes, offered his exhibits and solemnly announced, "If it please the Court, the prosecution rests its case."

CHAPTER FOURTEEN

DONATO DiIULIO HAD NOT UNDERSTOOD all of that which had transpired or had been said during the presentation of the State's evidence against him. Indeed, his comprehension of the formal proceedings calculated to secure the forfeiture of his own life was so deficient that he seemed to be entirely uninterested. The general perception of his appearance and demeanor was fairly described in a contemporary account which appeared in the *Miami Union*:

DiIulio is about 20 years old and can neither read nor write. He has no conception of the laws of any country. In intelligence he can only be compared to a five-year-old child. His powers for reasoning or distinguishing between right and wrong go no further.

During the trial he sits with his head down and eyes upon the floor. The whole proceeding is a mystery to him and his interest in the affair can only be likened to that of a dog or animal chained to a stake and surveyed by a curious crowd. His obviously deficient intelligence and his resultant inability to comprehend the language of this country have left him as ignorant of its ways, customs, laws and his own rights as the day he landed on its shores. He maintains a stoical indifference to his surroundings as his past experience has taught him it is useless to try to understand.

In appearance, on rare occasions, his face is pleasing as his features are regular and when in the company of Turnkey Landry, whom he seems to feel is his only friend, he is all attention and animation, smiling and chattering in his jargon. At other times he maintains a scowling demeanor, giving him a murderous appearance caused by the contraction of his heavy dark eyebrows, as he feels that every man's hand is against him and for reasons that he is unable to fathom or understand.

Should the law decree that he die, he would show about the same degree of interest in being strapped in the electrical chair that the average human being would exhibit in sitting down to a solitary meal.

The defendant's innings, such as they might be, began just after three o'clock that same afternoon.

Judge Jones had ordered that all of the State's exhibits be admitted into evidence and he had summarily overruled Bill Haines' perfunctory motions for dismissal and for directed verdict. Now, after a short recess, he nodded to Haines. It was an unspoken, yet clearly anticipated, invitation to proceed with the defense.

Had there existed any question as to whether the defendant would testify on his own behalf or invoke the Fifth Amendment privilege against self-incrimination, the issue was swiftly put to rest. In a single, fluid movement, Bill Haines drew himself to his feet and announced that his first witness would be the defendant himself. Then, as soon as the resultant commotion among the spectators had subsided, he asked the Court for an instruction to the jury concerning the use of an interpreter. Judge Jones granted the request and turned his attention to the twelve men in the jury box.

"Gentlemen of the jury," he began, "you have doubtless gleaned from the testimony thus far into the trial the fact that the defendant can neither speak nor comprehend the English language. You may also have gained the impression that he does possess some minimal ability to understand certain words or phrases. Whatever may be your private perception in this regard, I am required to instruct you that the parties have stipulated that, for the purposes of his own testimony, the defendant is conclusively presumed to be unable to speak, or to understand, a single word of English.

"For that reason, the parties have agreed that the defendant will testify with the intermediation of an interpreter." Judge Jones made a gesture in the direction of Charles Ginocchio, who had been seated just within the bar and behind the defense counsel table. "We are fortunate in having secured for this purpose the services of Mr. Charles Ginocchio of Cincinnati. Please stand up, sir.

"Mr. Ginocchio is the American consular agent for the Royal Italian government. He is a citizen of both countries, the United States and Italy, and, by reason of his education, background and training, he is readily conversant with both languages. I have appointed Mr. Ginocchio as official interpreter — he is to be considered by you as an officer of the court — for the express purpose of the taking of the defendant's testimony.

"Questions will be addressed to the defendant by counsel, in the same manner as you have seen with reference to other witnesses. These questions will be translated into Italian by Mr. Ginocchio and relayed to the defendant. The defendant's answers will, of course, be given in Italian and Mr. Ginocchio will then translate them into English in order that we can understand the complete dialogue between the examiner and the witness."

With a nod to the court reporter, he added, as an aside, "Renna, you'll be happy to learn that you need not try to record anything spoken in Italian. If you'll just take down the questions and the answers in English that'll have to suffice."

Turning back to the jury, he continued, "The jury is specifically instructed that you are to consider the defendant's answers to specific questions, together with any declarative statements, relayed to you by Mr. Ginocchio on behalf of the defendant, to be the defendant's own testimony. You are not to speculate concerning the substance of any colloquies between the defendant and the interpreter and you may not assume any of the testimony to be contrived or attenuated by the interpreter himself. I have already told you that Mr. Ginocchio is an officer of the court and I now admonish you to regard him only in such capacity.

"This entire process, the taking of the defendant's testimony, may well prove to be quite tedious, and I expect you will find it difficult to follow. Nonetheless, I urge you to pay close attention. Despite the existence of a language barrier, the defendant's evidence is entitled to receive no lesser consideration than that of the prosecution."

Having completed his admonition to the jury, Judge Jones gathered his robes, nodded a second time in Bill Haines' direction, and settled himself into his swivel chair at the bench. Haines, who had resumed his own seat at the counsel table during the court's instruction to the jury, now turned in his chair and affected a similar signal to Charles Ginocchio. In his own turn, then, Ginocchio arose, took two short steps towards the counsel table, placed a hand lightly on DiIulio's shoulder and spoke softly into his ear.

DiIulio's first response was both automatic and predictable. He responded not at all. He appeared, at least initially, to have been totally unaware of Ginocchio's presence or that he had spoken to him. It was only after Ginocchio had gained his full attention and repeated his urgings that DiIulio mumbled his assent and allowed himself to be led to the front of the courtroom and to take up station at the witness stand.

It would have been difficult to overlook the striking contrast in the appearance of the two men as they made their way across the courtroom. Ginocchio, older and somewhat smaller, was neatly attired in a freshly pressed dark business suit, white shirt and tie. His manner was confident and, despite the slight limp occasioned by his artificial limb, his movements were quick and surprisingly agile. And, though he carried his ebony walking stick, he depended on it not at all. In comparison, DiIulio seemed younger even than his twenty years and not yet fully formed. His dark pants and jacket were an obvious mismatch, both being of poor quality and badly worn. The want of a necktie seemed the more conspicuous by virtue of his having buttoned his frayed dress shirt clear to the top. He had plodded woodenly to the witness stand, following Ginocchio and, at the latter's direction, he had mounted the two carpeted steps to the sturdy armchair bolted to the platform. Once seated, he looked sheepishly about the courtroom, surveyed a veritable sea of strange faces, then found Ginocchio again, and affected a tentative, self-conscious grin. It made him appear to be not only callow and amorphous, but simple-minded as well. Donato DiIulio's over-all aspect was that of one who had suddenly and unexpectedly surfaced into a new and unfamiliar element, an environment wholly foreign to his own nature.

Charles Ginocchio had positioned himself next to the witness stand and at DiIulio's right shoulder. Standing erect, he was at eye level with DiIulio as the latter sat in the elevated chair located midway between the judge's bench and the jury box. When Brooks Johnson approached and inquired of the defendant whether he solemnly swore that the testimony he was about to give would be the truth, the whole truth and nothing but the truth, Ginocchio translated the question directly. Then, when DiIulio had answered, "*Si, la verita. Givro*", Ginocchio translated, "Yes, the truth, I swear."

Bill Haines began his direct examination of the defendant Donato DiIulio in a manner calculated to put him at ease and, at the same time, to demonstrate to the jury that he was a real person, a human being barely beyond his childhood, with his own set of values, hopes and sensitivities, rather than the brutish, insensate lout the prosecution and the newspapers had portrayed him to be.

It did, at first, seem painfully tedious:

Q.   *(By Haines) What is your full name and address?*
       (Colloquy between witness and interpreter)
A.   *(By Ginocchio) The witness says his full name is Donato DiIulio. He currently resides at the Miami County jail. His last non-custodial address was at the Hill House in Covington.*
Q.   *What is your present age?*
       (Colloquy)
A.   *The witness says he is twenty years old. He was born December 20th, 1887.*
Q.   *Where were you born?*
       (Colloquy)
A.   *In Civaqua, Italy. It is a small village located in the southern part of that country.*
Q.   *Do your parents still live in Italy?*
       (Colloquy)
A.   *Yes.*
Q.   *What are their names and in what community do they live?*

When Ginocchio translated Haines' last question, DiIulio balked. He shook his head emphatically, then folded arms across his chest and slumped back into the witness chair. His face clouded and his expression took on the aspect of a stubborn scowl. Ginocchio tried again. This time he placed his hand on DiIulio's arm in conciliatory fashion, paraphrased the question, and spoke to him in a conversational tone. DiIulio's retort was charged with emotion. His determination not to answer the question was obvious to everyone in the courtroom. Finally, after what appeared to be a series of assurances given by Ginocchio, the two men became engaged in a reluctant, but extensive discussion concerning the framing of a response to Haines' question.

That accomplished, Ginocchio gave DiIulio a reassuring pat on the shoulder and addressed the court.

"The witness says, your Honor, that he does not wish to answer the question. He has steadfastly refused, these many months, to provide the requested information for fear some communication might occur. Stated simply, Mr. DiIulio does not want his family to learn of his present difficulties. Rightly or wrongly, he says he prefers that they believe him to have died."

Judge Jones nodded his understanding and looked to the lawyers. "Mr. Haines?"

"Yes, your Honor," replied Haines quickly "with the permission of the court and counsel, I'll withdraw the question."

"Granted," said Judge Jones after Alva Campbell had signaled his own assent. "Please continue your examination."

Bill Haines studied the notes he had made in preparation for his examination of the defendant. He flipped casually through some three or four papers, made an entry at the end of a paragraph, and closed his notebook. He pushed his chair away from the counsel table, gained his feet and walked unhurriedly to the open area of the courtroom nearest the witness stand. There was method in his activity. It gave him the few moments necessary to recraft his intentions for the presentation of the defendant's testimony.

It would not do, he recognized, for DiIulio to project to the jury as a recalcitrant witness from whom his own counsel was required to drag grudging and carefully guarded answers to specifically worded questions. Better, he thought, to loosen the reins and give him his head. Better to guide him through the telling of his story than to attempt to force the matter. A subtle change in the technique of his examination was indicated and he would modify his approach accordingly.

Bill Haines turned to face the witness. He lifted his lean frame up onto the balls of his feet, held a moment, then relaxed into a more comfortable stance. He dropped his arms and clasped his hands loosely in front of his beltline. He allowed his facial features to soften and he looked encouragement and reassurance to the defendant as he addressed him in the most disarming manner he could muster, "Donato, I want you to understand that none of the people gathered here in the courtroom — the judge, the members of the jury, the spectators," he directed the defendant's attention, sequentially, to those persons to whom he had alluded, "none of these people know very much about you. They don't really know who you are."

He waited for Ginocchio to translate his remarks. Then when the dialogue between the interpreter and the defendant had ended and DiIulio had nodded his understanding, Haines continued, "Because, Donato, I think it important that we all come to know you better, I want you to tell us, in your own way, about your family, your childhood, your life in the old country. Will you do that for us?"

When Ginocchio had made him understand what was wanted, Donato DiIulio made a rueful smile, nodded briefly and began to speak softly and haltingly. His words were directed to Bill Haines, whom he considered to be his ally, and were translated, sentence by sentence, by Ginocchio. His delivery was, at first, both tentative and tortuous, but as he proceeded, he seemed to gain confidence. His voice became stronger and the continuity of his speech increased. He fell readily into a verbal lockstep with Ginocchio and he quickly learned to pause at appropriate intervals in order to accommodate the need for translation. Much to everyone's surprise, the anticipated tedium in the taking of the defendant's testimony did not materialize and the flow of his narrative seemed smooth and essentially uninterrupted.

He had been the youngest of four children, he said, having been born when his parents were in their forties. His mother, he reflected, would now be past sixty and his father was some five years her senior. His three sisters were considerably older than he and all of them had married before he was ten years old.

The family had lived in a small fieldstone villa located on a hillside near the edge of town. There was a scant parcel of rocky, uneven ground nearby and his father tended a handful of goats and a few sheep for the people who owned their villa. When there was work to be had at the local vineyards his father, and often his mother, had helped with the harvest and he had been left to tend the stock. It was an easy chore, one he had performed handily since before he was five, and he had enjoyed it immensely.

They were very poor, but so was everyone else in the area. All of the provinces of Italy, and especially those of the south, were greatly impoverished. The ground was unfit for the growing of crops, except for the grapes, and apart from the vineyards, there was no industry.

And, like everyone else, they managed. They had supplemented their income from the picking of grapes and the tending of goats with bartered goods received in exchange for goat-cheeses made by his mother, fresh eggs from her hens, and fagots of firewood and kindling which he and his father gathered in the hills.

What little education he received had come from the sisters, those of the local Catholic orders and those who were of his own family. He had learned the rudiments of language and mathematics from the nuns during the four years he had attended the town's parish school. Then, after he had left the school in order to devote more time to his chores, his older siblings took occasional and sporadic turns at helping him to refine and to build upon that which he had already assimilated from his limited formal education. The net result was that he was able to read and write passably well, he could count, add, multiply, divide and make change, he knew a little bit of geography and he had been exposed to a great deal of Catholicism.

And, as his family was no poorer than others of his acquaintance, neither was his education any more lacking than that of his fellows. His childhood, he said, had been a happy one. His family was close — even after his sisters had married and had children of their own — and caring. He had had many friends, boys his own age and of similar circumstance. They had played at children's games, roamed the hills and fished the streams together. His voice strained with emotion as he reminisced about the pleasures and contentments of an adolescence which was both carefree and pastoral in nature. Nostalgically, and in consideration of his present circumstance, he wished that those times had never ended.

But end they did. And when it happened, it served to remind how truly tenuous their situation had been. The owner of their villa died and his heirs served notice that they had other uses for the property. The DiIulios would have to find somewhere else to live.

This had come to them at a time when his parents were no longer young. His father was well past sixty and had lost much of his former vigor. Because of that fact they had had no opportunity to find another suitable accommodation. Ultimately, and after much discussion and many tears, it was decided that the parents would go to live with one of the married daughters and Donato, who had just turned fifteen, would enter into an indenture for passage to America.

Donato DiIulio's familiar place within both family and community — the essence of his security — as well as his childhood, had ended at a stroke.

CHAPTER FIFTEEN

TUESDAY, MARCH 3RD, HAD BEEN A LONG TRIAL DAY. Judge Jones had been loathe to interrupt the continuity of the defendant's descriptive account of his family circumstances and his old world childhood. It was nearly six o'clock when Bill Haines raised an admonitory finger to the witness and suggested to the Court that they had reached an appropriate point at which to conclude the testimony for the day.

Despite the lateness of the hour and the lengthening shadows thrown by the lowering sunlight through the west windows of the courtroom the members of the jury had seemed almost unwilling for the session to end. They had paid close attention to Ginocchio's cogent translations of Donato DiIulio's recitation and had been caught up in his history of life in the old country.

Even the spectators, who had spent more than nine continuous hours in their conjoined and unyielding seats behind the bar, were reluctant to leave when Judge Jones sounded his gavel and announced that court would be in recess until the following morning.

And if the day had been long, the evening seemed disproportionately short for most of the principal participants.

By the time Deputy Landry had returned Donato DiIulio to his cell at the county jail, supper had been served and the plates, cups and silverware collected. He was glad for the solitude in which to eat the meal that Nellie Gibson had assembled and reheated for him. Then, shortly afterwards, he was equally glad for the chance to play at draughts with George Landry. Their evening games had become a matter of routine and a source of pleasure for both.

Their final game of the evening was interrupted by Sheriff Gibson's announcement that the prisoner had visitors. They were waiting in the second-floor conference room. Gibson asked Landry to take DiIulio on up and lock the three of them in the room together.

The visitors could only be Bill Haines and Charles Ginocchio. There had been no others. The visit was wholly impromptu, a spur of the moment thing, Haines explained through Ginocchio's translations. He had reflected, during the course of his own dinner hour, on DiIulio's testimony, that which they had just completed and that which they would take tomorrow. And, in doing so, he said, it had occurred to him that it might be helpful to review with DiIulio some of the concepts they had discussed over the last several months. So, with that in mind, he had sought out Ginocchio for assistance and the two of them had simply dropped in on him.

"First off," he said reassuringly, "I wanted you to know that I was impressed with today's testimony. I think you came across as candid and..." he hesitated, groping for the right word, "and, as likeable," he finished. "Someone with whom the jurors might want to relate."

He waited for Ginocchio to complete the translation, ascertained that he had been understood, and continued.

"But that isn't the real reason I've come down here tonight. What I really want to talk about is tomorrow. Tomorrow is crucial. That which you tell the jury tomorrow will be of paramount importance. The outcome of this trial will likely depend on it."

Bill Haines looked to Ginocchio and then to DiIulio. When both had nodded, he stood up and began to pace. "Now then," he began conversationally, "first thing in the morning we'll put you back on the stand and let you tell your story. You should continue as you have. Be candid, be honest. Be forthright. We want the jury to like you. We want them to identify with you. *Capische?*"

Another pause, a look to Ginocchio and then to DiIulio, a nod from each, and Haines took a seat directly opposite DiIulio. He looked searchingly into his eyes, demanding the latter's full attention.

"Alright," he continued. "As you know, I have consistently advised you to tell the truth at all times. I have insisted that your testimony be truthful and nothing other than the truth. Do you remember that?"

Translation, followed by a nod.

"What I say to you now is that what you tell this jury must not only be the truth, it must be *your* truth." Bill Haines set his jaw firmly. His eyes bored into DiIulio's. "And only *you* can know what *your* truth is."

This time, the translation completed, both DiIulio and Ginocchio looked perplexed, quizzical.

Bill Haines tried it again. "You will remember," he said, "that I have more than once explained to you the precise nature of the charge against you. It was part of my job, my duty to you as your counsel, to have done so.

"Let's be very certain that you understand all the ramifications. The specific charge against you is that of murder in the first degree. If you are convicted, the judge will be required to sentence you to die in the electric chair." Haines' pause at this juncture was deliberately long and intensely pregnant. "Unless, of course, the jury should recommend mercy. In that case the judge will be required to sentence you to imprisonment for the rest of your life."

As soon as Ginocchio had translated this last, DiIulio exploded in remonstrance. He chirped, stubbornly and animatedly to Ginocchio who explained, "he says he doesn't want to be shut away for a lifetime. He prefers — if convicted — to be executed."

Bill Haines sloughed off DiIulio's irruption with a wave of his hand. "That's youthful bravado," he said. "He doesn't really mean it."

Then to the slowly subsiding DiIulio, "But I haven't finished. You must also remember that in order to convict you of first degree murder, the jury must find that you killed this woman *intentionally*, that you meant to kill her, and *also*, that you killed her with *premeditated malice*.

"Alright so far?" he asked pedantically. "I've just described separate elements, *intention*, *premeditation* and *malice*. The jury must find that all three of those elements were present in order to return a verdict which will forfeit your life."

He paused for translation. He held up his left hand to signal that he would brook no interruption. When satisfied that DiIulio was with him he continued, "If the jury should find that you *intended* to kill her, but that you had not pre-planned it, that there was no *premeditation*, or that there was no *malice*, then their verdict cannot be murder in the first degree. It will have to be second degree.

"If, on the other hand, they should find that you didn't really *intend* to kill her, they must either return a verdict of manslaughter — or they must acquit you entirely.

"We've talked about this before, right? *Capische*? I simply need to go through it one more time.

"*Intention* and *malice*," he continued, "are states of mind. *Your* mind. Only *you* can truly know what went on in *your* mind. That's what I mean when I speak of *your* truth.

"On the other hand, if the state of your mind was such that you were incapable of forming an intention or harboring malice, if you were so affected that you either did not know what you were doing or could not prevent yourself from doing it, then the jury cannot convict you of murder in any degree. Do you understand what I've just told you?"

Charles Ginocchio took pains to make sure that DiIulio had assimilated all that Haines had said to him. Because he had been educated as a lawyer he was uniquely qualified to explain the ramifications and the subtle nuances involved. A protracted exchange occurred and Ginocchio ultimately reported that the defendant had a general comprehension of the principles involved.

"Good," responded Haines, anxious to put the cap on it. "Now please understand that I would never tell you to be untruthful. I have, in fact, been most assiduous in my insistence that you speak only the truth."

He paused for confirmation, got it and continued, "However, please remember that it is *your* truth, and yours alone, that you must convey to the jury."

It was an invitation.

"Do you understand me?" asked the lawyer. "Completely?"

Another translation. Another dialogue. Then Charles Ginocchio answered the question. "I believe he understands you very well, Mr. Haines. He has asked me to thank you for your visit here this evening and to assure you that he intends to speak the truth, and only the truth, as he understands it. He says that the jury will hear *his* truth."

* (*

TRIAL RESUMED WEDNESDAY MORNING. It was precisely nine o'clock when Judge Jones gavelled the session into order and silenced the imperfectly muted rumblings emanating from the overflowing crowd of spectators waiting patiently in the gallery section located just behind the bar. There were even more of those, he noted, than at previous sessions. The outer doors of the courthouse building had been opened at eight and the corridors were immediately jammed with would-be observers. Then, half an hour later, the tall double doors of the courtroom itself were opened and the seats, aisleways and perimeter spaces were swiftly filled to capacity.

The case had, from the outset, generated considerable public attention and now that the event of trial approached its culmination, the prevalent and widespread interest in the proceedings appeared to have intensified.

Inside the bar it appeared that the landscape had not changed from the previous day. Donato DiIulio was once again seated in the sturdy chair atop the witness platform and Charles Ginocchio stood at his right shoulder. Judge Jones, in his full-length black robe, was comfortably ensconced in his upholstered swivel chair at the bench, Prosecutor Alva Campbell was at the State's counsel table, and Bill Haines had stationed himself near the center of the arena. It was obvious that they would begin today where they had left off yesterday.

At a nod from Judge Jones, Bill Haines addressed the witness, first by way of reprise, then to pick up the thread and to guide the testimony.

"Donato," he encouraged, "you have told us that a decision was taken within your family that you would enter into an indenture for passage from Italy to America. Have I stated that correctly?"

And after a short colloquy, Charles Ginocchio responded. "The witness acknowledges that to be correct."

The questioning continued:

Q.   (By Haines) And did you, at that time, enter into such an indenture?
     (Colloquy)
A.   (By Ginocchio) Yes.
Q.   And thereby came to this country?
A.   (By Ginocchio) Yes.

Q.   *When was that?*

A.   *(By Ginocchio) The witness says he arrived at the port of New York in July of 1903.*

Because Haines was anxious that the format for the taking of the defendant's testimony should quickly revert to yesterday's free and easy narrative style, his next remark to the witness was not so much a question as it was a directive.

"Please tell us about it."

Donato DiIulio readily obliged. He seemed more relaxed, more confident and better assured, than before. He described the course of an arduous and protracted odyssey overland from Civaqua to Napoli, Naples, where he had signed the documents which would provide him ship's fare in exchange for his agreement to work it off in America, the long ocean voyage to the land of opportunity and abundance, and through the frustrating, bureaucratic punctillio of Ellis Island. It was late July before he was released from immigration and his indenture assigned to a coal-mining concern which operated a series of mines in West Virginia. That company arranged for his transport, along with other immigrants, also Italian, by railroad boxcar across the mountains to a camp near Huntington.

He spoke of his life at the mining camp and his having been befriended by Johnny Bellini. Johnny Bell, everyone called him, was five or even six years older than DiIulio and was infinitely wiser in the ways of the world. He soon became DiIulio's mentor, his protector and his confidant. He was very much like *un fratello maggiore*, an older brother, and the young Donato relied on his judgment and trusted him implicitly. So when Johnny Bell assured him that he had served enough of his indenture to leave the mining camp with impunity and assured him of better working conditions and better pay in the railroading business, he hesitated not at all in joining his *fratello* as a gandy dancer for the Hoover-Kinnear Company.

He had liked railway construction work. The daily rigors involved in the clearing and grading of the roadway, the setting of the ties and the placement of the heavy rails, spiking them firmly into position, were more than compensated for by their pride, that of the entire work crew, as each new mile was completed. Better still, the pay was better than coal-mining and the work was above ground, outdoors in the open air.

It was railroading that brought him to Ohio, he said, first to Piqua, then westward with the progression of the Big Four to Covington. Actually, he and Johnny Bell had come together. Each time the company had proposed to relocate one of them the other had opted to go along. They had arrived in Covington in the late summer of '05. Donato DiIulio was then seventeen years old, Johnny Bell perhaps twenty-two or twenty-three. It was there they met the other Johnny, Johnny Nickel. He was a resident of Covington, along with his wife and children, and he was four or five years older yet than Johnny Bell. The three of them soon became great friends, *amicos*, and whiled away their spare time together, usually as a threesome.

Donato was very happy in the United States. He worked hard, made more money than he had thought possible, and sent most of it home to his parents. He got along well with virtually everyone he worked with, both in the mine and on the tracks, despite his inability to speak English. Some of the men had made fun of him, he knew, because of that fact, but he hadn't really minded. It was done with a good will and he laughed along with them. Besides, he knew he deserved whatever ribbing he got because it was his own fault he couldn't speak the language. He had tried, really hard, to pick it up on his own, but he seemed to have no aptitude for it. He was still trying to learn, he said. In fact, just last fall, while he was in jail, Deputy Landry told him that Sheriff Gibson was sending two young boys to a "reform school" and he had asked to be sent there also in order that he might be taught to read and write in English.

And he had liked Covington especially well. It reminded him of his home town in the old country. It was only slightly larger than Civaqua and had the same kind of terrain with gently rolling hills although it was also much greener and infinitely more lush than anything he'd known before. And it was the friendliest, most hospitable community he'd been in. There was a small Italian contingent located out at the edge of town and there was even an "Italian store" where he could make himself understood.

Donato DiIulio was so much enchanted by the village of Covington that he was determined to find living quarters there and to make it his permanent home in America. So as the Big Four construction job neared completion and the company prepared to move its crew to Steubenville, he began to cast about for another job, one that would permit him to stay in Covington. It would entail a parting of the ways with Johnny Bell, his *fratello maggiore*, who would be moving on to Steubenville, but Donato DiIulio was determined to remain. Then, when he'd been hired to work at the brickyard, it all became possible.

And if he had been happy during the first four years of his life in the United States, that happiness turned to rapture when he found the love of his life. Except that when he imparted that information to Ginocchio from the witness stand, he didn't look rapturous. His voice broke, he buried his face in his hands and choked back a sob. Ginocchio, along with everyone else in the courtroom, waited for Donato DiIulio to regain his composure.

Then, when he was ready to continue, he spoke of his introduction to Forest May Floyd — Frosty — and of the development of the relationship between them. He described, in infinite detail and in perfect chronology, each of their frequent meetings, assignations and trysts over the thirty-five day period April 5th through May 9th of 1907. As he spoke of those events, volubly and without notes of any kind, it was readily apparent to everyone in the courtroom that however deficient his language skills might have been, there was nothing wrong with his memory. He appeared to possess total recall as he testified concerning specific dates and places and provided a verbatim recapitulation of each of their significant conversations. In view of his obvious language deficit, it was a truly remarkable performance.

And because it was both thorough and specific as to all of the incidents of his relationship with Frosty, including those sexual in their essence, his testimony was perceived, at least by contemporary standards, to be both lurid and sensational. Speaking wistfully, without hindrance or interruption from either court or counsel, he chronicled for the benefit of the jury all of the particulars of his own seduction and all their subsequent intimate encounters. His depictions of matters carnal were so exceptionally graphic that the spectators in the rear of the courtroom strained forward in their seats and cupped their ears in order to better hear Ginocchio's translations. However scandalized they may have been, they were at pains to miss no word of it.

Bill Haines made no effort to stem the flow of the defendant's spicy descriptions. As a matter of trial strategy, it suited his purpose very well and, by means of occasional promptings, he actually encouraged the witness to be more specific. He wanted the jury to understand the true nature, and the full extent, of the defendant's obsession.

Donato DiIulio beamed radiantly when he reached the subject of their, his and Frosty's, betrothal. He spoke glowingly of his great love for her, an emotion that was at once sacred, total and all-encompassing. It was transcendent and eternal, such a love as could occur but once in a lifetime. And she had loved him as well. She had promised to marry him on their very first date. She had even begun a hope chest and had set about acquiring household goods and preparing her wedding trousseau.

They were to be married in the fall, he said proudly, in New York City, and then they would travel to Italy so that she could meet his family and he could show her off to the friends of his childhood. His happiness, just in the anticipation of their marriage, was complete.

They had had some arguments, he conceded, about one thing or another, but then what young couple had not had to work their way through the occasional spat? And, he grinned broadly, it was always so much fun making up afterwards. But despite their occasional disagreements they had remained constant in their determination to marry. There had never been any question on that score.

Until, that is, that terrible Tuesday, May 7th, when she had become so angry with him. He hadn't really understood, that night, why she was angry, but he thought on it and later concluded that she was upset because she believed him to be less firmly committed to their approaching nuptials than was she. He presumed she felt that if he really cared for her, he would husband his money better, or get a better paying job, so that they would be financially able to marry as planned.

He hadn't realized how really angry she was until she began to shun him and to treat him badly. Even then, he was certain that they could get through this thing, this lovers' misunderstanding, and that he could convince her of the depth of his commitment and the force of his determination.

And when he could not convince her, when she persistently refused to relent and to accept his protestations, he simply ran out of options. Frosty's obdurate contumacy, inexplicable and irrational, effectively foreclosed their further exercise of free choice, and made them captive to the cruel, immutable force of destiny, *la forza del destino*.

It was that force, pitiless and ineluctable, Ginocchio translated, that demanded the sacrifice of their separate lives in order that the two lovers might be conjoined through all eternity, *per sempre*. Donato DiIulio, in attempting to end both their lives, did that which he was constrained to do. The tragedy, he said, was that he had failed to die alongside his betrothed.

Thus concluded that portion of the defendant's testimony which was essentially narrative in character. It had begun tentatively, uncertainly. Then, as he'd spoken of his childhood and of his life in America, the defendant had gained confidence and the words came quickly, tinged slightly with an aura of nostalgia. He had seemed almost beatific when he described the events of his courtship with Frosty and their pledges to love one another forever. Finally, as his story drew to its ending, he was overcome by emotion and the words came painfully and with difficulty. The words and phrases conveyed to the jury by Charles Ginocchio had not been, in every case, precise verbatim translations of the words spoken by the witness, but it had been a fair and accurate rendition. And while Ginocchio may have unwittingly embellished the testimony in an effort to accomplish a comprehensible interpretation, he was entirely faithful in communicating the sense of it.

There remained but a few more matters to be covered before the direct examination of the defendant could be completed and Bill Haines confronted them directly.

Q. *On May 9th, 1907, the day Forest May Floyd died, how did you feel about her?*

A. *(By Ginocchio) I loved her more than anything in life.*

Q. *Were you angry with her?*

A. *(By Ginocchio) No. I was distressed because we had reached an impasse, but I was never angry with her.*

Q. *Did you feel any malice toward her?*

A. *(By Ginocchio) No, never. I loved her.*

Q. *Did you intend to hurt her?*

A. *(By Ginocchio) No, no, of course not.*

Q. *When you left your room that morning, when you set out to find her, what did you intend?*

A. *(By Ginocchio) I intended to speak with her, to assure her concerning my commitment. I wanted our lives to go on as before.*

Q. *You hadn't intended to kill her?*

A. *(By Ginocchio) No.*

Q. *And you'd formed no plan to do so?*

A. *(By Ginocchio) No.*

Bill Haines permitted himself an inward sigh of relief. He had touched on the three principle elements of murder in the first degree and had elicited satisfactory answers. He knew that Alva Campbell would challenge those answers on cross, but he couldn't help that. He had done what he could. He had but one further matter to explore:

Q. *Did I correctly understand you to say that you had sexual intercourse with Forest May on your very first date?*

A. *(By Ginocchio) Yes.*

Q. *Within hours of your acquaintanceship?*

A. *(By Ginocchio) Yes.*

Q. *Had you ever had sexual intercourse before? With anyone?*

A. *(By Ginocchio) No. I had had no experience with girls. There was only my mother and my sisters.*

Q. *Am I also correct in that you and Forest May had sexual intercourse on each and every occasion you were together?*

A. (By Ginocchio) Yes. That is, until the time of our final estrangement.

Q. And each time you had sex with her you gave her money. Is that true?

A. (By Ginocchio) For our hope chest.

Q. Let me ask it another way. Was there ever a time when you'd had sex with her and didn't give her any money?

A. (By Ginocchio) No.

Q. She insisted on it, didn't she?

A. (By Ginocchio) She wanted it for our hope chest. We both did.

Q. As a matter of fact, there was one particular occasion when you were a little slow in gettin' your money up and she just plain reached into your pocket and took it. Isn't that so?

A. No answer.

Q. And she ripped your pocket in the process?

A. No answer.

Donato DiIulio didn't like where this dialogue was going. He became sullen and balky. When Ginocchio translated his lawyer's questions, DiIulio simply glowered and declined to respond.

Haines forced the issue:

Q. Come on, Donato, I need an answer. Was there an occasion when Forest May tore your pants while trying to extract money from your pocket? Yes or No?

A. (By Ginocchio, after a protracted colloquy) Yes.

Q. And was that just after you'd had sex with her?

A. (By Ginocchio) Yes.

Q. Unless I am much mistaken, you are wearing that same pair of pants today. Is that correct?

A. (By Ginocchio) Yes.

Bill Haines instructed the witness, "Please stand up and show the jury the damage done to your pants by Forest May."

Donato DiIulio was very nearly recalcitrant. He understood what it was Haines was suggesting about the love of his life and he resented the implication. He felt betrayed by his counsel. Finally, after a lengthy discussion with Ginocchio during which he scowled darkly at Haines, he complied. A large tear from the beltline to the bottom of his pocket, clumsily repaired, could be discerned from the farthest corner of the jury box.

Q.   *Who made the repair to your pants?*
A.   *(By Ginocchio) I did. It's the best I was able to do. It doesn't matter.*

Bill Haines refused to let it go. He knew he had alienated his client, but he was determined to make the point and to press it home.

Q.   *Donato, you have told us that there was never a time when you had sex with Forest May and did not give her money?*
A.   *(By Ginocchio) You do not understand. The money was for the hope chest.*
Q.   *Please answer the question. Yes or no?*
A.   *(By Ginocchio, after repeating the entire question) Yes. I have already said so.*
Q.   *And the price, Donato, on these several occasions, how was it determined?*
A.   *(By Ginocchio) There was no "price"; I contributed what I could afford — for the hope chest.*
Q.   *The price, for the service, then, was pretty much what the market would bear. Is that right?*

And when DiIulio bridled, set his jaw and refused to answer, Bill Haines appeared to relent. "Never mind, Donato. I withdraw the question." Then to Judge Jones he said simply, "That completes my direct examination your honor. Tender the witness."

CHAPTER SIXTEEN

BILL HAINES SPENT MOST OF THE LUNCH BREAK trying to repair the damage he'd just done to the rapport he had so carefully cultivated with his client over the course of the past four months. Donato DiIulio was incensed, resentful of Haines' brutally frank insinuations concerning his beloved and his implicit characterization of their liaison as something cheap, venal and tawdry rather than the beatific, idyllic and perdurable love affair he had perceived it to be.

"I have no wish," he said as Ginocchio translated, "to shatter your illusions — or, indeed, to convince you that your relationship with this woman was anything other than what you have believed. Neither is it my intention to try to convince you that her character and her motives were anything other than chastely honorable. It would be cruel and insensitive for me to do so. I recognize that in spite of all that has happened you have loved her well, if perhaps too much, and that her memory will always be poignant for you.

"However," he continued earnestly, "if I am to be of any help to you in this matter, it is imperative that I convince the jury — not you, Donato, but the jury — that this young woman, by her own conduct, contributed to her death. I must show them that she herself set in motion those powerful forces which inexorably and irresistably produced this tragedy we have been replaying these past several days."

Haines looked to DiIulio as Ginocchio translated his words into Italian. DiIulio glared fiercely at the wall, the floor, the empty jury box. Arms folded across his chest, face closed, he fairly exuded his resentment as Ginocchio, in his own words, tried to convey the sense of what Haines had tried to communicate to him. And because it was Ginocchio speaking, he listened. He continued to sulk and to avert his gaze, but he did listen.

And when Haines asked, "Do you understand?" DiIulio swallowed hard, stared defiantly into space and, after a long, charged moment, nodded in apparent resignation.

It was the best he could hope for, Haines recognized. He patted DiIulio on the shoulder, gathered his papers, and signalled Deputy Landry that they had finished their conference and he could take the defendant back to the jailhouse for what was left of the lunch hour.

ALVA CAMPBELL'S CROSS-EXAMINATION of Donato DiIulio was thorough and painstaking as to detail. As a part of the process, he required the defendant to revisit much of his testimony on direct. If he had hoped, however, to ferret out and to develop inconsistencies or contradictions, he was sorely disappointed. DiIulio's answers to his questions, differently and less sympathetically worded than Haines', were the same he had given earlier. Until, that is, they got to the essential elements of intent, malice and premeditation:

Q.   *(By Campbell) You have told us, sir, that you never intended to harm or kill Forest May and that you had formed no plan to do so. Do I have that correctly?*

A.   *(By Ginocchio) Yessir. That was my testimony.*

Q.   *How was it then, that you happened to have a revolver in your pocket?*

A.   (*After a pause*) *I often carried it with me — for protection.*

Q.   *Protection, sir? From what?*

A.   (*Pause*) *I don't know. There are people who dislike me because I am Italian.*

Q.   *Did you carry your revolver with you the day before? On Wednesday?*

A.   *No.*

Q.   *Or the day before that?*

A.   *No.*

Q.   *Isn't it true, sir, that you had deposited your revolver with Mr. Hill for safekeeping more than a week earlier and that you retrieved it from him on the morning of the shooting?*

A.   *Yes.*

Q.   *Why?*

A.   *I thought I might need it.*

Q.   *Against Forest May?*

A.   *Yes.*

Q.   *And you did use it against her, didn't you?*

A.   *Yes.*

Q.   *You took it out of your pocket, pointed it at her back — at close range — and pulled the trigger, did you not?*

A.   *Yes. I did those things.*

Q.   *You shot her twice, didn't you?*

A.   *Yes.*

Q.   *Do you still want this jury to believe that you didn't intend to kill her?*

A.   *I meant that we should die together.*

Q.   *You intended to kill her first and then yourself, is that right?*

A.   *Yes.*

Bill Haines winced inwardly as Alva Campbell meticulously and relentlessly nailed down each of the essential elements of his case. One by one he closed off the defendant's potential escape routes. He was very nearly finished:

Q.   *And when you did this thing, when you pulled the trigger and fired two bullets into Forest May's back, did you know what you were doing?*

A.   *Yes.*

Q.   *You were in complete possession of your faculties, and fully aware of the nature and consequences of your acts, were you not?*

A.   *Yes. I was.*

The defendant's frank and unqualified admissions fell on Bill Haines' ears like hammer blows. Each new concession effectively scuttled another aspect of his projected defense. He reflected, as he listened to his client's testimony, on his admonition to DiIulio that he tell *his* truth. His thinly disguised invitation to rationalize had been blithely ignored and he was going to have to deal with it as best he could.

Alva Campbell had been standing at the far end of the jury box, just outside the railing. It was a station both favorite and familiar to him, one from which he could direct the flow of testimony towards the jury and simultaneously monitor the jurors' reactions to what was being said. Now he closed his notebook as if he had concluded his examination and strolled thoughtfully back to his chair at the counsel table. Before sitting down, he redirected his attention to the witness:

> Q.   *I believe, sir, that you were raised in the Roman Catholic religion?*
>
> A.   *Yessir.*
>
> Q.   *You are familiar with the Commandments?*
>
> A.   *Yessir.*
>
> Q.   *The Sixth Commandment, "Thou shalt not kill," do you know that one?*
>
> A.   *Yessir.*
>
> Q.   *One final question, then, Mr. DiIulio. On May 9, 1907, the day this event occurred, did you know it to be wrong — against the laws of God and man — to take the life of another human being?*
>
> A.   *(After a colloquy punctuated with pauses) Yes.*

Alva Campbell lowered his sturdy frame into the counsel chair, turned his eyes to Judge Jones and announced softly, "No further questions, Your Honor."

AS IF TO SHOW THAT THE GREAT STATE OF OHIO, the prosecution, didn't have a corner on the Commandment market, Bill Haines called Johnny Bell, Joseph Caserta and Tony Buttera to demonstrate that Blanche Floyd and Johnny Nickel had each borne false witness when they had testified for the state.

Johnny Bell was the first and the most compelling of all. He described his early friendship with Donato DiIulio and the course of their movements from the coal mines of West Virginia to the railheads of Piqua and Covington, Ohio.

He and DiIulio had come to Covington together in September of 1905. A few months later, just after the new year, they had met Johnny Nickel and the three had become fast friends. Then in May of that year he and Nickel had had their first assignation with the Floyd sisters, Blanche and Frosty, out at the electric plant. The girls had brought blankets and they paired off, he with Frosty and Nickel with Blanche, and each couple had sexual intercourse. They gave the girls five dollars apiece. The arrangement had worked well, seemed satisfactory to all, and the two couples continued in that vein for about a year. As a general rule they would be together one or two nights a week, usually as a foursome. Fridays were almost routinely reserved as "date nights", but they frequently came together on other occasions. Sometimes, on week nights, he and Nickel, either singly or together, would walk out the pike to the girls' home, wait till their parents had retired, and then call down one or both by jiggling the colored strings that hung down the side of the house.

There were a couple of times, he said, when they had switched partners "just for fun", but for the most part he had considered Frosty to be his girl and Blanche to be Nickel's. Then, in April of '07, the company required him to move to Steubenville to work on a new rail line. Before he left he thought he did Donato a favor by "fixing him up" with Frosty.

"I never dreamed it would end this way," he added dourly.

"When you and Nickel had sex with these girls," asked Haines, "did you always give them money?"

"Yessir, it was expected."

"How much money?" Haines wanted to know. "What was the going rate?"

"It varied, maybe two, three dollars. Sometimes more if we were flush. But there wasn't really any "set price"; it was more like a gift we'd wanted them to have. Kinda showed them our appreciation." He smiled ruefully. "If it wasn't enough, they'd generally let you know about it."

"Did you love Forest May?" asked Haines.

"No. No, sir, I didn't. I appreciated her a whole lot, but I didn't love her."

In an effort to directly confront and discredit the earlier testimony of Blanche Floyd and Johnny Nickel, both of whom had testified as a part of the prosecution's case in chief, Bill Haines segued from the general to the specific:

Q. *Mr. Bell, I will represent to you that Blanche Floyd came into this courtroom — just yesterday — and testified under oath that as of the night before her sister's death she had known Johnny Nickel "only slightly". Do you believe that testimony to be true?*

A. *Of course not. I've already said that she and Johnny Nickel were seeing each*

*other once or twice a week that I was aware of. I know he was screwin' her
pretty regular. I was there. (Winces.)*

*I'm sorry, Your Honor. I mean they were having sexual intercourse on a
regular basis.*

Q. *I will also represent to you that Blanche Floyd has asserted — again under
oath — that she had never so much as heard of you.*

Is that assertion true?

A. *Now that's almost funny. I've got a letter from her right here in my pocket.
She wrote me last summer to tell me what had happened to Frosty.*

Q. *You have the letter in your pocket?*

A. *Yes, I do. I got it out and read it again before I came here for the trial. Here
it is. (The witness hands the letter to counsel.)*

She even signed it "Love, Blanche F."

Q. *Are you familiar with her handwriting?*

A. *Oh, yes. I've seen notes she's sent to Johnny Nickel. It's hers.*

Q. *Alright, let's talk about Johnny Nickel. I'll represent to you that he also came
into this courtroom yesterday and testified under oath that he barely knew any
of the Floyd girls, that he knew Donato DiIulio only by sight, that he knew
you only slightly and that he had never been anywhere in company with either
of the Floyd girls, with Donato DiIulio, or with you.*

Do you believe that testimony to be true?

A. *No. It isn't true. Not a bit of it.*

*Johnny Nickel's married, got kids. I understand he don't want to tell about the
girls. But he and Donato — Danny, he wanted us to call him — and
me, we were together 'bout every day. We were good friends.*

*Matter of fact, I've got several letters from him since this happened. I don't
have them with me, I don't. I didn't think I'd need them.*

No. If that's what he said, it ain't true.

Johnny Bell was followed to the stand by Joseph Caserta and Tony Buttera.
Caserta said he had lived in Covington in 1907 and that he had seen Johnny
Nickel, Donato DiIulio and the two Floyd girls together two and three times
a week. Buttera told of his having seen the four of them having a midday
picnic in a boxcar parked on a siding near his commissary. He's spoken to
them briefly and they'd had something of an argument.

Alva Campbell had no cross-examination for any of them. He had suspected
that Blanche and Nickel had lied, for reasons that were abundantly obvious,
and he didn't want to argue the matter. Bill Haines, on the other hand, was
well content to have scored a point or two against the prosecution. It wasn't

much, he knew, but there weren't really that many opportunities. He'd have to take what he could get.

Thomas and Angie Hill had testified as a part of the prosecution's case in chief. Now they appeared again as a part of the defendant's evidence. In both instances their testimony was essentially neutral in character. It neither helped nor damaged either side. They simply told what they knew of DiIulio's routine comings and goings during the short period he had boarded with them at Hill House. The only nuance was Mr. Hill's off-hand observation that DiIulio had acted a "little crazy" the morning he had reclaimed his revolver. In response to further probing on the subject, Hill refused to elaborate. "He just acted kinda different," was all he would say.

Mrs. William Clark, a longtime Covington resident, professed herself to be familiar with the handwriting of Blanche Floyd. Asked to examine the letter which had been produced by Johnny Bell, she unequivocally pronounced the handwriting to be that of the ostensible signatory, Blanche Floyd.

The testimony of Edward Simmons, Barnhart Wagner and Adda Babylon was concise, unremarkable and essentially worthless. Each of them had seen the defendant at one time or another on the day of the shooting. Apart from their separate reports of isolated sightings, they added nothing whatever to the mix.

And then it was over. The evidence was in. Of the forty-nine witnesses ultimately subpoenaed by the defense, only ten apart from the defendant himself, had actually been called to testify. And, most remarkably, Alva Campbell had not seen fit to cross-examine any of them. Then, when Bill Haines announced to the court that the defense rested its case, Alva Campbell simply stated that there would be no rebuttal. There was no need. There was nothing for him to rebut.

It was precisely four o'clock and Judge Jones excused the jury. Tomorrow, he told them, they would hear the arguments of counsel and his own instructions concerning the law. The case would then be entrusted to them for decision. He recommended to them that they retire early, sleep soundly, and come back in the morning prepared to think well and to reason clearly.

BOTH OF MIAMI COUNTY'S TWO NEWSPAPERS had carried front-page, above-the fold, news coverage of the trial. Complete with banner headlines, photographs of the participants, and day-to-day, witness-by-witness accounts of the proceedings, their reportage was both thorough and professional. They differed subtly, and only slightly, in style — and perhaps in objectivity.

The fact that the trial had aroused a great deal of public attention and had attracted a full gallery of spectators was remarked upon by each newspaper. The staid and proper Piqua Leader-Dispatch primly reported that:

The case is satisfying the most sensational, and large crowds continue to attend.

And the more editorially-oriented Miami Union concluded its column with the observation:

The usual number of feeble-minded females are thronging the courtroom, seemingly reveling in the disgusting and degrading nature of the trial. The murderer is the recipient of dainty baskets of lunches and flowers contributed by this same class who appear to find an object of hero worship in a murderer.

CHAPTER SEVENTEEN

THE FINAL PERORATIONS OF COUNSEL, their respective summations of the evidence and their closing arguments to the jury, consumed all of Thursday morning's session of court. In accordance with prescribed standards of practice, and because he had the burden of proof, Alva Campbell was both entitled and obliged to open and close that phase of the trial during which the attorneys are permitted to comment upon the evidence and to plead their causes direct to the jury.

Campbell's remarks were, in large measure, an amplified reprise of his opening statement. He did not re-read the grand jury's original indictment of the defendant for first degree murder, but he did take the document into his hand and wave it about as he reminded the jury of its content and its significance. He reviewed and critiqued the testimony of the witnesses, those called by the defense as well as his own. He allowed, even, the possibility that two of the State's witnesses, Blanche Floyd and Johnny Nickel, might have been something less than fully truthful with reference to certain "sensitive, personal matters, having no real bearing on any of the matters at issue."

"Mr. Haines has taken great pains," he observed, "to convince you that Blanche Floyd and Johnny Nickel were less than candid in their denials of an affair between themselves and an acquaintanceship with Johnny Bell and with the defendant Donato DiIulio."

He looked at the jury askance. "To what end has he done so? Ask yourselves, gentlemen, what possible difference can it make in the outcome of this trial?

"Assume for the moment — and I certainly don't concede it — but assume for the sake of argument that these two people, Blanche Floyd and Johnny Nickel were romantically involved with one another and that they lied to conceal it. Assume that each of them testified falsely in order to protect their reputations, to avoid public scorn. It would be understandable for them to do so. Not commendable, but understandable.

"Assume all that to be true, as Mr. Haines would have you do, and then consider how any of it alters the basic, uncontroverted fact that this man DiIulio, the defendant, deliberately and maliciously fired two bullets into Forest Floyd's back, at point blank range and with every intention of taking her life.

"The conclusion, of course, is obvious. The ultimate fact that the defendant committed murder in the first degree is altered not a single whit, not an iota, by the existence or nonexistence of any kind of illicit relationship between Blanche Floyd and Johnny Nickel. The question itself is the rankest sort of red herring, an unfair tactic to divert your attention from the real issue to be decided."

Alva Campbell devoted the greatest part of his comments to the testimony of the defendant himself. More compelling, even, than the eye-witness accounts he had brought them, he told the jury, was the defendant's own account of his having pestered, harassed, stalked and finally murdered this hapless young woman whose only offense had been her unwillingness to requite her assassin's misdirected and unwholesome attentions.

"We have only to consult the defendant's own testimony," he emphasized. "He has described for us, in infinite detail, every event which occurred and every act which he performed that fateful day last May when he shot this unfortunate woman to death in the center of downtown Covington and in full view of her two sisters and other onlookers.

"Not only has he told you what he did, that he killed this young woman," Campbell began building steam, "he also told you, in no uncertain terms, why he killed her. He as much as admitted that he did so because she had rejected him. She had spurned his unwanted attentions and, for no better reason than that, he took her life. Without warning and from behind, gentlemen of the jury, the way of a coward. Cravenly and remorselessly, he shot her in the back so that she died within minutes. She had resisted his advances, so he simply executed her — ruthlessly and without the slightest show of sympathy or human compassion.

"Never mind that he has said he believed they were somehow engaged to be married. Never mind any of that kind of foolishness. Even if true, rather than delusional or merely perceptual on his part, such a relationship could scarcely justify her homicide. It would be ludicrous for the defense to suggest otherwise.

"The Court will instruct you concerning the legal concepts of malice, premeditation and intention, those specific elements which the State must prove in order to support a conviction of the crime of murder in the first degree. The giving of that instruction as to matters of law is within the sole province of the Court and it would be improper for me to intrude upon that function.

"However, against the backdrop of the court's anticipated instructions on the law, I will remind you that the defendant, Donato DiIulio, has admitted from the witness stand that he killed Forest May Floyd by shooting her twice in the back. He has also freely admitted that he had planned to do so hours beforehand, that he had armed himself for that very purpose prior to leaving his room at Hill House that morning, and that at the moment he pulled the trigger he had intended to take her life. Finally, of course, you will remember that he acknowledged that he was at all times in full possession of his faculties and was alertly aware, not only of the nature and quality of his acts, but that the taking of a human life was wrong, that it was against the laws of God and those of man.

"With those admissions, gentlemen, the defendant has effectively convicted himself of the offense charged in the indictment. He has confessed to each of the necessary elements and he has expressly eschewed any claim of justification or avoidance."

Alva Campbell had done his work well. Throughout the course of the trial he had presented his evidence in logical, orderly fashion and had conducted his cross-examinations thoroughly and shrewdly. He had constructed a compelling and seemingly irrefutable case against the defendant and he had slammed shut, one by one, all of the doors by which the defendant and his counsel might have sought to escape. Then, in his summation, he had meticulously parsed and examined all of the evidence and he had argued his cause fervently and eloquently. Now, after more than ninety minutes, he began to wind it down.

"The evidence in this case is overwhelming. It is also conclusive as to all matters potentially at issue. The State has proven to you, beyond any reasonable doubt, each and every element of the charge set forth in the indictment. We have shown to you those physical acts by which the defendant killed his victim; we have shown his intention to take her life and the malice aforethought which engendered his evil purpose; and finally, we have demonstrated the absence of any single circumstance which might conceivably mitigate the sheer depravity of his crime."

With an affectation of total candor, Alva Campbell offered, "I confess to you, gentlemen, that I have been unable to identify any real controversy between the parties as to any of the factual matters before us. Except for the wholly extraneous question as to the existence or nonexistence of an affair between Blanche Floyd and Johnny Nickel, the evidence presented by the defense has been entirely consistent with that presented by the prosecution. If there are any other discrepancies in the testimony, or any other factual issues anywhere in the case, I seem to have missed them.

"And if, for that matter, there has yet emerged any theory of defense, some rationale upon which to argue for a verdict other than guilty as charged, I seem to have missed that also. The evidence presented by the defendant has not only failed to contradict the State's case, it has actually confirmed and buttressed it in every particular.

"That circumstance is not, of course, the fault of the defendant's attorney. Mr. Haines is an able and experienced lawyer. He has championed Mr. DiIulio's cause to the best of his very considerable abilities. That is a part of his sworn duty to the Court and to our American system of laws and he has performed that duty well. Even so, Mr. Haines cannot create a defense or present evidence where none exists. Neither he nor his client can change the facts.

"You also, gentlemen of the jury, have a sworn duty to the Court and to our judicial system. Each of you has taken an oath to fairly try the issues in this case and to render a just verdict in accordance with the facts and the law as given to you by the Court. I have every confidence that you will discharge that duty faithfully and conscientiously. The totality of the evidence in this case — that produced by both sides — constitutes a solemn mandate that you perform that duty by returning a verdict of murder in the first degree *and*, gentlemen, that verdict must also be without recommendation. The defendant himself showed no slightest mercy to his victim and there is nothing in the evidence to evoke the least bit of our sympathy or compassion for him. The State of Ohio demands the imposition of the death penalty, and as the official representative of the State, in these proceedings, it is my duty to insist on it."

As he spoke these last imperative phrases, Alva Campbell had projected his head, torso and arms so far over the railing and into the box that he was very nearly at one with the jurors. Now he stood erect and retreated a step or so, toward the center of the room. He clasped his hands together at his beltline, allowed the tension to drain from his features, and addressed the jury in a relaxed and conversational tone.

"Gentlemen of the jury, all of us who live in this county have become aware of the developing class of young men, mostly immigrants and day-laborers, who are at large within our separate communities. They have no permanent homes, no familial or other local ties, and they have no history. For the most part they are ignorant, uneducated and without a shred of moral fiber. It has become the habit of these people, these young men, to prey upon our young women. Unhappily, and for one reason or another, perhaps because of the railhead, the town of Covington seems to have a greater concentration of these people than has the rest of the county. The daughters, and even the wives, of its good citizens, the girls and the young women of the town, are sorely at risk in such an environment. They deserve our protection from the ever-present menace posed by this motley class of unbridled rogues.

"Such a person as I have described is the defendant, Donato DiIulio. Ignorant and unlettered, alien and rootless, he has wreaked his own brand of havoc on this innocent young woman and her family. We cannot, in good conscience, permit such a disaster to pass unpunished.

Alva Campbell paused meaningfully. He stood stock-still in front of the jury box. One by one, he locked eyes with each of the twelve jurors. Then he released them with a single admonition, stern, yet softly spoken, "Gentlemen, do your duty."

NOT MORE THAN TWENTY MINUTES LATER, after the customary mid-morning recess, the players were once more in position, the jury in the box and the spectators returned to their seats and into the aisleways behind the bar. Judge Jones had experienced no difficulty in restoring order to the courtroom as a pervasive hush of anticipation settled over the ritually contrived, yet increasingly familiar tableau. The final arguments of counsel, especially those of experienced defense counsel in high profile cases, were unique and much-awaited highlights in the humdrum stream of events in Miami County, Ohio.

This case in particular had engendered an inordinate degree of interest and speculation concerning the defendant's argument to the jury. Alva Campbell had been quite correct in his assertion that no real theory of defense had yet emerged and it was difficult to imagine what sort of appeal might be made on the defendant's behalf.

Bill Haines, then, suffered no want of attention when he closed his trial notebook, pushed aside the copious notes he had taken during the course of the trial, and strode easily to his favorite station, near the center of the courtroom, directly in front of the jury box. He nodded in the direction of the prosecutor, then to Judge Jones, and surveyed the jury. His stance was erect, yet casual, his slight weight neatly balanced on the soles of his feet. With lean sinewy hands loosely gripping the lapels of his jacket, he seemed relaxed and unhurried. His manner and appearance conveyed to the jury that they were not to expect either a flowery oration or a pedantic lecture. It was as though a discussion were in the offing, a congenial discourse between colleagues mutually engaged in a common quest.

Bill Haines inclined his head in an implied salutation. He addressed them amiably, "Gentlemen," and several of the jurors bobbed their own heads in reply. He paused until the exchange had been completed. "Seems like we've been at it here a long time. I know that. And it's been hard work — for all of us. It's been hard for the Judge, hard for Mr. Campbell, hard for me, and it's been especially hard for you. I know that too.

"There's this much about it, though. However long it takes, this legal process we're going through, and however tiresome it gets, it's all necessary. It's vitally, critically, crucially necessary.

"We're only going to do this thing once, so we'd damn well better get it right the first time."

Haines' voice and aspect had grown stern as he said this last. Now he moderated both to signal a subtle shift onto another tack. "Coupl'a days ago — seems a lot longer, more like a week, but it was just last Tuesday — we talked about the six blind men from Indostan. Remember, they'd tried to learn about the elephant and none of them got it right?

"I said to you then that Mr. Campbell was like the six blind men, that because he hadn't yet seen the whole elephant, he couldn't really describe it for you. Because he hadn't yet heard all the facts in this case, he couldn't really tell it right. And I believed that.

"Problem is, we've all heard the facts now — the evidence is all in — and Mr. Campbell still hasn't got it worked out right.

"But I want you to understand, I don't blame Mr. Campbell for that. He's entitled to be mistaken. All of us, one time or another, make up our minds before we've got all the facts. We form a kind of 'mind-set'. Then when the facts come out we don't always hear them. We hear what's consistent with our mind-set and somehow miss everything else. It's like the fellow who went to the symphony to hear the trumpets. He accomplished precisely what he set out to do. He heard and registered the stirring martial sounds of the trumpets very well, but he missed the whole of Tchaikovsky.

"I'm afraid, gentlemen, with all due respect, that that's about what's happened to Mr. Campbell. I think he came into court this week expecting to hear the harsh, strident blare of accusatory trumpets. And he did. He heard the trumpets all right, but it seems like he missed the music.

"Mr. Campbell told you this morning that it didn't matter whether Blanche Floyd and Johnny Nickel lied when they denied they'd had any kind of a romantic affair or that they'd had an acquaintanceship with Johnny Bell and with the defendant. Matter of fact, he conceded the 'possibility' that they'd lied, said it would have been 'understandable' if they had. 'Not commendable,' he said, 'but understandable.'

"But whether they lied to you or not, Mr. Campbell said it didn't make any difference in what happened — or in the outcome of this case. In fact, he said he couldn't understand why I made such a big thing of proving they'd lied, that they'd all been seen together frequently. A 'red herring', he called it.

"And that, gentlemen, is what convinces me that he's missed the music."

Bill Haines had stepped closer to the jury box. His eyes moved from juror to juror, commanding their complete attention.

"Let me try to spell it out. Y'see, when Blanche and Nickel made their denials, they directly contradicted the testimony of the defendant. When they denied their own relationship, they also denied a relationship between Frosty and the defendant Donato DiIulio. You'll remember that he described the close interconnection between the events of his own burgeoning love affair with Frosty and the separate but parallel mating activities between Blanche and Nickel in such a manner as to compel your acceptance. It is not possible to disbelieve his testimony concerning their frequent meetings and rendezvous, all four of them, their trysts at the power plant, and their many times spent together in and around the town. To do so would impugn the testimony of virtually all of the disinterested witnesses who came into court to corroborate the defendant's version.

"Now then, for the sake of argument — and just for the moment — let's take these feckless, 'understandable' denials by Blanche and by Nickel clear out of the equation. We'll come back to them, but for right now let's just park them...somewhere," Haines looked around as though to find a suitable place. Then he made a basket of his hands, scooped them through the air in a gathering motion and deposited the imaginary denials firmly on the corner of the prosecutor's counsel table. "Here," he said. "This is limbo. We'll leave them over here for awhile.

"Alright," he continued, moving his glance from juror to juror. "Let's look at what we've got left, without the denials." He raised an eyebrow. "Without the convenient denials of Blanche and Nickel we've got ourselves a fully credible and consistent history and an uncontradicted, eminently realistic account of this entire tragedy.

"The history part tells about these two sisters, Blanche and Forest. They were a couple of good-time girls, loose and easy with the boys. And available. Remember their toe-strings? They were pretty generally available. So, of course, what with young people being what they are, it was inevitable that these two young fellas, Bell and Nickel, would get hooked up with them. Bell was footloose and uncommitted, and Nickel was faithless to his marriage vows. And both of them had money in their pockets.

"It was an arrangement that worked. Their mutual dalliance lasted for something over a year. The girls distributed their favors liberally and the two Johnnys bestowed cash gifts in appreciation. There were no commitments, no protestations of undying love — remember there were times when they swapped partners, 'just for fun' — it was an uncomplicated arrangement that was frankly carnal, venal and essentially frivolous.

"This was the landscape onto which the defendant Donato DiIulio stumbled in May of last year. When Johnny Bell opted to relocate to Steubenville, he unwittingly sowed the seeds of the present disaster. With the best of intentions he contrived to install his young friend DiIulio into his own fortuitous niche within the Floyd sisters' casual menage. In doing so, however, he completely overlooked the basic fact of the defendant's painfully unsophisticated innocence. Perhaps it should have occurred to Johnny Bell that his youthful protege, inexperienced and inarticulate in the language, was no fair match for the artful, older woman, but I doubt that it did at the time.

"Now, in retrospect, it seems that the course of events that followed hard upon the boy's seduction and enslavement was as inexorable as the passage of time. Raised, as he was, in an alien land and tutored in the cloistered classrooms of the Catholic sisters, he was genuinely naive as to the rites and customs of courtship in America. And that naiveté is the flaw that made him vulnerable.

"From that first moment when this woman first drew him into her body and promised they would marry, their fates were sealed. However flippantly she had given her body and her promise, his acceptance was solemn and unqualified. He became obsessed — not only with the woman herself, but with the concept of their marriage, the sharing of their lives, eternal conjugal bliss. She had promised, as had he, and their eternal souls had then and there become bonded together. He believed their exchanged pledges to be sacred and he never doubted their commitment, the sanctity of their union. And each time they met and mated anew his conviction — his obsession — grew stronger. They were destined for one another. He knew that unalterable truth with every fiber of his being."

Bill Haines voice had grown husky with intensity. He paused a moment to assess his audience, the twelve men in the box. Satisfied that he had their attention, he mastered his voice and continued, "Gentlemen, earlier this morning Mr. Campbell said to you that he hadn't yet heard a theory of defense in this case."

Another pause, this one for effect. "Well, I did," he said softly. "And so did you."

He looked to the defendant, then back to he jurors. "You heard it from the defendant himself. You may not have picked up on it because he said it in Italian. What he said was '*la forza del destino*' — the force of destiny.

"The phrase itself just happens to be the name of an Italian opera — by Mr. Verdi, I think — and that may be why I happened to catch the words. But the translation by Mr. Ginocchio made it very clear that the defendant wasn't referring to an opera. He used those words to tell us all that when Forest May became obstinate in her rejection of him — and made it crystal clear to him that she would never relent — from that moment forward he knew that he had no choice but to end both their lives. It was her own rebelliousness, he said, that foreclosed all their options and made them both captive to the powerful forces of their joined destiny.

"And, gentlemen of the jury, it was those forces, pitiless and immutable, that produced this double tragedy — the destruction of two young lives — for the defendant Donato DiIulio had no more power to impede the onslaught of their destiny or to prevent the tragedy than you or I. Whether or not his actions were wrong — morally or legally — he had no ability to stay his hand or to avoid the consequences of his actions."

Bill Haines drew a deep breath, let it out slowly, and retreated a step towards the prosecutor's counsel table.

"Now we have it all, gentlemen. The history, the whole story, the complete symphony. Did everybody hear the music? All of it?"

He sauntered the few remaining steps to the prosecutor's table. "But let's not forget the denials — those by Blanche Floyd and Johnny Nickel. Remember the denials? We parked them right over here." Haines' supple hands recreated the image of a basket as he symbolically collected the imaginary denials from the corner of the table.

"We parked those denials over here, in limbo, because they were the only inconsistencies in all the evidence we've heard these past three days. Now that we've got it right, heard the whole symphony, maybe those denials aren't as inconsistent as we thought they were. Maybe they are, after all, kinda like the trumpets. Heard alone, they're isolated and incomplete. Sometimes they'll seem at odds with the melody. But then when you combine them with the rest of the orchestra, each section in harmony with the whole, it all comes together as a finished symphony to produce a single consistent theme.

"And what, gentlemen, could be more consistent with the theme of this tragic story than for Blanche Floyd and Johnny Nickel to deny their own sorry roles — she, an arrant trollop and he a philanderer with a wife and children? In context with the whole, it is these very denials which balance and confirm the essence of truth in the defendant's testimony."

Bill Haines was nearly finished with his appeal to the jury. He dared not risk losing their attention now. He needed it for a few more moments.

"Sometime after lunch," he told them, "Judge Jones will instruct you concerning the law which you are to apply in arriving at your decision in this matter. I expect that instruction to be both comprehensive and exhaustive, not only as it pertains to your own proceedings as a jury, but as to all of the legal questions at issue. I expect, for example, that he will speak with you concerning the elements of the crime charged by the indictment as well as those other offenses potentially included. He will doubtless explain to you the legal concepts of malice, premeditation, and intention.

"Additionally, because the defendant has pleaded that he is not guilty by reason of temporary insanity, I expect the Court to instruct you concerning that specific defense.

"I would urge that each of you listen attentively to the Court's charge. It is important that you do so. I would hope that you will pay particular attention to the Court's instruction concerning the defense of temporary insanity. I fully expect the Court to tell you that if you determine that the defendant's state of mind was such that he was unable to control his actions, he is not legally responsible and must be acquitted."

Alva Campbell rose to his feet to lodge an objection. Instructions concerning the law were within the sole province of the Court and he thought that Haines was treading too close to the line. He exchanged a glance with Judge Jones, reconsidered his objection, and shrugged. Haines had moved on with his argument and the moment was lost. Campbell sat down quietly.

Bill Haines was aware of Campbell's having risen to object. He had anticipated it. When no actual interruption came, he simply concluded his argument.

"Gentlemen of the jury, you have listened well to the evidence and we have spoken about the cruel and powerful forces that can control our actions. You have heard the defendant's testimony, learned of his child-like vulnerability and his fatal obsession, and you have seen the inevitable result. I would ask now only that you first listen to the Court's instruction, then listen to the music — all of it — and do what is right."

Chapter Eighteen

THE CASE WENT TO THE JURY AT 2:40 THAT AFTERNOON. Judge Jones had allowed an extra half hour for lunch, in recognition of the onus that was about to devolve on the jury, and had then delivered his prepared instructions on the law. His reading of those formalized instructions, his charge to the jury, in measured, sonorous tones, had consumed a full seventy minutes. He had counseled them in general terms concerning the significance of an indictment, their responsibilities as jurors, and the legal concepts of reasonable doubt, weight of the evidence and the presumption of innocence.

His exposition on the law pertaining to the crime charged, that of murder in the first degree, had been both specific and exhaustive. He had begun by postulating the statute, Section 12400 of the Ohio General Code:

Whoever, purposely, and...of deliberate and premeditated malice...kills another, is guilty of murder in the first degree, and shall be punished by death unless the jury trying the accused recommend mercy, in which case the punishment shall be imprisonment in the penitentiary during life.

He had then proceeded to a detailed analysis of each of the constituent ingredients contained within the quoted language. These, he had charged them, were the necessary elements which they must find to have existed in order to support a conviction. They consisted of a purpose or intent to kill, malice, deliberation and premeditation. The presence or absence of each of such elements was a material issue of fact to be resolved by the jury.

And, of course, since the defendant DiIulio had pleaded not guilty by reason of temporary insanity, Judge Jones had also been obliged to instruct concerning that affirmative defense. His charge in that regard was precisely what Bill Haines had anticipated. The test, he had said was:

... whether at the time of the homicide the brain of the defendant was partially deranged to such an extent that his will power, his judgment, and the control of his mind was so impaired that the act of homicide was the result of such derangement and that by reason thereof he was unable to control his act.

Judge Jones had chosen his words carefully. He knew that the slightest misstatement of the complex legal principles involved in the case could form the basis of an appeal and perhaps even a reversal. He also knew that Bill Haines and Alva Campbell were each paying rapt attention to everything he said for precisely that reason.

Near the end of his remarks Judge Jones had explained the matter of those other and lesser offenses which were included within the indictment and told them of the five verdict forms which had been prepared for their use:

1. Guilty as charged in the indictment.
2. Guilty as charged with a recommendation of mercy.
3. Not guilty of murder in the first degree, but guilty of murder in the second degree.
4. Not guilty of murder, but guilty of manslaughter.
5. Not guilty.

Throughout the delivery of his charge, Judge Jones had commanded the jurors' attention by the sheer force of his personality and his judicial bearing. He concluded his instructions with no less intensity than that with which he had begun:

Upon your retirement to the jury room you will elect one of your number to be the foreman and when you have agreed upon a verdict you will cause your foreman to sign it and return with it to the Court. Because this is a criminal case the law requires that your verdict be unanimous. All twelve of you must be in agreement.
Individually and collectively, you have been called upon to discharge one of the highest duties that appertains to American citizenship. You have been selected as jurors in this case because of your fitness, intelligence and qualifications to determine a matter of so much consequence. It is of the highest importance to the community that a wrongdoer be punished when guilt is established beyond a reasonable doubt, and it is of equally high importance to the defendant and the community that a defendant be not convicted if there is reasonable doubt of his guilt.

Having weighed the evidence carefully, let your verdict satisfy your own minds that you have fairly and impartially tried this case, and when you have done that you will have discharged your whole duty and the obligation you took to well and truly try and true deliverance make between the state of Ohio and the prisoner at the bar.

NO ONE STIRRED UNTIL AFTER BROOKS JOHNSON had conducted the jurors out of the courtroom and into the cloistered jury room across the hall. They would remain there, sequestered, until their work was finished.

Bill Haines stood, rolled his shoulders and stretched his neck from side to side. Consciously, he willed his body to relax and his mind to let go the stresses of combat. He had done all that could be done and he could only hope it was enough. The matter was out of his hands now and within the collective conscience of those twelve men before whom they had played out their drama these past four days. My God, he reflected, had it only been four days? It had seemed so much longer.

He glanced about the courtroom. It seemed a sea of activity. The spectators had abandoned their seats and were milling about in small groups, talking with one another in low tones, all the while engaged in a spontaneous and unhurried exodus from their gallery. Inside the bar, Judge Jones had already gathered his notes, clutched up his robes, and repaired through the clerk's office to his own chambers across the hall. Renna Spitler, the court reporter, was collecting her store of pencils and steno pads and would soon follow the judge's pathway toward her own office. Alva Campbell hefted his well-stuffed briefcase from the floor beside his counsel chair, nodded respectfully to Haines, and exited through the narrow doorway reserved for court personnel.

Charles Ginocchio moved unobtrusively to Haines' side at the counsel table and drew his attention to Donato DiIulio. The defendant was still seated abjectly in his chair, staring blankly at the floor. He had obviously understood nothing of the court's charge to the jury and now appeared to be unaware that the trial had ended. Sheriff's deputy George Landry waited patiently, at a distance, for a signal to return the prisoner to his jail cell to await the verdict.

"I'd be obliged," said Bill Haines to Charles Ginocchio, "if you could take the time to explain it to him. The arguments of counsel, the charge by the court, and the jury's responsibility. Would you mind terribly?"

"Of course not," answered Ginocchio. "I want to tell him what's happened thus far. And I'll need to tell him what may or may not happen next."

He offered his hand to Haines. "I think you've made a marvelous effort on his behalf. I have been truly impressed."

Bill Haines exchanged the handshake, acknowledged the compliment, and answered wryly, "I only hope it was good enough to save his life."

Then, with a grimace, he inquired, "Will you stay for the verdict?"

"I'd like to do that," answered Ginocchio. "I want very much to see it through. Besides, whatever it is, I'll need to explain it to him."

"Good," replied Haines. "After you've finished with DiIulio, explained the proceedings, stop by the house. I'll ask Blanche to make some sandwiches. I expect the jury'll be out awhile."

LIFE HAS FEW MOMENTS MORE ANXIOUS — at least for the litigants and their lawyers — than those spent awaiting the verdict of a jury. And of course, the higher the stakes might be, the greater the anxiety.

Such was the ambiance that evening at the Haines' residence on South Cherry Street. The resident family, Bill, Blanche and daughters Mildred and Helen, had been joined by Elizabeth Haines and Charles Ginocchio.

Elizabeth Haines had followed the newspaper accounts of her son's defense of the Italian and had, these past two days, accompanied Blanche to the courthouse where the two of them had found seats in the gallery section and watched the proceedings. After the case had been submitted to the jury, the two women had walked the three blocks' distance to the Haines' residence to share a pot of tea and to await the verdict.

Bill Haines had arrived perhaps an hour later. He had stopped by his office in hopes of catching up on his mail and reviewing a new file that had come his way, but he found himself far too preoccupied to concentrate on anything other than the business at hand. Finally, after he had read the same letter for the third time without the slightest glimmer of comprehension, he simply laid it down, anchored it with a paperweight and closed up shop. Just as well, he reflected as he locked his office door. He had invited Ginocchio to join him for sandwiches and he wanted to be at home when his guest arrived.

Their party was complete when Ginocchio joined them at suppertime. He had been with DiIulio for over an hour, he said, and had then tended to a few personal items in preparation for his return to Cincinnati.

"That may not happen until tomorrow," Haines remarked languidly. He consulted the Regulator clock on the far wall. "The jury's been out nearly four hours already. Hard to tell when they'll come in."

"It surely won't be much longer," said Ginocchio.

"I wouldn't think so, Gino," answered Haines. "I figured somewhere between three and five hours. We're about midway right now."

They were gathered about the dining room table, making a meal of cold beef sandwiches and home-canned peaches. Conversation was sporadic at best because of the prevalent expectation that they would be summoned back to the courtroom to receive the verdict at any moment. Such conversation as there was, however, concerned only the life and times of Donato DiIulio and the trial itself.

"I must admit," said Blanche Haines to her husband, "that last fall, when you first became involved with the case, I felt no sympathy whatever for Mr. DiIulio. I considered him to be more animal than man, a species completely apart from the rest of us.

"And I'm sure I must have said as much," she acknowledged with a small smile.

"You did, indeed," agreed Haines.

"Well, I just want to tell you now that whatever the jury decides, you have accomplished one very significant result. You have pointed out this man's humanity, his terrible vulnerability. You have shown him to be not so much a brutish lout to be despised as a misdirected young boy who should be pitied for the terrible mess he's made of things. You have won for him, if nothing else, at least some small measure of sympathy."

"Well then," answered Haines. "There's that."

"Which is not to say," Blanche interrupted, "that he should not be executed. Nothing I have said changes the fact that he deliberately killed that poor young woman. However much we may pity him, he must answer for what he's done."

"And if you were on the jury?"

"I'd vote for the death penalty," she finished it for him. "I know you don't want me to say so, but I think he deserves to die."

"Happily," Haines replied wryly, "you are not a member of the jury."

"Nor ever likely to be," she pouted. "It all seems so stupid. Tell me again why it is that women can't serve as jurors?"

"It's because you can't vote, my love," he answered indulgently, knowing it to be a sore subject. "Jurors are selected from a list of qualified electors, and until such time as women win the right to vote, they cannot be considered to be electors."

"It's stupid," she repeated.

"Actually," Haines remarked equably, "I've always felt it would be helpful, at least for the defense, to have women jurors. I would expect them to be more sympathetic, more tolerant and less harsh in their judgments than men." He rolled his eyes playfully. "At least," he added, "I should think that to be true in most cases."

They marked the time on the wall clock. "Six hours, now," mused Ginocchio aloud. Then, to Haines, "What do you suppose it means?"

"Don't know, Gino," answered Haines. "Some cases you can speculate. A quick verdict often spells acquittal, a slow verdict usually means a conviction. But this case isn't typical. I won't even try to guess. We'll just have to wait."

They had finished supper, cleared the dishes and put the girls to bed. Blanche and Elizabeth had prepared fresh coffee and they were still gathered about the table, willing the time to pass and the jury to return its verdict.

"I thought I'd heard all the testimony," said Blanche Haines. "But I never learned who the other man was. You know who I mean. The tall man who stood on the rear platform of the traction car on which they traveled to and from Piqua. The one the girl said was her 'new fella'. Who was he?"

"You mean the one she was making eyes at, right in front of DiIulio?" asked Bill Haines.

"Yes, that's the one. Who was he?"

"Hmph," grunted Bill Haines. "I guess he was just somebody. He could have been anybody." He studied his saucer a moment and then added, "It doesn't really matter who he was, but I'm sure he was meant to be the next object of Frosty Floyd's coquetry."

Charles Ginocchio took up the thought. "And she would have taken a perverse delight in flaunting it in DiIulio's face," he added. "To make him jealous."

Bill Haines nodded his agreement. "It may also have made him kill her," he said. "Deep within his subconscious he may have resolved that if he couldn't have her, no one else would either."

"So he killed her, made her his woman forever?" asked Ginocchio.

"*Per sempre*," answered Haines softly. "That's what he said, wasn't it?"

"*Dio mio*," sighed Ginocchio. "It sounds like an Italian opera."

"French, actually," corrected Haines, "but without the music."

"And you supplied the music," said Ginocchio. "Complete with the 'fate' motif."

"I tried," said Haines. "God knows, I tried."

THE JURY WAS OUT ALL NIGHT. Shortly after six o'clock Friday morning, more than fifteen hours after the case had been submitted, the electric buzzer sounded outside the jury room to announce that a verdict had been reached.

Two hours later, at eight o'clock, Judge Jones looked about his courtroom and noted for the record that all of the principals were in attendance. Then, without further ado, he called for the verdict. Brooks Johnson received a folded sheet of white paper from foreman Hayes Stewart and handed it up to the bench. Judge Jones unfolded the paper, adjusted his reading glasses and scanned the writing.

"Will the defendant rise for the verdict?" he intoned, more in the manner of a directive than of a question. He waited another moment for Bill Haines and Charles Ginocchio to urge Donato DiIulio to his feet. He noticed that Haines and Ginocchio both looked every bit as tired as did the twelve jurors. He doubted whether any of them had gotten much rest. When Bill Haines and Donato DiIulio had gained their feet and faced the jury together, Judge Jones read the verdict aloud.

"'We, the jury in this case,'" he read, "'find the defendant Donato DiIulio guilty of murder in the first degree in manner and form as he stands charged in the indictment, and recommend him to mercy.' And," he continued, "the verdict appears to have been signed by J. Hayes Stewart, as Foreman."

Donato DiIulio reacted not at all to the verdict. He hadn't understood a word of it. Charles Ginocchio spoke to him quietly in an attempt to explain.

Bill Haines addressed the court, "Your Honor, the defendant asks that the jury be polled."

And, in response, Judge Jones asked each of the twelve jurors, in turn and by name, "Is this your verdict?" To which question each man solemnly declared, "It is." As soon as the last juror had affirmed the verdict Judge Jones ordered it to be entered of record, thanked the jurors for their service, ordered the defendant into custody, and adjourned the session. It had taken no more than fifteen minutes.

Bill Haines grasped his client's hand and patted him on the shoulder. Then as Deputy Landry led his prisoner out of the courtroom, Alva Campbell approached, shook hands with Haines and Ginocchio. The three men congratulated one another for the professionalism with which each had performed his respective role in the proceedings.

"I'll want to explain it to him," said Ginocchio and prepared to follow Landry and DiIulio back to the jail.

"I'll be in my office," Bill Haines replied.

LATE MORNING FOUND THE TWO MEN, Haines and Ginocchio, together again in Bill Haines' office. They were making the best of a half pot of warmed-over coffee. Charles Ginocchio had spent the last hour and a half with Donato DiIulio in an effort to help him to better understand the significance of the verdict and to offer such consolation concerning his predicament as he could muster.

"I think he's working his way through it," reported Ginocchio of his discussions with DiIulio. "I'm not at all certain that he has yet fully assimilated all the ramifications or felt the whole brunt of the matter, but he's getting there."

"I know," said Haines. "It'll take some getting used to."

"What happens next?" asked Ginocchio.

"It just plays itself out," Haines answered. "Like a Victrola. I'll file a routine motion for new trial, claim a lot of errors were committed, and Judge Jones will summarily overrule it and sentence DiIulio to life imprisonment. From here on in, it's virtually automatic and fully predictable."

They sipped tepid coffee simultaneously and stared out the window. Bill Haines spoke dolefully, as much to himself as to Ginocchio. "It wasn't the verdict I had wanted."

"Yes," replied Ginocchio, "but then it wasn't the verdict Mr. Campbell wanted either. You've persuaded the jury to spare your client's life — and if I remember our first meeting correctly, that was your principal goal"

"That's true, Gino," acknowledged Haines. Then, with a twinkle, he added, "But second degree would have been so very much finer. That was the argument, you know. Four of the jurors held out most of the night for murder two."

ONLY THE WEEKEND INTERVENED. On Monday morning Judge Jones convened court and promptly overruled Bill Haines' motion for new trial.

Then, at the judge's invitation, Bill Haines and Charles Ginocchio maneuvered Donato DiIulio to a station directly in front of the bench. The four men were positioned so closely together that, in any other setting, they would have seemed a congenial social gathering. It was precisely the effect Judge Jones had intended.

In soft-spoken tones and gentle manner, he expressed his sympathy for the defendant and his regret over the fact that the law afforded him no opportunity for the exercise of discretion. The sentence which he was required to pronounce, that of life imprisonment without the possibility for pardon or parole, was mandatory and he had no ability to mitigate it in any respect.

"Happily," he said, "the laws of God are not so immutable and impersonal as are those of man. I believe that He, who sees all things, will better understand and appreciate the strong forces that worked upon your mind and caused you to act as you did. And I profoundly believe that, even in prison, you will find the opportunity to rehabilitate your life and to redeem your immortal soul. I hope and pray that you may do so."

Charles Ginocchio translated Judge Jones' remarks, sentence by sentence, as they were spoken and the judge paused appropriately in order that he might do so. Donato DiIulio was deeply affected and moved to tears by Judge Jones' kindliness and by his expressions of compassion.

And, finally, when DiIulio replied that he had nothing to say as to why sentence should not be imposed, Judge Jones made the requisite pronouncement, "I therefore sentence you to be imprisoned in the Ohio State Penitentiary for the rest of your life. You are remanded to the custody of the sheriff for delivery to the penitentiary. May God have mercy on your soul."

Epilogue

LESS THAN 24 HOURS AFTER HIS SENTENCING, Donato DiIulio was conveyed by Sheriff Gibson to the Ohio State Penitentiary at Columbus where he was duly enrolled as Prisoner numbered 38218.

Two days later, the March 12th edition of *The Miami Union* carried a front page commentary concerning the trial itself and expressing concern over currently evolving social trends, both moral and demographic, which the commentator assigned as root causes of the Floyd-DiIulio difficulty. By way of excerpt:

IMMIGRATION LAWS

Sadly in Need of a Thorough Overhauling

MURDER TRIAL A WARNING

Sylvester on the Importance of Careful
Parental Supervision of the
Conduct of Your Child

Almost every one is supposed to know that there was a celebrated criminal case tried in the courts of this county last week and the result, but perhaps you don't know all the details. I have it from official authority that when the records were all ready at the beginning of that trial, they showed that ordinarily it would take about eight or nine days to try the case, but under the management of Judge Jones and his court officers it was tried in four days. The manner in which that jury was empaneled was a great saving of time and expense and there can be no legal exceptions taken to the plan. This, with other expediting measures taken, shortened the life of that trial and made the cost to the state a great deal less than they would have been in the hands of some men. The court officers deserve due credit. Many people have said to me that the case should have been tried behind closed doors. I don't know about that. I am willing to abide by the opinion of the court and it may be that he like myself thought that a good lesson taught right at home might be of some use to some people.

The lesson I want to impress by reference to this trial is the necessity for parental training. Too many of us let up on our young ones too soon. About the time the boys discard knee breeches and the girls' dresses get down to their shoe tops, they begin to think they are somebody, and that's all right. They should think so but they should be taught to reverence the old folks and get their consent as to where they go and what they do and who are going to be the performers. As a rule watchful parents can see signs that enable them to read pedigrees much quicker than young folks can and sometimes it happens that young people don't look or think about the pedigree just so there is a good time in view. And that is where we need to come down with both feet. I am well aware that we have people who will say that the old fool wants the children tied to their mother's apron strings until they are 21 years old. Be it so.

I want my readers to understand that I am casting no insinuations whatever but trying to point out the importance of a careful supervision of the conduct and whereabouts of the youth of this country.

The man convicted of murder last week in Troy is an Italian and of the class of undesirable immigrants. There have been so many crimes committed lately throughout the country by that class of people that the American blood in a fellow boils when we read of them. It is believed by many today that there is danger ahead of Judge Jones and that jury. I don't believe it myself but I do think its a great misfortune that the ornery Italian devil didn't stub his toe and fall on the gang plank into the sea and drown before he landed here. When we have men who can't control their dispositions any better than this fellow did, the sooner they are dead the better. What to do with this undesirable element of foreigners is a great problem for our statesmen. They are coming here by the thousands and will continue to come as long as we allow the steamship companies and their agents to contract for their transportation.

DONATO DIIULIO REMAINED IN THE PENITENTIARY a period of two years and eighty-one days. He died there on May 31, 1910 of heart failure with epilepsy listed as a contributing factor.

The official death certificate recites that he was twenty-two years old and had no known relatives.

AN AFTERWORD CONCERNING CHARLES GINOCCHIO

At the conclusion of the DiIulio murder trial, after the defendant had been sentenced and remanded into custody, the clerk was required to prepare and file an official "Cost Bill." This was an itemized statement of those expenses incident to the prosecution which were either authorized by statute or allowed by court order. They routinely included charges such as fees to the clerk, the sheriff, the court reporter and to witnesses subpoenaed into court. In this particular case, the allowable costs totalled $697.46 and specifically included compensation to the court-appointed interpreter in the amount of $58.00. The order for such payment contained no provision for travel or subsistence expenses.

In the course of my research into the DiIulio affair I came to be favorably and considerably impressed with the persona of Charles Ginocchio. He struck me not only as someone who was exceptionally well qualified for the assignment he so graciously accepted, but as someone I should have liked to have known personally.

I was gratified, then, to learn that my own judgment in that regard had already been confirmed by his colleagues of the Cincinnati Bar Association. Upon the event of his death in 1964 the full membership of that Association convened in special session and adopted the following somewhat extraordinary memorial resolution:

MEMORIAL TO CHARLES S. GINOCCHIO

Drawn together this morning by the most solemn of human impulses, and in obedience to the call to duty by the president of The Cincinnati Bar Association, I rise in all humility as the spokesman for our committee in presenting a tribute to the memory of Charles S. Ginocchio, one of the most beloved personages our association has ever produced.

While this system of public mourning transmits to posterity our sense of the sad event of his death, it only faintly represents our knowledge of the complete excellence of this man we so cordially honor this morning.

Charles S. Ginocchio was born in Cincinnati, Ohio, on January 7, 1873. When he was three years of age he accompanied his parents to Italy. There he obtained his elementary and preparatory education under the tutelage of the Falesian Fathers. At the age of eighteen he was graduated from the Falesian College of Alessio, Italy.

He returned to the United States, in 1891, with his widowed mother, and resided at her home in Newport, Kentucky. Shortly after his return he became seriously ill, and his physician declared that death was imminent. By a miraculous recovery he outlived all predictions and lived to be ninety-one years old.

He was appointed Italian Counsel in Cincinnati, in 1904, and held that office for thirty years. During World War One, he was knighted by the King of Italy for distinguished service to the Allies.

In 1907 he received his Bachelor of Laws degree from Chase College of Law, in Cincinnati.

For thirty-four years from 1904 to 1938, he was associated with the Old Union Savings Bank and Trust Co., and later with the Fifth-Third Union Trust Co., when these two institutions merged.

In 1938, he retired from the bank to enter the practice of law with his two sons, Charles B. Ginocchio and Louis A. Ginocchio. Due to failing health he retired from active practice of law in 1960.

In addition to his two sons, he is survived by a daughter, Miss Marguerite Ginocchio and eleven grandchildren, all of Cincinnati. His wife, the former Mary Brizzolara, a native of Cincinnati, died in 1952.

When a man like Charles S. Ginocchio dies he leaves a beam of light behind him upon the paths of life that will shine for ages on our mortal sight like a star traveling down from the sky. And in that light we shall see the reflection of his gay spirit, his exuberant laughter and optimistic enthusiasm which he exemplified during his life and in which there can be found consolation and inspiration for all of us, for all time.

He became endeared to us by reason of his sterling qualities, nobility of character, and kindly humor. Men sought his advice because they knew not only of his integrity in giving advice, but of the care and impartiality by which he arrived at the conclusion that helped govern his actions.

He radiated from his personality a charm and sweetness that left an unending impression upon all of us. He was one of nature's own noblemen. He touched nothing that he did not brighten and make better. He was a man who made friends without making enemies. He was a man you did not have to know all his life. He had a genius for finding out how to be kind. He was bold in his kindness. In all his social and civic life he manifested that affable regard for the happiness and interest of his fellowmen, which endeared him to them, and built a monument of regard in their hearts, which shall last longer than the proudest work of art.

— Such was the man the Cincinnati Bar has lost. Such was the man his family, his friends and associates mourn. We certainly should show such a man great honor and respect by not letting the sun set on his memory. The magic that can block the coldness and finality of death, the miracle of his resurrection and continued life among us lies right in our own heart. He will live forever if we keep on remembering him.

— So let us this morning promise to keep these true and sweet memories of him alive, for all years to come, thereby restoring life and breath and love to Charles S. Ginocchio, through the Simple Miracle of remembering.

AUTHOR'S NOTE

At the time of his appointment to defend Donato DiIulio, William A. Haines was already well on his way to becoming one of the finest trial lawyers in this part of the state. Over the next forty-odd years he managed to achieve that pinnacle of success at which all the traditional cliches become applicable. He grew to be, in every sense of the word, a legend in his own time and he did, indeed, bestride his profession like a colossus. The most frequently reported statistic, one that my father cited to me when I was a young boy, was that Bill Haines had defended nineteen first degree murder cases and had never lost a man to the electric chair — not a bad record for a small town practitioner in Arcadian middle America and at a time in our history when justice and retribution were swiftly exacted.

And while it was true that his enormous reputation was principally earned within his own especial metier, that of criminal defense work, it is also conceded that he was an equally formidable advocate in the civil trial arena.

A genial, affable man, he was nonetheless a fierce competitor and was adept at virtually everything he assayed. Whether in the courtroom, at a bridge table, or on the golf course, Bill Haines wanted to win. It was as though the fires within him, his own unique life force, burned with a special intensity.

I knew Bill Haines personally, played bridge with him at the old Troy Club, and watched him putter around the golf course. He was in his eighties and semi-retired when I came to practice, but I did come to know him as a colleague. And I remember that the most remarkable thing about him was the acute, fervid glistening of his eyes that revealed so much of his mettle.

Upon reflection it somehow seems right — and necessary — that he'd been made of the sterner stuff. The two most important challenges of his life involved him personally. They came at opposite ends of his career.

The first such challenge had the potential to scuttle his career before it began. In November of 1894, just as he was ready to apply for admission to practice law, the 25-year-old Haines was arrested on a warrant charging him with petty larceny. The proceeding had been initiated with the filing of an affidavit by "Squire" A. R. Hawthorne, a local lawyer with whom Haines had been reading law. The charge was that fifteen months earlier, in August of 1893, Haines had stolen one of Hawthorne's law books, a volume entitled *Maxwell on Code Pleading* and having a value of $6.00.

In retrospect, it seems obvious that the Squire's charge was more likely the product of spite and malice than of any real offense, but the matter was nonetheless one of serious importance. Conviction of a crime would have effectively disqualified Haines from ever being admitted to the practice of law. He retained the ablest and most prominent firm in the county, Byrkett and Gilbert, and vigorously defended against the charge. The cause was tried to a jury in the Probate Court beginning January 12, 1895. Finally, after a protracted and hotly contested proceeding involving no less than thirty-seven witnesses, the jury found for the defendant. He was admitted to the practice of law directly after his acquittal.

The second and last of such challenges came sixty-one years later. In the summer of 1956, Bill Haines was in his 88th year and his intellectual acuity had been sufficiently compromised by the aging process that his family found it necessary to file an application with the Probate Court, alleging him to be incompetent by reason of mental disability and seeking the appointment of a guardian.

Predictably, and characteristically, Bill Haines' reaction to the allegation was vigorous and combative. He immediately retained four of the most prominent lawyers in the county and served notice that he intended to resist the application in open court. There would be a trial and the issue would be that of his own alleged incompetence.

And though he had the benefit of the best legal counsel available, Bill Haines ultimately elected to handle his own defense. After a full lifetime spent in the trial arena, he could not do otherwise. The case was tried before Judge John M. Kiracofe of nearby Preble County, sitting by special assignment, and lasted four days. Bill Haines, with four able lawyers sitting as associate counsel, conducted all of the principal aspects of the trial, specifically including the examination and cross-examination of the witnesses.

At the conclusion of the evidence Judge Kiracofe took the matter under advisement and indicated that he would issue a written decision at a later time.

Then, on September 25th, 1956, Bill Haines died. He died as he would have chosen to do, resting on a couch in his office. Two days later Judge Kiracofe filed an order terminating the action:

DECISION

This case is closed. The application will be denied.

Could it be that the Judge in the Court above, fearing that we humans might err, saw fit to remove the subject from the jurisdiction of this Court and Himself assume such guardianship as might be needed now and throughout eternity?

It would seem to be proper that the last case tried by W. A. Haines was in defense of himself and his ability to handle the property which he had been able to accumulate during his life. It is also fitting and proper to remind counsel that some of his cross examination during the trial was ably done and very impressive.

From this, we might all learn that more patience is needed in our association with our elderly associates.

An entry of dismissal may be prepared which Judge Faust will gladly sign with costs to be paid by the applicant.

The Troy Historical Society, principally in the person of Juda Moyer, has been an invaluable resource to me in the preparation of this work, particularly with reference to the provision of old newspaper accounts and photographs.

This is the third such effort in which my good friend, secretary and former classmate, Martha Crouse, has been involved. And on each succeeding occasion, her involvement has been greater, more valuable and better appreciated than before. I suspect that if we should do another, she'll not need me at all.

About the author

John Fulker is a native of Troy, Ohio. Educated at Miami University and Columbia Law School, one of the highlights of his law school experience was driving a taxicab in New York City.

He has been joined in the practice by his two sons, Andy and Bill; his daughter, Cameron, is a graphic artist. He and his wife, Nancy, reside in Troy, at sufferance with their Labrador retriever, Irish setter and too many cats.

Mr. Fulker has a wide variety of interests which include chess, classical music, literature, swimming, canoeing, sailing, and particularly, waterfowling. He is a conservationisr and has been active in Ducks Unlimited.

Chicken Soup:

The Miami County Courthouse, 1841–1887, in which Jane Ragan and George Mitchell were tried for murder.

Sheriff's residence and Probate Court built in 1854; site of Jane Ragan's preliminary hearing and incarceration.

Cheap Whiskey and Bad Women:

The bullpen area at the Miami County Jail in which Jane Ragan, George Mitchell and Donato DiIulio were held.

George Mitchell, photograph taken immediately after having been cut down from the gallows.

The portable gallows which was assembled, disassembled and moved from county to county for public hangings performed in accordance with the law at the time of the Mitchell execution.

Ticket for hanging George Mitchell (first scheduled for May 28,1880; respite by Governor until September 3rd, 1880; second respite granted on September 2nd, and hanging rescheduled for September 17th, 1880, on which date he was finally hanged); this ticket for September 3rd, 1880 was given out to William Miller, but was not used, as the hanging did not take place that day.

More Bad Women:

Contemporary newspaper
sketch of Donato DiIulio.

William A. Haines, court
appointed counsel for Donato
DiIulio; photograph taken 40
years later.

Contemporary photo of
Judge Walter Jones who
presided over the DiIulio
trial.

Charles Ginocchio, Royal Italian
Counsel for Cincinnati who
served as interpreter for the
DiIulio trial; photograph taken
several years later.

Gandy dancers, a typical railroad gang, circa 1906.